About this book

This book has been written specifically to help you implement the Framework for Teaching Mathematics with students who have gained Level 2 or 3 at the end of KS2. It is designed to help students consolidate their achievement at Level 3.

The content is based on the Year 4 and 5 teaching objectives from the Primary Framework but provides access to Year 7 objectives. To make the most of the material contained in this book it is strongly recommended that your students use the corresponding Student Book as shown on the back cover.

The authors are experienced teachers who have been working with students of a similar ability for years and so are well qualified to provide appropriate classroom practice.

The book is made up of units that provide access to the Support tier of the sample medium term plans that complement the Framework for Teaching Mathematics at KS3.

The units are:

A1	Sequences	1–14
N1	Number calculations	15–28
S1	Perimeter and area	29–38
N2	Fractions, decimals and percentages	39–52
D1	Data and probability	53–66
A2	Using symbols	67–78
S2	Angles and shapes	79–86
D2	Handling data	87–98
N3	Multiplication and division	99–116
A3	Functions and graphs	117–130
S3	Triangles and quadrilaterals	131–142
N4	Percentages, ratio and proportion	143–154
A4	Linear equations	155–164
S4	Transformations	165–178
N5	More number calculations	179–196
D3	The handling data cycle	197–208
D4	Probability experiments	209–216
A5	Equations and graphs	217–234
S5	Angles and symmetry	235–248

Each unit comprises double page spreads that should take a lesson to teach. These are shown on the full contents list.

Problem solving is integrated throughout the material as suggested in the Framework.

How to use this book

This book is organised into double page spreads that should take an hour to teach. The page numbers correspond with those in the Student Book, making the books very easy to use.

The spreads have been written to correspond to those in the Support tier as much as possible to make it easier to teach the two tiers alongside each other in the classroom. On the first page of each unit there is a **Bridging** table suggesting how to organise the class if you are teaching the two tiers together.

Three-part lesson plans

The spread gives an off-the-shelf **lesson plan**.

There is a practical overview of the **three-part lesson** that you can read and implement with minimal preparation:

1. The mental starter is designed to provide a lead-in to the concepts of the main lesson, and often overlaps with the starter in the Support tier.
2. The introductory activity helps you bring the associated Student Book to life, providing engaging questions to help students discuss and appreciate the mathematical ideas.
3. The plenary suggests a way of rounding up the learning and helping to overcome any difficulties students faced during the lesson.

Homework

A **homework activity** is suggested for each spread.

▶ The activities have been written to ensure students don't need to take home books or sheets of paper and are intended to be short activities that students can do. You may ask students to write down the question in their exercise books or diaries so they can remember what to do.
▶ There are frequent references to **Springboard 7** pages that are suitable as homework activities, so you can send a sheet home if you prefer.

Framework references

Each spread starts by listing the relevant Year 7 teaching objective so you can see what students are aspiring to access.

Framework page references from the **Primary Framework** document are included so you can see what each spread is covering.

The book provides coverage mainly from the **Year 5 Teaching Programme** although parts are taken from Years 3, 4 and 6.

At the end of each lesson plan, there is a reference to other parts of the curriculum that link in with the key ideas on the spread.

Framework MATHS

7

A

Teacher's Book

Ray Allan

Martin Williams

Claire Perry

OXFORD

UNIVERSITY PRESS

Great Clarendon Street, Oxford OX2 6DP

Oxford University Press is a department of the University of Oxford.
It furthers the University's objective of excellence in research,
scholarship, and education by publishing worldwide in

Oxford New York

Auckland Bangkok Buenos Aires Cape Town Chennai
Dar es Salaam Delhi Hong Kong Istanbul Karachi Kolkata
Kuala Lumpur Madrid Melbourne Mexico City Mumbai Nairobi
São Paulo Shanghai Taipei Tokyo Toronto

Oxford is a registered trade mark of Oxford University Press
in the UK and in certain other countries

British Library Cataloguing in Publication Data

Data available

ISBN 019 914 940 2

10 9 8 7 6 5 4 3 2

Typeset by Mathematical Composition Setters Ltd.

Printed in Great Britain by Ashford Colour Press Ltd., Gosport.

Acknowledgements

The photograph on the cover is reproduced courtesy of Pictor International
(UK).

Differentiation

The exercises in the Student Book are graded, and start with the simplest questions and build up gradually. There are three tiers of difficulty: lead-in, focus and challenge. These three levels are highlighted to make it easier to differentiate within ability groups and to manage the learning environment effectively.

Misconceptions

Common misconceptions are highlighted and there are suggestions for helping students overcome difficulties. This is designed to help prevent longer-term problems arising.

Answers

The answers are given to the questions in the Student Book and also to the worksheet questions where appropriate.

Resources

The right-hand page of every spread consists of a photocopiable page.

There are two types:

- ➤ OHPs, which provide a useful visual aid to promote discussion
- ➤ Worksheets to either support weaker students or to provide consolidation of the key ideas. The Worksheets are also available in a useful Workbook format.

There are also some general resources (Rs) from the Framework Maths scheme that are reproduced at the end of the book for your convenience.

The relevant resources are listed on each spread and also on the first page of each unit to help you plan in advance.

Schemes of Work

On the last page of each unit there is a photocopiable Scheme of Work. Each Scheme of Work details the relevant teaching objectives from the Primary Framework (Y456), and the Access Year 7 resources, both in the Student Book and Teacher's Book.

Assessment

At the end of the book is a bank of photocopiable assessments. There is an assessment for each unit. Each assessment is designed so the students can write on their answers. The assessments are 10 minutes long.

The questions are based on past paper National Test questions from KS2 and are mostly at Level 3 with two or three marks at Level 2.

Students should be able to score around 70% on each assessment.

The answers are provided at the end of the book.

Contents

A1 Sequences   1–14

A1.1   Patterns   2
A1.2   Introducing sequences   4
A1.3   Sequences and rules   6
A1.4   Sequences in diagrams   8
A1.5   Doing and undoing   10
A1.6   Operation machines   12
     Summary   14

N1 Number calculations   15–28

N1.1   Place value   16
N1.2   Negative numbers   18
N1.3   Adding and subtracting with negatives   20
N1.4   Mental addition   22
N1.5   Mental subtraction   24
N1.6   Multiplying by 10   26
     Summary   28

S1 Perimeter and area   29–38

S1.1   Measurements and scales   30
S1.2   Perimeter   32
S1.3   Area   34
S1.4   Perimeter and area   36
     Summary   38

N2 Fractions, decimals and percentages   39–52

N2.1   Understanding fractions   40
N2.2   Comparing fractions   42
N2.3   Fractions of amounts   44
N2.4   Decimal scales   46
N2.5   Decimals and percentages   48
N2.6   Finding tenths of amounts   50
     Summary   52

D1 Data and probability   53–66
  D1.1   The mode   54
  D1.2   What's in the middle?   56
  D1.3   Levelling   58
  D1.4   Introducing chance   60
  D1.5   Describing chance   62
  D1.6   The probability scale   64
       Summary   66

A2 Using symbols   67–78
  A2.1   Using letters   68
  A2.2   Adding and subtracting with symbols   70
  A2.3   Solving algebra problems   72
  A2.4   Symbols and values   74
  A2.5   Substitution   76
       Summary   78

S2 Angles and shapes   79–86
  S2.1   Time   80
  S2.2   Reading coordinates   82
  S2.3   Coordinates and shapes   84
       Summary   86

D2 Handling data   87–98
  D2.1   Sorting   88
  D2.2   Reading diagrams   90
  D2.3   Organising data   92
  D2.4   Displaying data   94
  D2.5   Interpreting data   96
       Summary   98

N3 Multiplication and division   99–116

N3.1   Rounding numbers   100
N3.2   Mental multiplication   102
N3.3   Multiplying decimals by 10   104
N3.4   Dividing whole numbers by 10   106
N3.5   Number and measure   108
N3.6   Multiplying by partitioning   110
N3.7   Division on a number line   112
N3.8   More division ideas   114
       Summary   116

A3 Functions and graphs   117–130

A3.1   Factors   118
A3.2   Multiples   120
A3.3   Square numbers   122
A3.4   Multiplication mappings   124
A3.5   Plotting pairs   126
A3.6   Mappings and graphs   128
       Summary   130

S3 Triangles and quadrilaterals   131–142

S3.1   Compass turns   132
S3.2   Angles   134
S3.3   Measuring angles   136
S3.4   Drawing angles   138
S3.5   Parallel and perpendicular lines   140
       Summary   142

N4 Percentages, ratio and proportion   143–154

N4.1   Fractions   144
N4.2   Fractions and decimals   146
N4.3   Fractions, decimals and percentages   148
N4.4   Percentages of amounts   150
N4.5   Ratio   152
       Summary   154

A4 Linear equations 155–164

A4.1 Using letters 156
A4.2 Equalities 158
A4.3 Inequalities 160
A4.4 Equations 162
Summary 164

S4 Transformations 165–178

S4.1 Symmetry 166
S4.2 Reflection symmetry 168
S4.3 Symmetry on a grid 170
S4.4 Translating shapes 172
S4.5 Rotation 174
S4.6 Movement on a grid 176
Summary 178

N5 More number calculations 179–196

N5.1 Estimating 180
N5.2 Approximations 182
N5.3 Using factors 184
N5.4 Written calculations 186
N5.5 Written division 188
N5.6 Equivalent fractions 190
N5.7 Finding fractions of amounts 192
N5.8 Finding percentages 194
Summary 196

D3 The handling data cycle 197–208

D3.1 Collecting data 198
D3.2 Drawing pictograms 200
D3.3 Drawing charts and graphs 202
D3.4 Using statistics 204
D3.5 Discussing findings 206
Summary 208

D4 Probability experiments   209–216

    D4.1   Describing probabilities   210
    D4.2   A probability experiment   212
    D4.3   More experiments   214
         Summary   216

A5 Equations and graphs   217–234

    A5.1   Solving equations   218
    A5.2   Using formulas   220
    A5.3   Using symbols in formulas   222
    A5.4   Making sequences   224
    A5.5   Rules   226
    A5.6   Rules and graphs   228
    A5.7   Graphs of formulas   230
    A5.8   Coordinates in all quadrants   232
         Summary   234

S5 Angles and symmetry   235–248

    S5.1   Angle facts   236
    S5.2   Triangles and quadrilaterals   238
    S5.3   Solid shapes   240
    S5.4   Line symmetry   242
    S5.5   Rotational symmetry   244
    S5.6   Tessellations   246
         Summary   248

Assessment   249–287
Assessment answers   288–292
Resources   293–310

Overview

This unit aims to build on students' previous understanding of sequences and to lay a foundation for further algebra work. It focuses on the idea of extending a sequence by using a rule and by continuing patterns using spatial awareness. It develops to introduce the idea of inverse operations that will allow students to start to solve equations.

Spreads A1.1, A1.2 and A1.3 form the focus of the unit.

Framework references

The unit covers objectives from the Framework (Y456) on pages: 17, 19, 53, 55, 59

Introduction

Discuss sequences that students may see every day such as tiling patterns. Emphasise that understanding how patterns develop is a useful skill for other subject areas such as ICT and Design.

Use the Check in activity to find out what students know about the content of the unit, in particular their understanding of even and odd numbers.

Check in activity

Count on

Give students a start number, and ask them to count up in 3s.
Use a number line (**R6**) to illustrate jumps of 3.
Start at 0, ask students to count up in 2s. List the numbers.
Ask students if they can name this group of numbers (even).
Start at 1 and repeat. (odd)

Useful resources

Worksheets
A1.1WS – continuing patterns
A1.2WS – using rules
A1.3WS – following rules
A1.4WS – odd and even numbers
A1.5WS – robot instructions
A1.6WS – function machines

General resources
R6 – number lines
R7 – function machines
R17 – 100 square
R19 - ruler
R24 – squared grid
Multilink cubes

Springboard 7 pages
47, 50, 51, 52

Differentiation – spanning the bridge

Spread	Bridge to the Support tier
A1.1	Develop to look at numerical sequences, and in particular discuss the information required to generate a sequence: **start term and rule**.
A1.2	Extend to consider the different rules that could describe the first 2 terms of a sequence. Essentially, the two tiers work alongside one another, but Access tier needs to recap keyword: **terms**.
A1.3	Progress to consider pictorial sequences, emphasising the pattern, and the corresponding numbers of each pattern. Emphasise the difference between the term number, and the value of the term.
A1.4	The Support tier covered sequences in diagrams in A1.3 but the Access tier provides a useful recap. Extend to consider function machines, and relate the input and output to the term and value of the term.
A1.5	Access tier needs to progress to identify functions/rules given input and output values. Discuss the different rules that could be applied to a given set of input/output values, and emphasise the need to check that the function fits all values given.
A1.6	Support tier have worked on function machines in A1.4 and A1.5, and can be used to support Access tier. Progress the Access tier to consider algebra to represent **variables**, and the conventions of algebra (numbers then letters, and no multiplication sign).

A1.1 Patterns

Access

This spread provides access to the Year 7 objective:
▸ Describe simple integer sequences (144).

Lesson Plan

Mental starter

▸ Choose a number to start with, say 7. Go around the class, with each student adding 3.
▸ Use different start numbers and step sizes. **R6** (number lines) may be useful.
▸ Develop to include subtraction. For example, start at 20, count back in 3s.

Introductory activity

Write the first 10 numbers on the board. Encourage students to describe any patterns they can see.

Highlight the **even** numbers and discuss the pattern made by the other numbers (**odd**).

Discuss the meaning of the term 'sequence'

Discuss 'patterns' in everyday life: bricks in a wall, plate decoration, pattern on a tie.

Use the examples in the Students' Book. Discuss what comes next in each case.

▸ For the necklace: blue, yellow, red.
▸ For the squares: 8, 10 (add 2).
▸ For the dots: 16, 20 (add 4).

Encourage students to describe each pattern in words. Emphasise the keywords: **repeat**, **increase**.

Plenary

Repeat the mental starter, but focus on subtraction. Introduce the term: **decrease**.

Develop briefly to patterns that jump the positive/negative number divide, for example, start at 13, subtract 2: 13, 11, 9, 7, 5, 3, 1, ...

Encourage students to consider what happens below zero. Use **R6** to show the sequence on a number line.

Homework

▸ Ask students to make up five number sequences of their own, and write a rule in words for each one.
▸ Springboard 7: Page 50.

Exercise Commentary

Coverage

The questions assess objectives on Framework (Y456) Pages 16–17.

Useful resources

R6 – number lines.
A1.1WS – provides support for weaker students.

Differentiation

▸ Question 1 focuses on recognising the next part of a pattern.
▸ Questions 2–4 focus on continuing a pattern.
▸ Question 5 extends to abstract sequences.

Support tier: focuses on generating sequences given a start number and rule.

Misconceptions

Students will find it easier to **increase** a number pattern. Students can use a number line (**R6**) as a visual prompt in the plenary to help illustrate that the sequence can continue into negative numbers.

Links

Negative numbers: Framework (Y456): Page 15.

Exercise Answers

1 a z b y
2 Continuation of pattern
3 a Red b Green c Red d Green e Red f Red
4 a Diamond b Circle
5 a 10 dots b 50 boxes c 66

Worksheet Answers

1, 2 Continuation of pattern
3 12 dots, 15 dots
4 a 10, 12 b 25, 30

1 Continue these patterns.

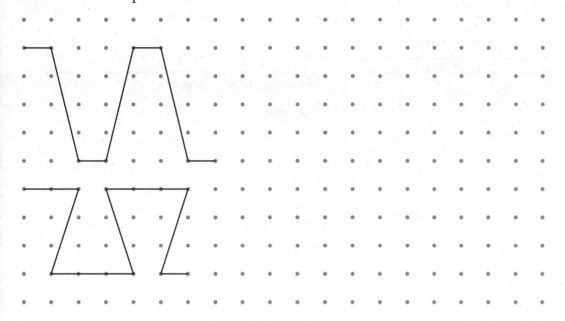

2 Use three colours to make a repeating pattern on these beads.

3 Here is a pattern that grows. Complete the last two parts of this pattern.

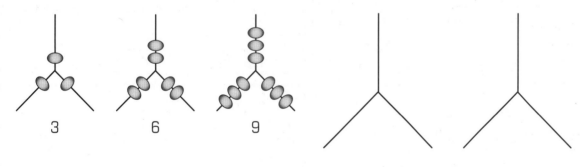

3   6   9

4 Each set of cards shows a number pattern.
   Complete the pattern.

a

| 2 | 4 | 6 | 8 | | |

b

| 5 | 10 | 15 | 20 | | |

A1.2 Introducing sequences

Access

This spread provides access to the year 7 objective:
▶ Generate and describe simple integer sequences (144).

Lesson Plan

Mental starter

▶ Choose a number to start with, say 6. Go around the class, with each student adding 2.
▶ Use harder start numbers, and step sizes. **R6** (number lines) may be useful.
▶ Emphasise correct use of keywords: **sequence**, **rule**, **increase**.

Introductory activity

Give students a rule such as 'increase by 5', and ask them each to generate the first six numbers in the sequence. Discuss the different sequences.

Discuss what other information you need to ensure each student writes the same sequence.

Emphasise that you need the same start number and rule.

Give a start number and rule and ask students to generate the first four numbers of these sequences. For example:
▶ Start at 3, add 4
▶ Start at 13, minus 2

Show some further numerical sequences, and ask students for the start number and rule.

Plenary

Discuss some multiplicative rules. For example: 2, 4. Other than start at 2, add 2, is there any other rule to describe this sequence?

What comes next? (6 or 8). Emphasise that you can have a rule 'times 2' that gives the same sequence.

Extend to division (by 2), providing an opportunity to progress to fractions.

For example: 8, 4, 2, 1, $\frac{1}{2}$, $\frac{1}{4}$.

Homework

▶ Ask students to generate and describe three sequences where the third number is 17.
▶ Springboard 7: Page 51.

Exercise Commentary

Coverage

The questions assess objectives on Framework (Y456) Page 17.

Useful resources

R6 – number lines.
A1.2WS – provides further practice of the key ideas.

Differentiation

▶ Question 1 focuses on using a number line to extend a sequence.
▶ Questions 2 and 3 focus on continuing a sequence using a rule.
▶ Question 4 extends to finding the rule.
Support tier: involves generating sequences using all four operations.

Misconceptions

Students will be less comfortable developing sequences to include fractions, decimals and so on.
Using a number line (**R6**) will help, especially to illustrate the division by 2 between each term and zero.

Links

Negative numbers: Framework (Y456): Page 15.

Exercise Answers

1 a 13, +3 b 3, −5   2 a 10 b 13 c 11
  d 18 e 25 f 50 g 1 h 3 i 4 j 20
3 a 2, 6, 10, 14 b 5, 8, 11, 14 c 21, 18, 15, 12
  d 50, 40, 30, 20 e 11, 16, 21, 26 f 24, 20, 16, 12
4 a 3, 5, 7, 9, 11 b +2 c 13

Worksheet Answers

1 a 10 b 15 c 22
2 a 13, 16   Increases by 3
  b 50, 60   Increases by 10 or is in the 10 times table
  c 16, 20   Increases by 4 or is in the 4 times table
  d 23, 28   Increases by 5   e 5, 3   Increases by 2
  f 12, 9   Increases by 3
3 a 0, 3, 6, 9, 12 b 2, 4, 6, 8, 10 c 7, 12, 17, 22, 27
  d 19, 16, 13, 10, 7 e 30, 26, 22, 18, 14

1 Write the next number in each sequence in the box.

a

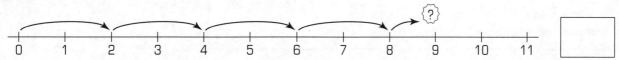

b

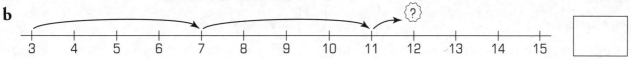

c

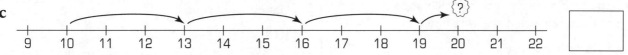

2 Complete each sequence and explain the pattern.
Here are some words to help you.

> This sequence increases by _____ each time.
> This sequence decreases by _____ each time.
> This sequence is in the _____ times table.

a 1 , 4 , 7 , 10 , ___ , ___   This sequence _____

b 10 , 20 , 30 , 40 , ___ , ___   This sequence _____

c 0 , 4 , 8 , 12 , ___ , ___   This sequence _____

d 3 , 8 , 13 , 18 , ___ , ___   This sequence _____

e 24 , 21 , 18 , 15 , ___ , ___   This sequence _____

3 Use the rule to write the first five numbers in each sequence.

a The first number is 0. The rule is +3.   ___ , ___ , ___ , ___ , ___

b The first number is 2. The rule is +2.   ___ , ___ , ___ , ___ , ___

c The first number is 7. The rule is +5.   ___ , ___ , ___ , ___ , ___

d The first number is 19. The rule is −3.   ___ , ___ , ___ , ___ , ___

A1.3 Sequences and rules

Access

This spread provides access to the Year 7 objective:
▸ Generate and describe simple integer sequences (144).

Lesson Plan

Mental starter

▸ Start with a number, say 50. Ask students to generate a sequence by decreasing in steps of 2.
▸ Repeat with different start numbers and step sizes and extend to include negative numbers.

Introductory activity

Give students the rule: subtract 6 each time. Discuss whether there is one sequence to fit this rule.

Emphasise the need for a start number **and** a rule. **Introduce the keyword: term**.

Show a 100 square (**R17**) and ask students to describe patterns in it. For example:
▸ third column: start at 3 and add 10
▸ leading diagonal: start at 1 and add 11.

Discuss strategies for identifying the rule. **Encourage students to consider the difference between terms.** Discuss examples.

Plenary

Use the 100 square (**R17**). Encourage students to describe a pattern for the rest of the class to identify. For example, the sequence, start at 4, add 10 is in column 4.

Homework

▸ Ask students to generate terms of a sequence given a start number and multiplicative rule. For example, start at 3 and double.
▸ Springboard 7: Page 52.

Exercise Commentary

Coverage

The questions assess objectives on Framework (Y456) Page 17.

Useful resources

R17 – 100 square.
A1.3WS – provides further practice of the key ideas.

Differentiation

▸ Question 1 focuses on continuing a sequence given a rule.
▸ Questions 2 and 3 focus on finding the rule.
▸ Question 4 extends to finding intermediate terms.

Support tier: involves generating sequences using all four operations.

Misconceptions

Emphasise that sequences can continue infinitely, or can be finite. Use the 100 square (**R17**) to challenge understanding of what happens after the 10th row.

Use a number line (**R6**) with students who have difficulty imagining the difference between successive terms.

Links

Negative numbers: Framework (Y456) Page 15.

Exercise Answers

1 **a** 4, 9, 14, 19, 24 **b** 23, 20, 17, 14, 11 **c** 0, 4, 8, 12, 16 **d** 21, 17, 13, 9, 5 **e** 30, 32, 34, 36, 38
2 **a** 1, +3 **b** 17, –3 **c** 9, +4 **d** 80, –10 **e** 29, –5 **f** 8, +7   3 **a** 2, 3, +3, 14, 17, 20 **b** 2, 1, +1, 6, 7, 8
 c 20, 2, –2, 10, 8, 6 **d** 5, 2, +2, 15, 17, 19 **e** 2, 8, +8, 34, 42, 50 **f** 3, 3, +3, 18, 21, 24   **g** 30, 4, –4, 10, 6, 2
 h 20, 10, +10, 60, 70, 80   4 **a** 7, 13 **b** 5, 8, 11, 14, 17

Worksheet Answers

1 **a** 3, 8, 13, 18, 23, 28, 33   **b** 19, 16, 13, 10, 7, 4, 1   **c** 12, 16, 20, 24, 28, 32, 36 **d** 28, 24, 20, 16, 12, 8, 4
 e 0, 7, 14, 21, 28, 35, 42   2 **a** 5, 7, 9, 11, 13, 15;   add 2   **b** 2, 7, 12, 17, 22, 27;   add 5
 c 20, 18, 16, 14, 12, 10;   subtract 2   **d** 20, 30, 40, 50, 60, 70;   add 10   **e** 30, 26, 22, 18, 14, 10;   subtract 4

1 Start at the bottom and follow the sequence to work out who is who!

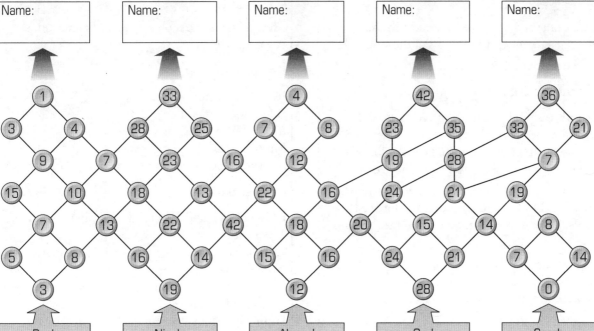

a Write the sequence for Paul.   ___ , ___ , ___ , ___ , ___ , ___ , ___

b Write the sequence for Nicole.   ___ , ___ , ___ , ___ , ___ , ___ , ___

c Write the sequence for Ahmed.   ___ , ___ , ___ , ___ , ___ , ___ , ___

d Write the sequence for Carl.   ___ , ___ , ___ , ___ , ___ , ___ , ___

e Write the sequence for Sarah.   ___ , ___ , ___ , ___ , ___ , ___ , ___

2 Write the start number and rule for each sequence.

a 5 , 7 , 9 , 11 , 13 , 15 , ...   Start at _____   The rule is _____.

b 2 , 7 , 12 , 17 , 22 , 27 , ...   Start at _____   The rule is _____.

c 20 , 18 , 16 , 14 , 12 , 10 , ...   Start at _____   The rule is _____.

d 20 , 30 , 40 , 50 , 60 , 70, ...   Start at _____   The rule is _____.

A1.4 Sequences in diagrams

Access

This spread provides access to the year 7 objective:
▶ Generate sequences from simple practical contexts (146, 154).

Lesson Plan

Mental starter

Give a start number (3), and a multiplicative rule (× 2). Students generate the first five terms of the sequence.

Change the start number and rule.

Introductory activity

Discuss students' understanding of **even** and **odd** numbers. Use the bench example in the Students' Book to emphasise the pattern of odd and even numbers. (odd numbers have one 'left over' when halved.)

Emphasise that number sequences can be illustrated using pictures. Discuss a suitable diagram for the two times table. There is one in question 3 of the Students' Book.

Encourage students to work in groups with multilink cubes to design a pattern which describes the three times table, and briefly discuss answers.

Plenary

Use squared paper or **R24** to show the first three terms of the square numbers (1, 4, 9). These are also shown on **A3.3OHP**. Encourage students to describe the sequence and give it a suitable name.

Discuss how the sequence progresses and what the next term will be.

Homework

▶ Ask students to draw a pattern to illustrate the first five odd numbers.
▶ Springboard 7: Page 47.

Exercise Commentary

Coverage

The questions assess objectives on Framework (Y456) Pages 18–19.

Useful resources

R17 – 100 square.
R24 – squared grid.
A3.3OHP – square numbers
Multilink cubes, squared paper
A1.4WS – provides support for weaker students.

Differentiation

▶ Questions 1 and 2 focus on extending a numerical sequence.
▶ Question 3 focuses on pictorial representations of times tables.
▶ Question 4 extends to recognising and completing number patterns.

Support tier: involves complex picture patterns.

Misconceptions

In question 3 students may use an odd multilink cube to match the representation of five in the five times table. Emphasise that the five times table progresses odd, even, odd, even, etc. Students can use multilink cubes to help visualisation.

Students may have difficulty visualising the progression of square numbers in the plenary. Encourage the use of squared paper or a square grid (**R24**).

Links

Multiplication facts: Framework (Y456) Page 59.

Exercise Answers

1 a 1, 3, 5, 7, 9, 11, 13, 15   b 2, 4, 6, 8, 10, 12, 14, 16, 18, 20   2 a Even   b Odd   3 a E, C   b B, D   c A, F
4 a, b Across: 2, 4, 6, 8; 3, 6, 9, 12; 4, 8, 12, 16; 5, 10, 15, 20   Down: 2, 3, 4, 5; 4, 6, 8, 10; 6, 9, 12, 15; 8, 12, 16, 20
  Diagonally: 2, 6, 12, 20   c 5

Worksheet Answers

1 a 1, 3 or 5   b 1, 3 or 5   c 2, 4 or 6   d 2, 4 or 6   e 1, 3 or 5
2 a 3, 5, 7, 9, 11, 13, 15, 17;   C;   add 2   b 2, 6, 10, 14, 18, 22, 26, 30;   E;   add 4

1 The dots on this domino add up to 9 – an odd number.

Draw dots onto these dominoes to make an ...

a  **b**  **c**  **d**  **e**

... even number   ... odd number   ... even number   ... odd number   ... even number

2 In this zigzag you can only move to a joining square.

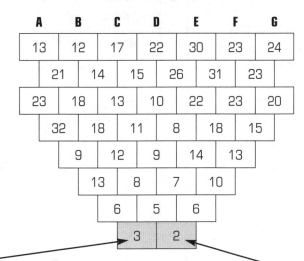

a Start at 3.

Follow only increasing odd numbers.

Write the sequence of odd numbers:

3 , ____ , ____ , ____ , ____ , ____ , ____ , ____

Which letter do you arrive at? _____

Write the rule.

The rule is: _____ ____

_____ ____

b Start at 2.

Follow only increasing even numbers.

Write the sequence of even numbers:

2 , ____ , ____ , ____ , ____ , ____ , ____ , ____

Which letter do you arrive at? _____

Write the rule.

The rule is: _____

_____

A1.5 Doing and undoing

Access

This spread provides access to the Year 7 objective:
▸ Understand the four operations as they apply to whole numbers (82–84).

Lesson Plan

Mental starter

▸ Start with a number, say 13. Ask students to add 5. Ask how to get back to 13 from the new number.
▸ Change numbers, and develop to use subtraction then addition.

Introductory activity

Refer to the mental starter. Introduce keyword: **undo**.

Discuss how to **undo** this movement: walk forward five steps. Introduce keyword: **opposite**.

Develop movement to include turning left, going upstairs, etc.

Use the Students' Book example of Harry walking up five steps, turning the light on and going into the bathroom, discussing how to reverse his actions.

Discuss a numerical example, such as $4 + 2 = 6$; $6 - 2 = 4$ and stress the 'start' and 'finish' of the calculation.

Formalise the two sets of inverse operations: add and subtract, multiply and divide.

Plenary

Challenge students to use their understanding of inverses to informally solve equations.
For example, I have a number. I add 6. The answer is 14. What was my number?
Extend to include all four operations and their inverses.

Homework

▸ Give students a copy of **R24** with four paths for a robot shown. They must give the reverse instructions. Ask students to devise a path for a robot on a squared grid and to give the reverse instructions.

Exercise Commentary

Coverage

The questions assess objectives on Framework (Y456) Pages 53 and 55.

Useful resources

A1.5WS – provides further practice of the key ideas.

Differentiation

▸ Questions 1 and 2 focus on reversing everyday actions.
▸ Question 3 focuses on inverse operations.
▸ Question 4 extends to undoing calculations.
Support tier: focuses on using function machines to find outputs.

Misconceptions

Students may have difficulty linking reverse operations to rearranging formal calculations using the inverse operation. They may make mistakes such as, if $4 + 6 = 10$, then $4 - 6 = 10$. This is using the inverse operation, but not thinking through the calculation itself. Encourage the use of checking procedures.

Links

Multiplication facts: Framework Page 59.

Worksheet Answers

1 a -3 b $+7$ c $\div 4$ d $\times 5$
2 a Path of F2–R–F1–R–F3   b Path of F1–L–F3–R–F2
3 a F1–L–F3; T–F3–R–F1
  b F5–L–F2–R–F2; T–F2–L–F2–R–F5

Exercise Answers

1 a Turn a tap off
  b Sit down
  c Close your eyes
  d Drive uphill
  e Breathe out
  f Take your shoes off
  g Climb down a ladder
  h Open the door
2 Joe woke up. He breathed out and shut the book. He stood up. He put his book in his bag and then put in his pen. He closed his bag.
3 a -3 b $\div 5$
  c $+7$ d $\times 6$
4 a 6   b 5   c 4   d 4
  e 3   f 2   g $\div$ h $\times$

1 Fill in the second operation that undoes the first one.

a   **b**   **c**   **d**

2

> F moves a robot forwards.
> F3 means go forwards 3 squares.
> R means turn right.
> L means turn left.
> T means turn around.

To move the robot from
A to B you write:
F3 – R – F2

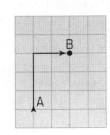

To take the robot back you reverse
all the instructions:
T – F2 – L – F3

Draw the path of the robot for:

a F2 – R – F1 – R – F3

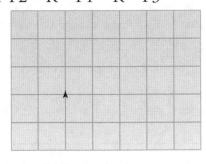

b F1 – L – F3 – R – F2

3 For each diagram:

▶ Give instructions to move the robot from A to B.
▶ Give the reverse instructions to move the robot back to B.

a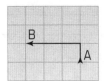

b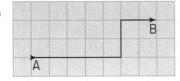

A to B: _____

B to A: _____

A to B: _____

B to A: _____

A1.6 Operation machines

Access

This spread provides access to the year 7 objective:
▶ Understand the four operations as they apply to whole numbers (82).

Lesson Plan

Mental starter

▶ Write a rule on the board, say +7. Give students a number, and ask them to apply the rule and give the answer.
▶ Change the inputs and the rule to include all four operations.
▶ Emphasise keywords: **input, output**.

Introductory activity

Link the mental starter to function machine representation. Emphasise that you put in an input, then do the operation to give the output.

Use **R7** (function machines) to discuss the output for different inputs and functions.

Encourage students to give outputs for given inputs. Use consecutive numbers from one for inputs, to allow confident students to describe the sequence represented by the outputs.

Develop to two-step machines emphasising the use of 'jottings' to break down the mental calculations.

Plenary

Using a ruler (**R19**), discuss the conversion from cm to mm.

Formalise this as a function machine with cm as input and mm as output ($\times$ 10 as a function) and discuss some examples.

Alter the cm values and ask for corresponding mm values. With confident students give an output value, and discuss how to **reverse** the machine. Link to the previous lesson on doing and undoing.

Homework

▶ Give students a copy of **R7** with inputs and functions given. They find the output for each machine. Students design their own function machines for the class to solve.

Exercise Commentary

Coverage

The questions assess objectives on Framework (Y456) Page 59.

Useful resources

R7 – function machines.
R19 – a ruler.
A1.6WS – provides support for weaker students.

Differentiation

▶ Questions 1 and 2 focus on one-step machines.
▶ Question 3 focuses on two-step machines.
▶ Question 4 extends to finding the function.
Support tier: focuses on using function machines to find functions and inputs.

Misconceptions

Recording results may be difficult for some students. **A1.6WS** and emphasising the use of jottings will help.

Some students will consider there to be two outputs for two-step machines. This can be addressed through the use of jottings at the interim stage (between the first and second operations).

Links

Choosing appropriate operations: Framework (Y456) Page 75.

Exercise Answers

1 a 7   b 12   c 16   d 30
2 a 9   b 2   c 18   d 3
3 b 8   c 8   d 8   e 20
4 a +4   b +9 or ×4

Worksheet Answers

1 a 7   b 6   c 20   d 5   e 8   f 4   g 40   h 18   i 4
2 a 10   b 4   c 15   d 8

1 Work out these calculations:

a $2 + 5 = $ _____   **b** $9 - 3 = $ _____   **c** $10 \times 2 = $ _____   **d** $15 \div 3 = $ _____

e $12 - 4 = $ _____   **f** $16 \div 4 = $ _____   **g** $4 \times 10 = $ _____   **h** $6 + 12 = $ _____

i $20 \div 5 = $ _____   **j** $30 + 50 = $ _____   **k** $5 + 27 = $ _____   **l** $38 - 4 = $ _____

m $22 - 15 = $ _____   **n** $6 \times 7 = $ _____   **o** $24 \div 4 = $ _____   **p** $20 \div 10 = $ _____

2 In this machine:

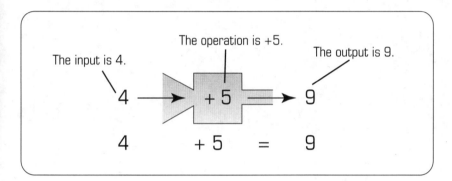

The operation is +5.

The input is 4.

The output is 9.

$$4 \longrightarrow +5 \longrightarrow 9$$

$$4 \qquad + 5 \qquad = \qquad 9$$

Complete these machines with the correct output.

a
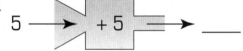
$$5 \longrightarrow +5 \longrightarrow \underline{\quad}$$

b

$$7 \longrightarrow -3 \longrightarrow \underline{\quad}$$

c
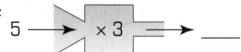
$$5 \longrightarrow \times 3 \longrightarrow \underline{\quad}$$

d
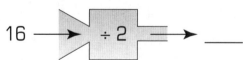
$$16 \longrightarrow \div 2 \longrightarrow \underline{\quad}$$

e
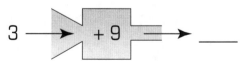
$$3 \longrightarrow +9 \longrightarrow \underline{\quad}$$

f
$$12 \longrightarrow -5 \longrightarrow \underline{\quad}$$

g
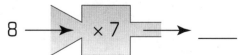
$$8 \longrightarrow \times 7 \longrightarrow \underline{\quad}$$

h
$$49 \longrightarrow \div 7 \longrightarrow \underline{\quad}$$

Framework MATHS   Scheme of work   Year 7

A1 Sequences (6 hours)	Teaching objectives	Framework Maths resources	Other resources
Properties of numbers and number sequences (16–17)	Recognise and extend number sequences formed by counting from any number in steps of constant size, extending beyond zero when counting back.	7A Student Book: A1.1, A1.2, A1.3 7A Teacher's Book: A1.1WS, A1.2WS, A1.2WS, A1.3WS, R6, R17	
Properties of numbers and number sequences (18–19)	Make general statements about odd or even numbers, including the outcome of sums and differences.	7A Student Book: A1.4 7A Teacher's Book: A1.4WS, A3.3OHP, R17, R24	
Understanding multiplication and division (52–5)	Understand the effect of and relationships between the four operations.	7A Student Book: A1.5 7A Teacher's Book: A1.5WS, R18	
Rapid recall of multiplication and division facts (58–9)	**Know by heart all multiplication facts up to 5 x 10.**	7A Student Book: A1.6 7A Teacher's Book: A1.6WS, R7, R19	
Reasoning and generalising about numbers or shapes (78–9)	Solve mathematical problems or puzzles, recognise and explain patterns and relationships, generalise and predict. Suggest extensions by asking 'What if...?'	7A Student Book: A1.1 - A1.6	

Overview

This unit aims to consolidate and extend students' mental addition and subtraction skills. It uses place value to lay the foundations for column addition and subtraction, and introduces negative numbers through the context of temperature. It introduces the idea of multiplying by 10.

Spreads N1.1, N1.4 and N1.5 form the focus of the unit.

Framework references

The unit covers objectives from the Framework (Y456) on pages: 3, 7, 15, 29, 41, 43, 45

Useful resources

Worksheets
N1.1WS – understanding place value
N1.2WS – negative number lines
N1.3WS – adding and subtracting using number lines
N1.4WS – adding using jottings
N1.6WS – multiplying by 10

OHP
N1.5OHP – adding to 20

General resources
R4 – place value table
R6 – number lines

Springboard 7 pages
50, 55, 56, 70, 72, 78

Introduction

Discuss when students may need to use mental strategies. Emphasise that they are everyday skills that everyone needs to be able to use effectively.
Use the Check in activity to find out what students know about the content of the unit, in particular their strategies for mental addition and subtraction and what they know about negative numbers.

Check in activity

Ask students to find the difference between 26 and 29.
Discuss strategies.
Emphasise counting on from 26.
Repeat for other differences.

Differentiation – spanning the bridge

Spread	Bridge to the Support tier
N1.1	Develop the Introductory Activity to consider hundredths, and extend them to compare numbers with tenths, with numbers with tenths and hundredths.
N1.2	Both tiers can work alongside one another in this lesson. Include some discussion around decimal negative numbers, and increasing or decreasing temperatures (touching on addition and subtraction) for Support tier students.
N1.3	Develop the Introductory Activity to consider the mathematical operation of temperatures falling (subtraction) and rising (addition). Progress to consider sequences of negative numbers.
N1.4	Support tier students need to develop strategies for mental addition and subtraction of numbers including HTU and decimals - discussion around decimal place value will help. Highlight the compensation method during the Introductory Activity.
N1.5	The Introductory Activity can be used as a recap for Support tier students who covered mental subtraction strategies in N1.4. Extend it to include complex numbers including decimals. Discuss how to formalise written methods (addition and subtraction).
N1.6	The Support tier involves the use of a calculator for more complex additions and subtractions. The Access Introductory Activity is not very relevant to the Support tier exercises. Support tier students can gain confidence with their calculators by working through the various examples in the Support student book. Discuss when to use a calculator, and emphasise the strategy of approximating first as a checking procedure.

Access

This spread provides access to the Year 7 objective:
▸ Understand and use place value (36).

Lesson Plan

Mental starter

Guess my number

▸ Write five numbers each made with the same digits. For example, 1845, 4815, 8451, 8514, 1548.

▸ Pick one number. Ask students to guess the number by asking questions such as: does it have four hundreds?

▸ Emphasise that the same digits are used, but place value determines the number.
You can use **R4** (place value table).

Introductory activity

Refer to the mental starter. **Discuss the place value of the number 324.**

▸ Ask: how many hundreds/tens/units?

Encourage students to place it on a number line (**R6**). Emphasise that 10 units make each ten. Repeat with 431.

Repeat with 3.6. Ask:

▸ How many units?

▸ What does the 6 stand for?

▸ How many tenths in a unit?

Emphasise tenths and decimals as part of a whole number. Encourage students to place 3.6, and other one decimal place numbers on a number line.

Plenary

Repeat 'guess my number' from the mental starter. Include decimal numbers, and develop to hundredths for confident students.

Homework

▸ Challenge students to use the digits 1–4 and one decimal point to create the largest and smallest numbers possible.

▸ Springboard 7: Page 70.

Exercise Commentary

Coverage

The questions assess objectives on Framework (Y456) Pages 3, 28 and 29.

Useful resources

R4 – place value table.
R6 – number lines.
N1.1WS – provides support for weaker students.

Differentiation

▸ Questions 1–3 focus on partitioning whole numbers.
▸ Question 4 involves positioning decimals.
▸ Question 5 extends to comparing decimals.

Support tier: focuses on place value including hundredths.

Misconceptions

In question 5 students may confuse the signs and place them incorrectly. Encourage students to discuss strategies for remembering as a group so ideas are shaped.

Links

Ordering integers: Framework (Y456) Page 15.

Exercise Answers

1 a 312   b 133   c 601   d 424   e 142   f 80
2 a 100, 100, 10, 1, 1, 1, 1, 1
  b 100, 100, 100, 1, 1, 1, 1   c 10, 10, 10, 10
  d 100, 100, 1, 1   e 100, 100, 100, 100, 100, 10, 1, 1
  f 10, 10, 10, 1, 1, 1, 1
3 a 840   b 563   c 751, 101 or 211
4 a 2.8   b 3.2   c 4.3   d 5.4
5 c >   d >   e >   f <   g >   h >

Worksheet Answers

1 a 135   b 531   2 a 123   b 322   c 313
3 a 100, 10, 10, 10, 10, 1, 1   b 100, 100, 10, 10, 10, 1
  c 100, 100, 100, 100, 10, 10   d 100, 100, 1, 1, 1, 1, 1
4 Arrows at: a 2.6   b 4.9   c 5.2   d 0.7

1 Here are three digits:

   a What is the smallest number you can make?

   b What is the largest number you can make?

2 What numbers are shown here?

   a  _____

   b  _____

   c 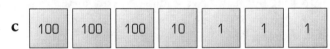 _____

3 Write these numbers as 100s, 10s and units on the cards like question 2.

   a 142

   b 231

   c 420

   d 205

4 Point to these decimal numbers using arrows.

   a 2.6

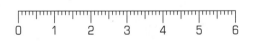

   b 4.9

   c 5.2

   d 0.7

Access

This spread provides access to the Year 7 objective:
▸ Understand negative numbers as positions on a number line (48).

Lesson Plan

Mental starter

▸ Write a positive temperature on the board, 23 °C. Ask students questions such as:

  ▸ In the next town it is 4 °C hotter. What is the temperature?

  ▸ The temperature decreases by 10 °C. What is the new temperature? Is that hotter or colder?

▸ Change the variation of temperature to ask more challenging questions.

Introductory activity

Discuss a temperature estimate of the day outside. Discuss what the temperature might be in Alaska. Emphasise that negative values are used to describe freezing temperatures that are below zero.

Link **colder** to **smaller** and **hotter** to **bigger**. Link to thermometer as a vertical number line as in the Students' Book. Encourage students to place negative numbers on a number line (**R6**).

Emphasise that ⁻4° is smaller (colder) than ⁻1°. Ask questions such as:
▸ Which is colder, ⁻14° or 8°?
▸ Which is bigger, ⁻5 or ⁻2?

Plenary

Use the values from question 5, and discuss the difference in temperatures of different pairs of cities, for example, London and Bangkok (22 °C).

Homework

▸ Ask students to find examples of negative numbers used in everyday life (weather forecast/goal differences in newspapers).

▸ Springboard 7: Page 70.

Exercise Commentary

Coverage

The questions assess objectives on Framework (Y456) Page 15.

Useful resources

R6 – number lines
N1.2WS – provides support for weaker students.

Differentiation

▸ Question 1 involves reading a thermometer.
▸ Questions 2–4 involve ordering and comparing temperatures.
▸ Question 5 involves a real-life context.

Support tier: extends to include temperature rises.

Misconceptions

Students commonly think ⁻5 is bigger that ⁻2. Linking to ideas of cold and hot can help, and the use of number lines (**R6**) will enable students to see the relative sizes. Emphasise that as a horizontal line with positive numbers, how numbers to the right are larger, whilst numbers to the left are smaller.

Links

Ordering numbers: Framework (Y456) Page 9; Sequences: Page 17.

Exercise Answers

1 a 10° b 4° c 15° d 23° e 0° f ⁻5° g 6°
  h ⁻1° i 19° j ⁻9° k 13° l 7°
2 a ⁻6° b ⁻4° c ⁻10° d ⁻2° e ⁻10° f ⁻7°
  g 3° h 0°   3 a < b < c < d >
4 a ⁻9°, ⁻5°, ⁻3° b ⁻3°, ⁻2°, ⁻1° c ⁻7°, ⁻5°, 0°
  d ⁻10°, ⁻8°, 0° e ⁻10°, ⁻6°, 5° f ⁻9°, 4°, 9°
5 a Montreal b Bangkok c London, Bangkok

Worksheet Answers

1 a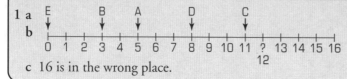
  b
  c 16 is in the wrong place.

2 a 2, ⁻2 b ⁻1, ⁻2 c ⁻3, ⁻4, ⁻5 d ⁻6, ⁻8
3 ⁻5, ⁻4, 4, 5
4 ⁻8, ⁻6, ⁻5, ⁻4, ⁻3, ⁻2, ⁻1

1 On this number line the arrow points to position 9.

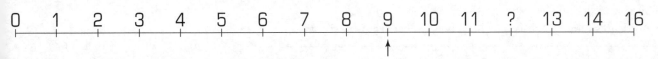

| 0 | 1 | 2 | 3 | 4 | 5 | 6 | 7 | 8 | 9 | 10 | 11 | ? | 13 | 14 | 16 |

a Draw arrows to point to these positions.
Label the arrows with their letters.

A 5   **B** 3   **C** 11   **D** 8   **E** 0

b Find the ? mark on the line. Write the correct number above it.

c Which number is in the wrong place? Answer: _____

2 Thermometers measure temperature.

Write the missing temperatures on these thermometers.

a
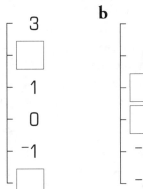
3
□
1
0
$^-$1
□

b
1
0
□
□
$^-$3
$^-$4

c
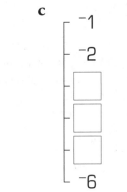
$^-$1
$^-$2
□
□
□
$^-$6

d
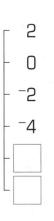
2
0
$^-$2
$^-$4
□
□

3 Put the missing numbers into the boxes on this number line.

□ □ $^-$3 $^-$2 $^-$1 0 1 2 3 □ □

4 Complete this number line that starts at $^-$10.

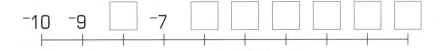
$^-$10 $^-$9 □ $^-$7 □ □ □ □ □ □

Access

This spread provides access to the Year 7 objective:
▶ Add and subtract positive and negative numbers in context (50).

Lesson Plan

Mental starter

▶ Choose a temperature to start with, 7 °C. Go around the class, with each student increasing the temperature by 4 °C.
▶ Use different start temperatures, and step sizes. Develop to decreasing temperatures.

Introductory activity

Encourage students to demonstrate an addition of two positive integers on a number line (**R6**). For example, 2 + 5. Emphasise the starting number and direction. You move to the right to get larger/warmer.

Discuss how to extend to a negative start temperature **rising** by 5 degrees as in the Students' Book.

Develop to subtraction, linking the calculation with finding the **difference** of two numbers and a change of **direction** (moving to the left).

Model the difference between 4 and ⁻3 using a number line (**R6**) (taking integer jumps) as in the Students' Book.

Plenary

Place 20 in the centre of the board, and ask students for number chains that add to make 20. For example, 18 and 2. This is shown on **N1.5OHP**.

Develop to include negatives: ⁻1 + ? = 20. Use a number line (**R6**) to support weaker students.

Homework

▶ Ask students to create three addition calculations where the answer is ⁻12 (For example, ⁻15 + 3 = ⁻12), and three subtraction questions (7 − 19 = ⁻12).
▶ Springboard 7: Page 78.

Exercise Commentary

Coverage

The questions assess objectives on Framework (Y456) Page 15.

Useful resources

R6 – number lines
N1.3WS – provides further practice of the key ideas.
N1.5OHP – pairs adding to 20 for the plenary.

Differentiation

▶ Question 1 focuses on reading a number line.
▶ Questions 2 and 3 involve temperature changes.
▶ Questions 4 and 5 involve calculating differences.

Support tier: extend to include number sequences.

Misconceptions

Students will be unsure as to whether to include zero as they move backwards and forwards on the number line. Emphasise the use of a drawn number line and encourage students to count in 1s until they recognise the pattern.

Links

Ordering numbers: Framework (Y456) Page 9.

Exercise Answers

1 a ⁻15°C b ⁻11°C c ⁻8°C d ⁻5°C e ⁻2°C
  f ⁻1°C g 1°C h 4°C i 6°C j 12°C
2 a 0°C b 0°C c 0°C d 0°C e ⁻7°C f ⁻12°C
3 a 4°C b 6°C c 2°C d 7°C e 1°C f 5°C
  g ⁻8°C h ⁻3°C i ⁻9°C
4 a 7° b 4° c 7° d 15° e 8° f 8° g 4°
  h 3° i 7°
5 a 7° fallen b 7° risen c 9° fallen d 7° fallen
  e 8° risen f 6° risen

Worksheet Answers

1 a 2 b 2 c 4 d 1 e 4 f ⁻2 g 0 h 6 i ⁻2 j 6
2 a ⁻8 b ⁻7 c ⁻9 d ⁻11 e ⁻8 f ⁻11 g ⁻12 h ⁻13 i ⁻13 j ⁻15
3 a 5 b ⁻10 c ⁻17 d ⁻3 e 0 f ⁻10 g 7 h ⁻17

1 Complete these problems.
Use the number line to help you.

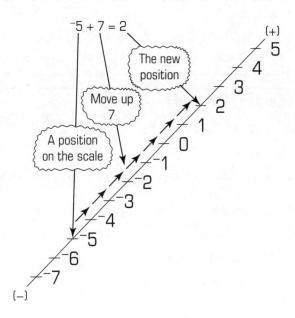

a $^-5 + 7 =$ _____   b $^-3 + 5 =$ _____

c $^-4 + 8 =$ _____   d $^-6 + 7 =$ _____

e $^-2 + 6 =$ _____   f $^-7 + 5 =$ _____

g $^-6 + 6 =$ _____   h $^-2 + 8 =$ _____

i $^-9 + 7 =$ _____   j $^-4 + 10 =$ _____

2 Complete these problems.
Use the number line to help you.

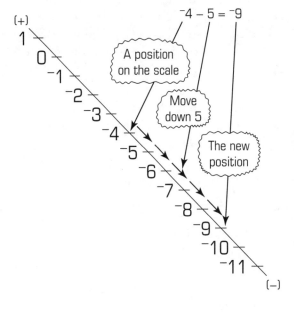

a $^-5 - 3 =$ _____   b $^-3 - 4 =$ _____

c $^-1 - 8 =$ _____   d $^-6 - 5 =$ _____

e $^-2 - 6 =$ _____   f $^-7 - 4 =$ _____

g $^-6 - 6 =$ _____   h $^-5 - 8 =$ _____

i $^-9 - 4 =$ _____   j $^-5 - 10 =$ _____

3 Complete these problems.

a $^-4 + 9 =$ _____   b $^-3 - 7 =$ _____

c $^-5 - 12 =$ _____   d $^-9 + 6 =$ _____

e $^-9 + 9 =$ _____   f $^-5 - 5 =$ _____

g $^-12 + 5 =$ _____   h $^-8 - 9 =$ _____

Access

This spread provides access to the Year 7 objective:
▸ Consolidate mental methods of calculation (92).

Lesson Plan

Mental starter

Target 20

▸ Write 20 in the centre of the board or use **N1.5OHP**. Ask for chains of two numbers which add to 20. Continue until you have each of the pairs.

▸ Discuss the order: is 20 + 0 different from 0 + 20?

Introductory activity

Refer to the mental starter.

Discuss how to work out 3 + 10. Encourage the use of a number line (**R6**): start at number 3 and jump up 10. Emphasise how to add a ten using a place value table (**R4**), and discuss the pattern. Discuss more examples and give weaker students the opportunity to gain confidence.

Progress to adding 30, using a number line (**R6**) to demonstrate 3 jumps of 10, and again link to the addition of tens in a formal place value context.

Finally, discuss 15 + 33 as starting at 15, jumping 3 jumps of 10, and 3 unit jumps. Encourage the use of a 'jotted' number line to help students progress.

Plenary

Write a variety of positive integers on the board, and challenge students to find two (extending to three) numbers that add to make 10, 20, 40, 80, ...

Extend to include numbers including hundreds and discuss the addition of 100, and multiples of 100.

Homework

▸ Ask students to make a poster to illustrate how to work out 43 + 19.

▸ Springboard 7: Page 55.

Worksheet Answers

1 27   2 55   3 71   4 73   5 42   6 31   7 73
8 59   9 40   10 47

Exercise Commentary

Coverage

The questions assess objectives on Framework (Y456) Pages 41 and 43.

Useful resources

R4 – place value table
R6 – number lines
N1.5OHP – adding to 20.
N1.4WS – provides support for weaker students.

Differentiation

▸ Questions 1–3 focus on complements to 20.
▸ Questions 4 and 5 involve adding 10 to numbers.
▸ Questions 6 and 7 involve adding 2-digit numbers.

Support tier: includes addition and subtraction involving 3-digit numbers.

Misconceptions

In question 7, students may experience difficulty jotting a basic number line. Use **N1.4WS** to support weaker students and help them to practise these skills.

Links

Written methods: Framework (Y465) Pages 48–51.

Exercise Answers

1 a 10   b 11   c 9   d 5   e 13   f 19   g 8   h 4
 i 14   j 12   k 17   l 7   m 16   n 0
2 a £7   b £11   c £17   d £9   e £13
3 a False   b True   c False   d False   e True
 f False
4 a 17   b 15   c 19   d 11   e 21   f 25   g 22
 h 31   i 42   j 29   k 37   l 30
5 a £13   b £23   c £19   d £22   e £35   f £50
6 a £29   b £57   c £45   d £57   e £51   f £95
7 a 54   b 56   c 73   d 39   e 59   f 69   g 88
 h 56

Use these number lines to help you add these numbers.
The first one is done for you.

1 13 + 14 = 27

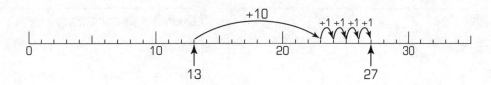

2 20 + 8 = ____

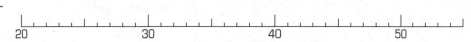

3 50 + 18 = ____

4 40 + 29 = ____

5 23 + 20 = ____

6 10 + 19 = ____

7 40 + 32 = ____

8 26 + 33 = ____

9 11 + 29 = ____

N1.5 Mental subtraction

Access

This spread provides access to the Year 7 objective:
▸ Consolidate mental methods of calculation (92).

Lesson Plan

Mental starter

Target 20
▸ Write 20 in the centre of the board. Ask for complements which add to 20. Continue until you have each of the pairs. This is also shown on **N1.5OHP**.
▸ Discuss subtraction facts you can derive from the complements: $3 + 17 = 20$ so $20 - 13 = 7$.

Introductory activity

Recap the mental addition from N1.4, in particular the number line jottings, and partitioning of numbers.

Discuss strategies for subtracting 10 from a number, giving students a start number, and a jump of ten. Emphasise that you take a ten from the tens place value digit.

Allow students to gain confidence through repetitive questions.

Progress to subtracting multiples of 10, and develop to discuss an example of subtracting any 2-digit value by partitioning into tens and ones.

Plenary

Challenge students to work out $65 - 48$. Encourage them to model their methods on the board. Share alternative strategies and discuss the compensation method ($65 - 50 + 2$).

Discuss the order of a calculation. Emphasise that $20 - 17$ is different to $17 - 20$.

Homework

▸ Ask students to make a poster to illustrate how to work out $83 - 46$.
▸ Springboard 7: Page 56.

Exercise Commentary

Coverage

The questions assess objectives on Framework (Y456) Pages 41, 43 and 45.

Useful resources

R6 – number lines
N1.5OHP – pairs of numbers that add to 20.

Differentiation

▸ Questions 1 and 2 focus on subtracting from 20.
▸ Question 3 involves subtracting 10.
▸ Questions 4 and 5 involve subtracting 2-digit numbers.

Support tier: focuses on written addition and subtraction of decimals.

Misconceptions

Students may have difficulty with the number line 'jottings', wanting to calibrate a given line exactly. Emphasise that it is a 'rough diagram', and emphasise the importance (or not) of interval values when they take a jump of ten.

Students may change the order of a subtraction, confusing $20 - 17$ with $17 - 20$. Encourage students to look at each calculation on a number line. Link to the work on negative numbers (N1.2).

Students are likely to lose track of the partitioned parts. The use of jottings as a supportive tool should help structure students' working, Encourage the use of checking strategies for every question.

Links

Negative numbers: Framework (Y456) Page 15.

Exercise Answers

1 a 10   b 8   c 3   d 16   e 4   f 7   g 12   h 9   i 19   j 0   k 12   l 11   m 13   n 14   o 18
2 a £6   b £11   c £9   d £12   e £8   f £3
3 a 3   b 13   c 16   d 29   e 44   f 66
4 a 35   b 25   c 32   d 27   e 33   f 22   g 9   h 64   i 28
5 a 12   b 24   c 24   d 22   e 13   f 22   g 23   h 22   i 22

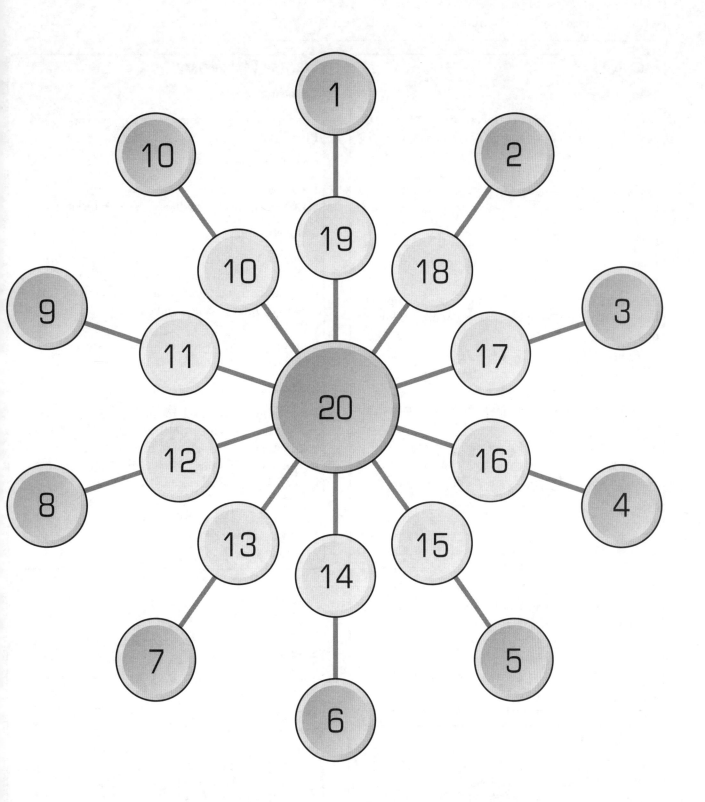

Access

This spread provides access to the Year 7 objective:
▸ Multiply integers by 10, 100, 1000, and explain the effect (36).

Lesson Plan

Mental starter

Ask students to perform multiplications of 10 (3 × 10 and so on) using a calculator. Write results on the board. Challenge them not to use a calculator as soon as they have realised a pattern.

Encourage students to explain the effect of multiplying by 10 in a sentence.

Introductory activity

Refer to the mental starter. Discuss the effect of multiplying by 10. (Use **R4**.)

Emphasise and discuss the common misconception of just 'adding a zero'. Emphasise that you move all the digits one place to the left.

Use a decimal example, say 5.7 × 10, and discuss the effect of adding a zero after a multiplication of 10. Discuss the place value of the digits in turn to determine that this rule does **not** apply for decimal numbers.

Demonstrate shifting digits one place to the left with integer values (requiring the introduction of a **zero place holder**) and decimal values. For example, 5.07 × 10.

Plenary

Discuss how to work out multiplies of 10, such as 4 × 70. Emphasise the calculation can be written as 4 × 7 × 10.

Extend to examples where both numbers are multiples of 10, such as 30 × 60 (3 × 6 × 10 × 10).

Homework

▸ Ask students to find 3.2 × 40, showing all working.
▸ Springboard 7: Page 72.

Worksheet Answers

1 a 60 b 90 c 50 d 80 e 100 f 120
 g 230 h 400 i 510 j 830
2 Clockwise, from top: 100, 210, 170, 400, 130, 420, 60, 190, 550, 240

Exercise Commentary

Coverage

The questions assess objectives on Framework (Y456) Page 7.

Useful resources

R4 – place value table
N1.6WS – provides further practice of the key ideas.

Differentiation

▸ Questions 1 and 2 focus on multiplying by 10.
▸ Questions 3 and 4 involve real-life situations.
▸ Questions 5 and 6 involve understanding the link between multiplication and division.

Support tier: focuses on using a calculator for harder calculations.

Misconceptions

Students may revert back to 'adding a zero'. Encourage them to formalise their work, with digits in place value columns, and showing the shift. **R4** will support students who find this process difficult and lengthy, but will also act as a checking aid.

Links

Place value: Framework (Y456) Page 3;
Measures: Page 91.

Exercise Answers

1 a 30 b 50 c 80 d 10 e 70 f 40 g 60
 h 90 i 20
2 a 160 b 130 c 170 d 120 e 150 f 190
 g 140
3 a 30 m b 50 m c 70 m d 100 m
4 a 90 m b 110 m c 190 m d 230 m e 70 m
 f 350 m g 420 m h 440 m
5 a 4 b 9
6 a 5 b 4 c 3 d 40 − 3 = 37 kg

When you multiply a number by 10 you move the digits one place to the left:

$3 \times 10 = 30$ $\qquad\qquad$ $16 \times 10 = 160$

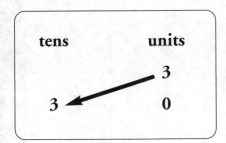

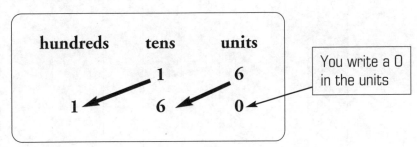

You write a 0 in the units

1 Multiply these numbers by 10. Put the digits in the correct place.
Remember to put a 0 in the empty units place.

		hundreds	tens	units
a	$6 \times 10 =$			
b	$9 \times 10 =$			
c	$5 \times 10 =$			
d	$8 \times 10 =$			
e	$10 \times 10 =$			

		hundreds	tens	units
f	$12 \times 10 =$			
g	$23 \times 10 =$			
h	$40 \times 10 =$			
i	$51 \times 10 =$			
j	$83 \times 10 =$			

2 Complete this spider diagram.
Multiply the numbers in the circles by 10 and write the answers in the squares.

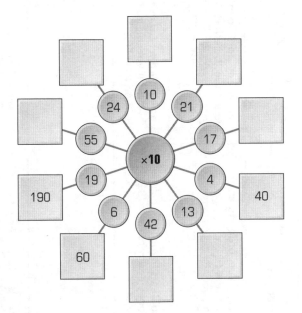

Framework MATHS — Scheme of work — Year 7

N1 Number calculations (6 hours)	Teaching objectives	Framework Maths resources	Other resources
Place value, ordering and rounding (2–3)	Read and write whole numbers in figures and words, and know what each digit represents.	7A Student Book: N1.1 7A Teacher's Book: N1.1WS, R4, R6	
Fractions, decimals and percentages, ratio and proportion (28–9)	Use decimal notation for tenths.	7A Student Book: N1.1 7A Teacher's Book: N1.1WS, R4, R6	
Place value, ordering and rounding (14–15)	Order a given set of positive and negative integers.	7A Student Book: N1.2 7A Teacher's Book: N1.2WS, R6	
Place value, ordering and rounding (14–15)	Calculate a temperature rise or fall across 0 °C.	7A Student Book: N1.3 7A Teacher's Book: N1.3WS, R6	
Mental calculation strategies (+ and −) (40–1)	Partition into T and U, adding the most significant digits first.	7A Student Book: N1.4 7A Teacher's Book: N1.4WS, R4, R6	
Rapid recall of addition and subtraction facts (38–9)	Derive quickly or continue to derive quickly all two-digit pairs that total 20.	7A Student Book: N1.4, N1.5 7A Teacher's Book: N1.4WS, N1.5OHP, R4, R6	
Mental calculation strategies (+ and −) (44–7)	Use place value for mental addition and subtraction.	7A Student Book: N1.4, N1.5 7A Teacher's Book: N1.4WS, N1.5OHP, R4, R6	
Place value, ordering and rounding (6–7)	Multiply any positive integer by 10 and understand the effect	7A Student Book: N1.6 7A Teacher's Book: N1.6WS, R4	
Using a calculator (70–1)	Develop calculator skills and use a calculator effectively.	7A Student Book: N1.6 7A Teacher's Book: N1.6WS, R4	
Problems involving 'real life', money and measures (82–9)	Use all four operations to solve simple word problems involving numbers and quantities based on 'real life', money and measures.	7A Student Book: N1.4–N1.6	

Access

Overview

The aim of this unit is to build students' understanding of perimeter and area, focusing on rectangles. Students need to be confident in using a ruler to measure lengths, and opportunities are provided to practise this skill.

Spreads S1.2 and S1.3 form the focus of the unit.

Framework references

The unit covers objectives on Framework (Y456) Pages 91, 93, 95, 97

Introduction

Ask students for examples of rectangles from everyday life. Show students more examples of rectangles, and generalise the properties of rectangles. Use the Check in activity to revise the properties of rectangles. Emphasise that opposite sides are equal, so if you know the length of two sides, you know the lengths of the other two sides.

Check in activity

Show students a rectangle.
Discuss:
▸ What is the name of this shape? (rectangle)
▸ How many sides does it have? (4)
▸ What do you notice about the angles? (all right angles)
▸ What do you notice about the lengths of the sides? (opposite sides are equal)

Useful resources

Worksheets
S1.1WS – measurements and scales
S1.2WS – perimeter
S1.4WS – perimeter and area

OHP
S1.3OHP – rectangles on a grid

General resources
R1 – digit cards
R7 – function machines
R19 – ruler
R21 – multiplication table
R24 – squared grid

Springboard 7 pages
112, 114, 129

Differentiation – spanning the bridge

Spread	Bridge to the Support tier
S1.1	Extend to consider the perimeter and area of rectangles where length and width are labelled, but there are no squares marked to count.
S1.2	Recap on area of a rectangle and develop to consider the area of an L-shape by splitting it into rectangles. Support tier students also need discussion about finding the length of a rectangle given the area/perimeter.
S1.3	Develop the Support tier to consider which units they would use for areas and perimeters of real-life objects. Remind students of reading scales, in particular the accurate use of a ruler to measure and draw lines accurate to the nearest millimetre.
S1.4	Support tier students need to progress to consider 3D shapes. Take time to discuss dimension, and to look at the 'flat' representation of a 3D shape. Define **net**, and link with area to extend to surface area of a 3D shape.

S1.1 Measurements and scales

Access

This spread provides access to the Year 7 objectives:
▸ Use units of measurements to measure and estimate (228)
▸ Read and interpret scales (230)

Lesson Plan

Mental starter

Students hold up answers to: 6 × 10, 12 × 10, 54 × 10, and so on using **R1** digit cards. Extend to decimals.

Introductory activity

Discuss students' understanding of the size of mm, cm, m, km. Encourage students to offer examples of objects to use as 'benchmarks'.

Discuss what units they would use to measure a leaf, the classroom length, the distance from here to France, and so on.

Discuss how to draw and measure a line with a ruler. Use an OHP of **R19** to demonstrate.

Emphasise that you always start at zero.

Discuss how to change cm to mm, linking with work on multiplying by 10 (N1.6) and operation machines (A1.6).

Discuss how to read the scales on page 31.

Plenary

Ask students to estimate heights, widths, lengths of various items (distance to the bus stop, height of classroom). Discuss the benchmarks they use and strategies to help (comparing with known lengths).

Challenge students to close their eyes and estimate one minute passing.

Homework

▸ Ask students to sketch a basic house shape (rectangle and isosceles triangle) with given dimensions, and challenge them to construct it accurately.
▸ Springboard 7: Page 114.

Exercise Commentary

Coverage

The questions assess objectives on Framework (Y456) Pages 91, 93 and 95.

Useful resources

R1 – digit cards
R19 – ruler
S1.1WS – provides further practice of the key ideas.

Differentiation

▸ Question 1 focuses on choosing correct units.
▸ Questions 2 and 3 focus on drawing and measuring accurately.
▸ Questions 4 and 5 focus on reading scales.

Support tier: focuses on finding perimeter and area of shapes in cm. S1.3 focuses on measurement and scales.

Misconceptions

Students often begin drawing and measuring lines from 1 cm.

Emphasise that you start from 0.

Encourage students to hold the pencil and ruler 'firmly' but not too rigidly. Accuracy should be stressed over speed.

Many students count each division on a scale as one unit. Link to fractions work – if there are 5 marks, each one is one fifth of the range, so you divide by 5.

Links

Multiplying by 10: Framework (Y456) Page 7.

Worksheet Answers

1 Lengths: centimetre, kilometre, millimetre, metre
  Times: month, second, year, week, hour, day
  Weights: kilogram, tonne, gram
2 a 26 kg b 35 km/h c 250 ml d 475 g
3 a 5 cm b 9 cm c 4 cm d 7 cm e 2 cm
4 8 cm by 2 cm

Exercise Answers

1 a centimetre b kilometre c metre d millimetre
  e metre f centimetre g metre h kilometre
  i millimetre j centimetre
2 a 4 cm b 3 cm c 8 cm d 2 cm e 5 cm
3 a Accurate lines: 3 cm, 7 cm, 5 cm, 8 cm, 10 cm, 1 cm.
4 a 36 b 143 c 250 d 260 e 77 f 83
  g 95 h 115 i 124 j 138   5 15.6

1 Write these units of measurement in the correct list.

month	kilogram	second	centimetre	
year	minute	tonne	week	kilometre
hour	gram	millimetre	day	metre

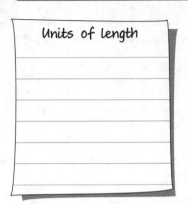

Units of length

Units of time

Units of weight

2 What readings are shown on these scales?

a `20    ▼    30` = _____ kg

b `30  40  50` = _____ km/h

c `200  ▲  300` = _____ ml

d `300    400    500    600` = _____ g

3 Measure these lines using a ruler.

a |————————————————| _____ cm

b |——————————————————————————| _____ cm

c |——————————| _____ cm

d |————————————————————| _____ cm

e |————| _____ cm

4 Measure the length and width of this rectangle and write on your answers.

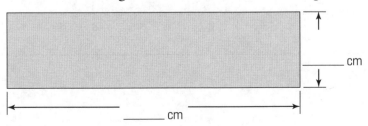

_____ cm

_____ cm

S1.2 Perimeter

Access

This spread provides access to the Year 7 objectives:
▸ Calculate the perimeter of shapes made from rectangles (234)

Lesson Plan

Mental starter

Slowly read a string of four one-digit numbers.

Students mentally calculate the sum of the string.

Repeat three or four times

Develop to using larger numbers.

Introductory activity

Ask questions to assess students' existing understanding:
▸ What is perimeter?
▸ What units is it measured in?

Walk around the edges of the classroom or table, emphasising that you are walking around the perimeter of the classroom. Emphasise that perimeter is a length – the total distance around a shape.

Discuss how to find the perimeter of a rectangle, given the length and width. Emphasise the use of addition.

Emphasise the property of a rectangle – given one length dimension, we know the opposite side length.

Discuss the L-shape in the Students' book with one dimension missing.

Discuss how to calculate the missing length and the perimeter.

Plenary

Draw a 3 cm × 4 cm rectangle with the diagonal (5 cm) marked. Tell students that:
▸ Emily says the perimeter is 3 + 4 + 3 + 4 = 14 cm.
▸ Sam says it is 3 + 4 + 3 + 4 + 5 = 19 cm.

Who is right?

Homework

▸ Draw as many rectangles as possible that have a perimeter of 24 cm.
▸ Springboard 7: Page 112.

Exercise Commentary

Coverage

The questions assess objectives on Framework (Y456) Page 97.

Useful resources

S1.2WS – provides support for weaker students.

Differentiation

▸ Question 1 focuses on finding the perimeter of shapes by counting squares.
▸ Questions 2 and 3 involve finding perimeters of shapes, some with lengths missing.
▸ Question 4 involves finding a missing length.

Support tier: combines perimeter and area and progresses to using a formula for area. S1.2 focuses on simple perimeter and area calculations.

Misconceptions

Students often use all the numbers given in a question, rather than just those that are needed. Encourage students to imagine themselves walking around the shape.

Links

Properties of rectangles: Framework Page (Y456) 103

Exercise Answers

1 C = 22 cm   E = 22 cm   H = 24 cm
2 a 14 cm   b 28 cm   c 22 cm   d 27 cm
  e 26 cm   f 20 cm
3 a 5 cm   b 11 cm   c 8 cm
4 7 cm

Worksheet Answers

1 a 14 cm   b 26 cm   c 16 cm   d 22 cm
2 a 18 cm   b 18 cm   c 18 cm   d 16 cm
3 5 cm

1 What is the perimeter of each shape?

a

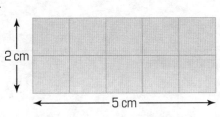

Perimeter = _____ cm

b

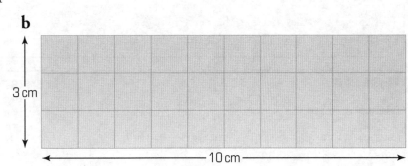

Perimeter = _____ cm

c

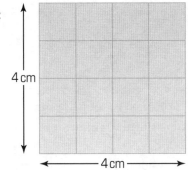

Perimeter = _____ cm

d

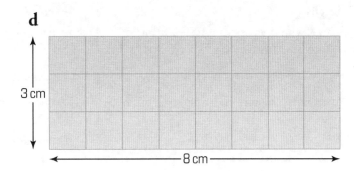

Perimeter = _____ cm

2 Measure the perimeter of each shape.

a

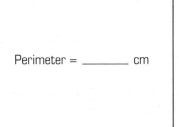

b

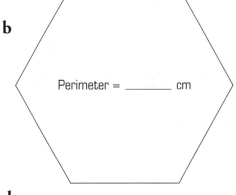

c

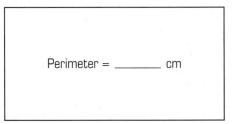

d

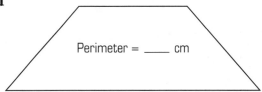

3 Challenge

This is a square.
The perimeter is 20 cm.
What is the length of each side? _____ cm

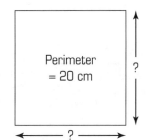

S1.3 Area

Access

This spread provides access to the Year 7 objectives:
▸ Calculate the area of shapes made from rectangles (234)

Lesson Plan

Mental starter

Call out a multiplication question, say 4 × 6. Students stand if they know the answer.

Choose a student, who then asks a division question based upon the answer, say 24 ÷ 3. Students stand if they know the answer.

Choose a student, who then asks a multiplication question based upon the answer (say 8 × 5), and so on.

Introductory activity

Ask questions to assess students' existing understanding:
▸ What is area?
▸ What units is it measured in?

Emphasise that area is the space inside a shape and is measured in squares.

Look at a rectangle on a squared grid (use **S1.3OHP**).

Discuss how to find the area. Model counting squares.

Repeat for other areas.

Emphasise that each square is 1 cm² and formalise notation (cm²).

Discuss finding the area of a large rectangle (9 × 8). Emphasise that the number of squares in the top **layer/row** is repeated for each row.

Progress to the formula: length × width = area.

Plenary

Look at the area of an irregular shape on a squared grid (**R24**), say a leaf.
Discuss how to estimate non-whole squares to give an approximate value of area.

Homework

▸ Draw as many rectangles as possible with a perimeter of 24 cm.
  Which has the largest area?
▸ Springboard 7: Page 129.

Exercise Commentary

Coverage

The questions assess objectives on Framework (Y456) Page 97.

Useful resources

R21 – multiplication table
R24 – squared grid
S1.3OHP – rectangles on a squared grid

Differentiation

▸ Questions 1 and 2 focus on counting squares.
▸ Question 3 involves using the formula and correct notation.
▸ Question 4 involves finding a missing length, given the area.

Support tier focuses: on measurement and scales. S1.2 combines perimeter and area and uses the formula.

Misconceptions

Students need a good grasp of multiplication facts, and a multiplication grid (**R21**) may be helpful.

Students may not be confident when only given the dimensions of a rectangle. Encourage them to draw the 3 × 5 example in their books, counting how many squares are in the top row, and how many rows there are. Link this to the dimensions given.

Links

Properties of rectangles: Framework (Y456) Page 103.

Exercise Answers

1 5 cm², 7 cm², 11 cm²
2 a 12 squares   b 20 squares   c 25 squares
  d 30 squares
3 a 15 cm² b 12 cm² c 9 cm² d 18 cm²
  e 25 cm² f 20 cm² g 12 cm² h 50 cm²
4 2 cm

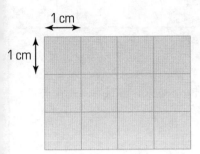

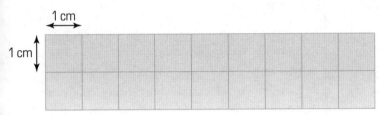

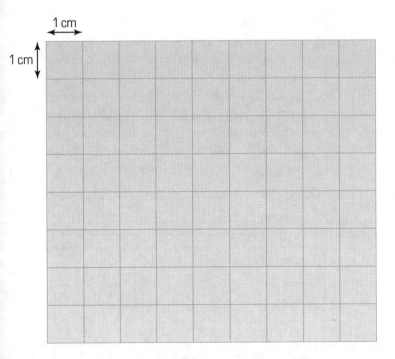

S1.4 Perimeter and area

Access

This spread provides access to the Year 7 objectives:
▸ Calculate the perimeter and area of shapes made from rectangles (234)

Lesson Plan

Mental starter

Show an empty operation machine (use **R7**).

Students suggest an input value. You supply the operation (use division if possible).
Students give the output.

Introductory activity

Show a rectangle on a squared grid and recap key points on perimeter and area.

▸ What is perimeter/area?

▸ How do you calculate it?

▸ What units is it measured in?

Discuss how to calculate the perimeter and area of the rectangle. Emphasise that perimeter is measured as a length, and requires **addition** of **all** the outside dimensions, while area is measured using squares, and can be calculated by **multiplication** of width and height.

Progress to a compound shape on a squared grid (**R24**).

Discuss how to calculate the perimeter, and extend to area. Encourage students to start from facts they know – the shape can be split into two rectangles.

Plenary

Given perimeter and width of a rectangle, discuss how to find the missing length. Link to inverse operation machines from the mental starter.

Given a square with perimeter of 40 cm, discuss strategies for finding the area.

Homework

▸ Draw as many rectangles as possible that have an area of 36 cm². Calculate the perimeter of each.

▸ Springboard 7: Pages 124, 125, 126.

Exercise Commentary

Coverage

The questions assess objectives on Framework (Y456) Page 97.

Useful resources

R7 – function machines

R24 – squared grid

S1.4WS – provides further practice of the key ideas.

Differentiation

▸ Questions 1 and 2 focus on counting squares.

▸ Questions 3 and 4 involve using the formula and metre notation.

▸ Question 5 involves finding a missing length and then the area.

Support tier focuses: on 3-D shapes. S1.2 focuses on compound shapes using the area formula.

Misconceptions

Students are likely to confuse perimeter and area.

Encourage them to share reminder strategies and think about everyday examples (perimeter fence) to keep in mind for reference.

Students will be tempted to calculate perimeter using only the lengths given, and area using all the values given. Encourage them to return to first principles – imagine walking once around the shape for perimeter, and drawing the squares onto a shape for area.

Links

Properties of rectangles: Framework Page 103.

Worksheet Answers

1 a 20 m **b** 50 m **c** 34 m **d** 32 m **e** 30 m **f** 28 m
2 a 25 m² **b** 40 m² **c** 54 m² **d** 150 m²
  e 72 m² **f** 63 m² **g** 40 m² **h** 12 m²

Exercise Answers

1 a 16 cm **b** 7 cm²
2 a perimeter = 40 cm, area = 70 cm²
  b perimeter = 28 cm, area = 28 cm²
3 a perimeter = 14 cm, area = 12 cm²
  b perimeter = 14 cm, area = 10 cm²
  c perimeter = 20 cm, area = 24 cm²
4 a 20 m² **b** 30 m² **c** 40 m²
5 a 9 m **b** 81 cm²

This is a plan of the ground floor of a palace.
The measurements of each room are in metres.

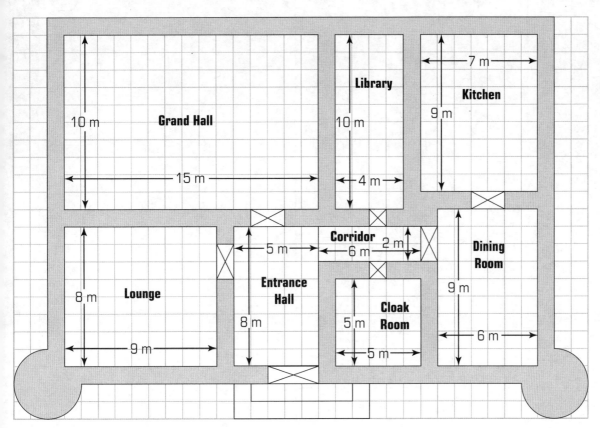

1 What is the perimeter of:

a The Cloak Room _____ m   **b** The Grand Hall _____ m

c The Lounge _____   **d** The Kitchen _____

e The Dining Room _____   **f** The Library _____

▶ Area of a rectangle = length × width.

Your answers should be in square metres (m²)

2 What is the area of:

a The Cloak Room _____ m²   **b** The Library _____ m²

c The Dining Room _____ m²   **d** The Grand Hall _____ m²

e The Lounge _____   **f** The Kitchen _____

g The Entrance Hall _____   **h** The Corridor _____

Framework MATHS Scheme of work Year 7

S1 Perimeter and area (4 hours)	Teaching objectives	Framework Maths resources	Other resources
Measures (90–1)	Use, read and write standard metric units.	7A Student Book: S1.1 7A Teacher's Book: S1.1WS, R19	
Measures (92–5)	Suggest suitable units and measuring equipment to estimate or measure length. Measure and draw lines to the nearest millimetre. Record estimates and readings from scales.	7A Student Book: S1.1 7A Teacher's Book: S1.1WS, R19	
Measures (96–7)	Understand and calculate perimeters of rectangles.	7A Student Book: S1.2, S1.4 7A Teacher's Book: S1.2WS, S1.4WS, R24	
Measures (96–7)	**Understand area measured in square centimetres. Understand and use the formula in words for the area of a rectangle.**	7A Student Book: S1.3, S1.4 7A Teacher's Book: S1.3OHP, S1.4WS, R21, R24	
Reasoning and generalising about numbers or shapes (80–1)	Explain a generalised relationship (formula) in words.	7A Student Book: S1.3, S1.4	

Access

Overview

This unit aims to develop students' understanding of parts of a whole, focusing on recognising $\frac{1}{2}$, $\frac{1}{4}$ and $\frac{1}{10}$. It develops to consider decimal equivalents and finding 10% of an amount.

Spreads N2.1, N2.3 and N2.5 form the focus of the unit.

Framework references

The unit covers objectives on Framework (Y456) Pages 22, 23, 25, 29, 31, 33

Introduction

Ask students for examples of when amounts need to be shared equally. (For example, sharing a cake, as in the Students' Book.) Emphasise that these are everyday skills that everyone needs to be able to use.

Use the Check in activity to find out what students know about finding halves and quarters of quantities. Discuss strategies for sharing amounts equally into two or four groups.

Check in activity

Split the class into pairs, and give each pair 12 multilink cubes.

Ask them to find half. Discuss methods for dividing the cubes into two equal parts.

Ask the class to divide the cubes into four equal groups.

What fraction does each group represent?

Ask quick questions such as:
What is half of 30 students? What is a quarter of 8 sweets?

Would you rather have half a pizza or a quarter? Students can justify their choice using diagrams.

Useful resources

Worksheets

N2.1WS – understanding fractions
N2.2WS – comparing fractions
N2.3WS – fractions of amounts
N2.4WS – decimal scales
N2.5WS – decimals and percentages
N2.6WS – finding tenths of amounts

General resources

R4 – place value tables
R6 – number lines
R7 – function machines
R19 – ruler
R21 – multiplication table
R24 – squared grid

Springboard 7 pages

178, 179, 181, 185, 188, 423, 424, 427

Differentiation – spanning the bridge

Spread	Bridge to the Support tier
N2.1	Progress Support tier students to consider writing an amount as a fraction of another, e.g. 71p as a fraction of £1. Emphasise that they need to use the same units.
N2.2	Support tier students need to consider equivalent fractions. Demonstrate finding equivalent fractions, using the same multiplier for numerator and denominator, and complement with some visual representations. Extend to comparing the size of non-unitary fractions.
N2.3	Support tier students will benefit from the introductory activity as a basis for N2.5. They need to progress to adding and subtracting fractions with the same denominator, and converting between mixed numbers and improper fractions.
N2.4	Progress Support tier students to consider hundredths as well as tenths, and their fractional/decimal equivalents. Emphasise that $\frac{2}{10}$ is $\frac{20}{100}$.
N2.5	Support tier students need to progress to finding non-unitary fractions of amounts. Encourage students to first find the unitary fraction and then multiply by how many parts they require (indicated by the numerator).
N2.6	Extend the mental starter to consider multiplication and division by 100. Highlight simple equivalences from N2.5, and emphasise the conversion of fraction to percentage through finding an equivalent fraction where the denominator is 100.

N2.1 Understanding fractions

Access

This spread provides access to the Year 7 objective:
▸ Use fraction notation to describe a proportion of a shape (60)

Lesson Plan

Mental starter

Ask two students with different attributes to stand up – one boy, one girl, or one blond hair, one brown hair.

Ask the class what fraction is blond. Ask similar questions to assess students' understanding of fractions.

Introductory activity

Show two circles or rectangles: one split into 2 equal pieces, the other into 2 unequal pieces.

Discuss which shows a half.

Emphasise that fractions show equal parts.

Draw representations of different fractions on a squared grid (**R24**): $\frac{1}{4}$, $\frac{1}{2}$, $\frac{3}{4}$ etc. Encourage students to identify the fractions shaded.

Discuss where the **numerator** of a fraction comes from.

Emphasise that it tells you the number of parts you have.

Discuss where the **denominator** of a fraction comes from. Emphasise that it tells you how many equal parts there are.

Plenary

Discuss these problems.

▸ I shaded one quarter of a circle. What fraction is unshaded?

▸ John ate two thirds of his chips. What fraction is left?

▸ Tina spent four fifths of her pocket money. What fraction is left?

Homework

▸ Draw diagrams to represent different fractions, say one fifth, two thirds and five sixths.

▸ Springboard 7: Page 179.

Exercise Commentary

Coverage

The questions assess objectives on Framework (Y456) Page 22.

Useful resources

R24 – squared grid

N2.1WS – provides support for weaker students.

Differentiation

▸ Questions 1 and 2 focus on equal parts.

▸ Questions 3 and 4 involve fraction notation.

▸ Question 5 extends to consider fractions that make a whole.

Support tier: focuses on writing one number as a fraction of another.

Misconceptions

Students may consider the numerator to indicate that number of parts shaded, while the denominator indicates unshaded.

Use the common representation of $\frac{1}{2}$ to help emphasise the meanings of the numerator and denominator.

Links

Division: Framework (Y456) Page 55.

Worksheet Answers

1 b 5, 1, $\frac{1}{5}$ c 10, 1, $\frac{1}{10}$ d 4, 1, $\frac{1}{4}$ e 6, 1, $\frac{1}{6}$
  f 9, 1, $\frac{1}{9}$
2 a $\frac{2}{5}$ b $\frac{2}{3}$ c $\frac{3}{4}$ d $\frac{3}{8}$ e $\frac{5}{6}$ f $\frac{7}{10}$

Exercise Answers

1 a Y   b X
  c Z   d Z
2 a 3   b 4
  c 2   d 6
3 a $\frac{4}{6}$ of the shape is shaded blue.
  b $\frac{5}{8}$ of the shape is shaded blue.
  c $\frac{2}{5}$ of the shape is shaded blue.
  d $\frac{1}{3}$ of the shape is shaded blue.
4 a $\frac{2}{6}$ b $\frac{3}{8}$
  c $\frac{3}{5}$ d $\frac{2}{3}$
5 a No   b No   c Yes
  d No   e Yes

1 Complete these sentences by looking at each shape.

The first one is done for you.

a

▶ There are **3** parts.

▶ **1** part is shaded.

▶ $\frac{1}{3}$ is shaded.

b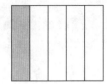

▶ There are ____ parts.

▶ ____ part is shaded.

▶ ____ is shaded.

c

▶ There are ____ parts.

▶ ____ part is shaded.

▶ ____ is shaded.

d

▶ There are ____ parts.

▶ ____ part is shaded.

▶ ____ is shaded.

e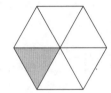

▶ There are ____ parts.

▶ ____ part is shaded.

▶ ____ is shaded.

f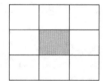

▶ There are ____ parts.

▶ ____ part is shaded.

▶ ____ is shaded.

2

This shape is divided into 3 parts.
2 parts are shaded.
$\frac{2}{3}$ of the whole shape is shaded.

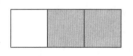

What fraction of each shape is shaded?

a 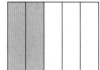 _____

b   _____

c   _____

d 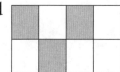 _____

e 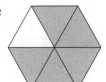 _____

f 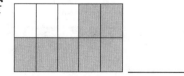 _____

N2.2 Comparing fractions

Access

This spread provides access to the Year 7 objective:
▸ Compare two or more simple fractions (64)

Lesson Plan

Mental starter

Write unit fractions on the board: $1, \frac{1}{2}, \frac{1}{3}$, up to $\frac{1}{7}$.

Discuss which is the biggest and which is the smallest.

Encourage students to think about each fraction as part of a big cake – would they prefer to have one piece of a cake split into two, or into five?

Discuss how to put the fractions in order of size.

Introductory activity

Draw two 6×4 rectangles on a squared grid (**R24**).

Split one vertically into two equal parts, and one vertically into three equal parts.
Shade one part of each diagram and discuss how to write this as a fraction. Recap on keywords **numerator** and **denominator**.

Discuss which fraction is bigger. This will be intuitive from the diagram.

Draw another 6×4 rectangle and shade a $\frac{1}{4}$ strip.
Discuss which is bigger: $\frac{1}{3}$ or $\frac{1}{4}$.

Emphasise that although the denominator is increasing, the size of the part is decreasing.

Introduce < and > notation and discuss an example containing an improper fraction ($\frac{6}{5}$).

Plenary

Go through question 5, and discuss fractions where the numerator is larger than the denominator.

Introduce the terms **improper fractions** and **mixed numbers**. Encourage the use of keywords **numerator** and **denominator**. Discuss what $\frac{3}{2}$ means and looks like.

Homework

▸ Find as many ways as possible of shading $\frac{1}{4}$ of a 3×4 grid.
▸ Springboard 7: Pages 178, 181.

Worksheet Answers

1 a $\frac{1}{4}$ coloured b $\frac{1}{2}$ coloured c $\frac{1}{2}$ is larger than $\frac{1}{4}$
2 a $\frac{1}{2}$ coloured b $\frac{1}{6}$ coloured c $\frac{1}{6} < \frac{1}{2}$ d $\frac{5}{6} > \frac{1}{2}$

Exercise Commentary

Coverage

The questions assess objectives on Framework (Y456) Page 23.

Useful resources

R24 – squared grid

N2.2WS – provides further practice of the key ideas.

Differentiation

▸ Question 1 recaps fraction notation.
▸ Questions 2–4 involve comparing fractions.
▸ Question 5 extends to include improper fractions.

Support tier: focuses on equivalent fractions and cancelling.

Misconceptions

Students will intuitively think that larger denominators indicate larger fractions. Question 2 highlights this problem. Encourage students to use rectangles to illustrate each fraction (a 6×4 grid is useful). A fraction wall may be clearer to some students.

Improper fractions in question 5 may confuse students who will naturally invert the fractions to make them more familiar. Discuss each fraction, using the key vocabulary to help avoid this problem.

Links

Division: Framework (Y456) Page 55.

Exercise Answers

1 a $\frac{1}{5}$ b $\frac{1}{4}$ c $\frac{1}{3}$ d $\frac{1}{8}$ e $\frac{1}{2}$
2 a $\frac{1}{4} < \frac{1}{2}$ b $\frac{1}{4} < \frac{1}{3}$ c $\frac{1}{3} > \frac{1}{8}$ d $\frac{1}{2} > \frac{1}{8}$ e $\frac{1}{2} > \frac{1}{3}$ f $\frac{1}{3} > \frac{1}{5}$
 g $\frac{1}{4} > \frac{1}{5}$ h $\frac{1}{8} < \frac{1}{5}$
3 $\frac{1}{8}, \frac{1}{5}, \frac{1}{4}, \frac{1}{3}, \frac{1}{2}$
4 a $\frac{1}{4} > \frac{1}{6}$ b $\frac{1}{2} > \frac{1}{3}$ c $\frac{1}{8} > \frac{1}{10}$ d $\frac{1}{5} < \frac{1}{3}$ e $\frac{1}{7} < \frac{1}{2}$
 f $\frac{1}{6} < \frac{1}{3}$ g $\frac{1}{4} > \frac{1}{9}$ h $\frac{1}{20} < \frac{1}{6}$ i $\frac{1}{12} > \frac{1}{15}$
5 a $\frac{5}{5} = 1$ b $\frac{7}{5} > 1$ c $\frac{2}{5} < 1$ d $\frac{5}{6} < 1$ e $\frac{10}{10} = 1$
 f $\frac{3}{2} > 1$

1 a Divide this rectangle into quarters ($\frac{1}{4}$s). **b** Divide this rectangle into halves ($\frac{1}{2}$s).

   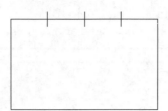

Colour in $\frac{1}{4}$ Colour in $\frac{1}{2}$.

c Compare the $\frac{1}{4}$ and the $\frac{1}{2}$.

Which is the larger area? _____

2 a Colour $\frac{1}{2}$ of this hexagon.   **b** Colour $\frac{1}{6}$ of this hexagon.

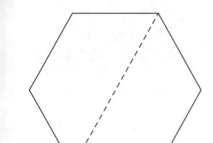   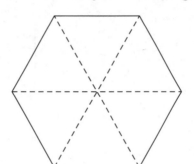

The hexagons are exactly the same.

c Write in a greater than (>) or less than (<) sign to compare the fractions.

$\frac{1}{6}$ ☐ $\frac{1}{2}$

d Colour $\frac{5}{6}$ of the second hexagon.
Write in a > or < sign to compare the fractions.

$\frac{5}{6}$ ☐ $\frac{1}{2}$

3 Steve and Claire have to share these marbles fairly.
Claire wants $\frac{6}{12}$ of the marbles.
Show on the drawing that this is a fair share.

Access

This spread provides access to the Year 7 objective:
▶ Calculate fractions of numbers, quantities or measurements (66)

Lesson Plan

Mental starter

Give students a calculation, say 5×7.
Use a multiplication table (**R21**) as support.
Ask for other calculations that fit these three numbers.
($7 \times 5 = 35$, $35 \div 7 = 5$, $35 \div 5 = 7$)
Repeat for other multiplication and division facts.

Introductory activity

Ask students for $\frac{1}{2}$ of: 10, 60, 30, 18
Encourage students to explain their method.
Emphasise that to find $\frac{1}{2}$ of something you divide by 2.
Discuss how to find $\frac{1}{4}$ of an amount.
Emphasise that to find $\frac{1}{4}$ of an amount you divide by 4.
Discuss how to find $\frac{1}{4}$ of 24. Refer to the mental starter and link the division fact to multiplication facts they might know:

▶ **What number multiplied by 4 gives 24?**

Plenary

Show a 4×6 rectangle on a squared grid (**R24**).
Explain that $\frac{1}{4}$ of the squares are yellow, the rest are red.
Discuss how many to shade in yellow.
Discuss the fraction of the squares that are red. How many squares are red?
Discuss the two methods – calculating $\frac{1}{4}$, and then finding how many are left, **or** multiplying $\frac{1}{4}$ of the amount by 3.

Homework

▶ Write five questions involving fractions that have answer 4 (for example, $\frac{1}{2}$ of $8 = 4$)
▶ Springboard 7: Pages 188, 423, 424.

Exercise Commentary

Coverage

The questions assess objectives on Framework (Y456) Page 25.

Useful resources

R21 – multiplication table
R24 – squared grid
N2.3WS – provides support for weaker students.

Differentiation

▶ Questions 1 and 2 focus on finding $\frac{1}{2}$ of an amount.
▶ Questions 3–5 focus on finding $\frac{1}{4}$ of an amount.
▶ Question 6 is a word problem involving finding quarters.

Support tier: focuses on adding and subtracting fractions.
N2.5 focuses on finding any fraction of an amount.

Misconceptions

The most common difficulty will be calculating divisions. Using a multiplication table (**R21**) can help link multiplication and division facts.
Students will have difficulty finding $\frac{3}{4}$ of an amount in the plenary. Saying 'three quarters' aloud will help them understand that this is 3 lots of one quarter.

Links

Multiplication facts: Framework (Y456) Page 59.

Worksheet Answers

1 5   2 5   3 a 4 b 3 c 4 d 3 e 6
 f 6 g 4 h 6 i 6 j 5
4 a 9 b 12 c 20   5 a 7 b 10 c 8
6 a 8 b 10 c 12

Exercise Answers

1 a 3 b 6 c 8 d 10
2 a 3 b 4 c 5 d 6
 e 7 f 10 g 20 h 30
 i 40 j 50 k 15 l 25
 m 35 n 45 o 55
3 a 1 b 2 c 5 d 6 e 12
4 a 5 b 8 c 4 d 6
 e 1 f 10 g 7 h 9
5 a £14 b 8 kg c 6 cm
6 a 10 b 100 c 25

1 Here are 10 cubes. Put them in two equal groups.

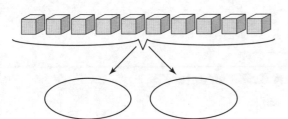

What is $\frac{1}{2}$ of 10?

Answer: ⎯⎯⎯

2 Here are 15 counters. Put them in three equal groups.

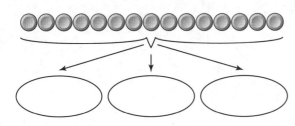

What is $\frac{1}{3}$ of 15?

Answer: ⎯⎯⎯

3 Use the multiplication grid to help you find:

a $\frac{1}{2}$ of 8 = ___   **b** $\frac{1}{3}$ of 9 = ___

c $\frac{1}{4}$ of 16 = ___   **d** $\frac{1}{5}$ of 15 = ___

e $\frac{1}{3}$ of 18 = ___   **f** $\frac{1}{4}$ of 24 = ___

g $\frac{1}{6}$ of 24 = ___   **h** $\frac{1}{2}$ of 12 = ___

i $\frac{1}{5}$ of 30 = ___   **j** $\frac{1}{6}$ of 30 = ___

×	1	2	3	4	5	6
1	1	2	3	4	5	6
2	2	4	6	8	10	12
3	3	6	9	12	15	18
4	4	8	12	16	20	24
5	5	10	15	20	25	30
6	6	12	18	24	30	36

4 Find:

a $\frac{1}{2}$ of 18 = _____   **b** $\frac{1}{2}$ of 24 = _____   **c** $\frac{1}{2}$ of 40 = _____

5 Find:

a $\frac{1}{4}$ of 28 = _____   **b** $\frac{1}{4}$ of 40 = _____   **c** $\frac{1}{4}$ of 32 = _____

6 Find:

a $\frac{1}{3}$ of 24 = _____   **b** $\frac{1}{3}$ of 30 = _____   **c** $\frac{1}{3}$ of 36 = _____

N2.4 Decimal scales

Access

This spread provides access to the Year 7 objective:
▸ Understand and use decimal notation (36)

Lesson Plan

Mental starter

Show a number line, from 5 to 6, with tenths highlighted (use **R6**).

Encourage students to count on from 5 in tenths. Point to each number on the number line to support weaker students, and to avoid the usual 5.9, 5.10 misconception.

Change the start number and increase steps to 0.2.

Introductory activity

Use a ruler (**R19**) to measure a line 4 cm long. Discuss what happens if the line stops halfway between two numbers.

Emphasise that we use fractions and decimals to describe parts of a whole. Highlight the decimal point as separating the whole from parts of the whole.

Show place value columns: thousands, hundreds, tens, units, tenths on **R4**.

Discuss how many:
▸ hundreds in a thousand?
▸ tens in a hundred?
▸ units in a ten?

Emphasise that any unit can be split into ten equal parts and that each part is one tenth.

Discuss fraction and decimal equivalents ($\frac{1}{10} = 0.1$, $\frac{2}{10} = 0.2$), giving examples to help build confidence.

Plenary

Write '1' in the middle on the board.

Ask students for number chains that add to make 1.

Encourage use of fractions and decimals.

Homework

▸ Find three examples of decimals in everyday life, from newspapers or magazines.
▸ Springboard 7: Page 185.

Exercise Commentary

Coverage

The questions assess objectives on Framework (Y456) Pages 29 and 31.

Useful resources

R4 – place value table
R6 – number lines
R19 – ruler
N2.4WS – provides further practice of the key ideas.

Differentiation

▸ Questions 1–3 focus on fraction/decimal equivalents.
▸ Questions 4 and 5 focus on ordering and comparing fractions and decimals.
▸ Question 6 involves estimating lengths.
Support tier: includes hundredths.

Misconceptions

Students may continue tenths past nine, saying 5.9 is followed by 5.10. Direct students to think about the patterns of 'carrying over' in an integer context. A number line is a useful support.

Links

Measures: Framework (Y456) Page 91.

Worksheet Answers

1 a $\frac{3}{10}$ b $\frac{5}{10}$ c $\frac{8}{10}$ d $\frac{4}{10}$ 2 b 2.7 c 3.3 d 2.5
3 A = 2.5   B = 5.3   C = 1.7   D = 0.4   E = 3.7
   F = 2.2   G = 1.8

Exercise Answers

1 a 0.2, $\frac{2}{10}$ b 0.7, $\frac{7}{10}$ c 0.3, $\frac{3}{10}$
   d 0.4, $\frac{4}{10}$ e 0.1, $\frac{1}{10}$ f 0.4, $\frac{4}{10}$
   g 0.6, $\frac{6}{10}$ h 0.9, $\frac{9}{10}$
2 a 0.4 b 0.1 c 0.8 d 0.2 e 0.9 f 0.7
3 a 1 shaded b 3 shaded c 8 shaded d 5 shaded
   e 6 shaded f 9 shaded
4 0.1, 0.3, 0.4, 0.5, 0.6, 0.7, 0.9, 1.0
5 a $\frac{7}{10} > 0.5$ b $0.6 = \frac{6}{10}$
   c $0.3 > \frac{2}{10}$ d $\frac{8}{10} < 0.9$
   e $1.0 = 1$ f $0.1 = \frac{1}{10}$
   g $0.7 > \frac{4}{10}$ h $0.5 = \frac{1}{2}$
6 a 3.3 b 8.7 c 9.9

1 What decimal part of each circle is shaded?

a 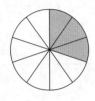   b   c   d

_____ is shaded.   _____ is shaded.   _____ is shaded.   _____ is shaded.

2 Each square is one tenth. What decimal numbers are shown here?
The first is done for you.

a

b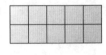

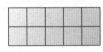

c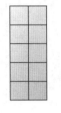

d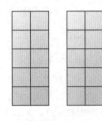

= 1.4   = _____   = _____   = _____

3 What reading does each dial show?
Write your answer as a decimal.

A = _____

B = _____

C = _____

D = _____

E = _____

F = _____

G = _____

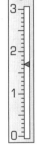

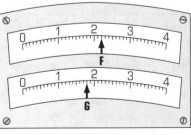

Access

This spread provides access to the Year 7 objective:
▶ Recognise the equivalence of fractions, decimals and percentages (70)

Lesson Plan

Mental starter

Call out a number for students to multiply by 10.

Ask students for a corresponding division fact.

Change the number, and use multiplication or division.

Extend to multiplying by 100.

Introductory activity

Discuss what students already understand by percentage and where they have come across it. Introduce the notation %.
Emphasise per cent as 'out of 100'.

Ask students for other words containing **cent**, and discuss their meaning (**cent**ury – 100 years).

Discuss what 50% of something means. Link to a half, and 0.5 from N2.4 (recap 0.5 as 5 tenths).

Show a number line (**R6**) from 0–1, 0–100%, (with 10 equal intervals) and mark five tenths, 0.5 and 50%. Encourage students to come up to the board to complete the number line (as in the Students' book).

Plenary

Ask some quick-fire questions:
▶ What percentage is equivalent to 0.1?
▶ What percentage is the same as 0.3?

Encourage students to answer without the support of the number line.

Extend to find 50% of 8.

Homework

▶ Find five examples of percentages in everyday life.
▶ Springboard 7: Page 185.

Exercise Commentary

Coverage

The questions assess objectives on Framework (Y456) Page 33.

Useful resources

R6 – number lines

N2.5WS – provides further practice of the key ideas.

Differentiation

▶ Questions 1–3 focus on fraction and percentage equivalents.
▶ Question 4 involves comparing fractions, percentages and decimals.
▶ Question 5 focuses on the whole: 100%.

Support tier: focuses on finding fractions of amounts. N2.6 focuses on equivalent fractions, decimals and percentages.

Misconceptions

Students may naturally think of 0.4 as 4%. Build upon 50% as the 0.5 equivalent, and encourage students refer to the equivalence number line in the Students' book.

Links

Shading fractions: Framework Page (Y456) 23.

Worksheet Answers

1 $\frac{1}{10}$, 0.1, 10%; $\frac{3}{10}$, 0.3, 30%; $\frac{9}{10}$, 0.9, 90%; $\frac{2}{10}$, 0.2, 20%; $\frac{7}{10}$, 0.7, 70%; $\frac{10}{10}$, 1.0, 100%; $\frac{8}{10}$, 0.8, 80%; $\frac{6}{10}$, 0.6, 60%; $\frac{5}{10}$, 0.5, 50%

2 b 50% < 0.8   c $\frac{1}{10}$ = 10%   d 30% < $\frac{6}{10}$
  e $\frac{8}{10}$ = 80%   f 0.2 > $\frac{1}{10}$ g 0.5 < $\frac{8}{10}$ h 60% > $\frac{3}{10}$
  i 30% = 0.3   j $\frac{7}{10}$ = 0.7   k 1.0 > 80%
  l 0.6 < 70%   m 0.4 < $\frac{5}{10}$ n 50% = 0.5   o $\frac{3}{10}$ > 20%

Exercise Answers

1 a 10%   b 20%   c 30%   d 50%   e 90%
  f 30%   g 40%   h 70%   i 60%   j 80%

2 a $\frac{9}{10}$ b $\frac{8}{10}$ c $\frac{7}{10}$ d $\frac{5}{10}$ e $\frac{1}{10}$ f $\frac{7}{10}$ g $\frac{4}{10}$ h $\frac{3}{10}$
  i $\frac{4}{10}$ j $\frac{2}{10}$

3 a 1 part shaded   b 7 parts shaded
  c 4 parts shaded   d 2 parts shaded
  e All parts shaded

4 a 40% < $\frac{8}{10}$ b $\frac{7}{10}$ = 70%   c 10% < 0.7
  d $\frac{9}{10}$ > 80%   e 50% = 0.5   f 90% = $\frac{9}{10}$
  g $\frac{8}{10}$ < 100%   h 100% = $\frac{10}{10}$

5
Full	80%	30%	40%	50%	15%	100%
Empty	20%	70%	60%	50%	85%	0%

1 Use arrows to join fractions, decimals and percentages of the same value.
The first is done for you.

Fraction	Decimal	Percentage
$\frac{4}{10}$ ●	● 0.9 ●	● 10%
$\frac{1}{10}$ ●	● 0.2 ●	● 40%
$\frac{3}{10}$ ●	● 0.6 ●	● 80%
$\frac{9}{10}$ ●	● 0.4 ●	● 30%
$\frac{2}{10}$ ●	● 0.1 ●	● 100%
$\frac{7}{10}$ ●	● 0.8 ●	● 90%
$\frac{10}{10}$ ●	● 0.3 ●	● 60%
$\frac{8}{10}$ ●	● 0.5 ●	● 70%
$\frac{6}{10}$ ●	● 1.0 ●	● 50%
$\frac{5}{10}$ ●	● 0.7 ●	● 20%

2 Use these signs to compare these fractions, decimals and percentages.
The first is done for you.

> > means 'is bigger than'
> < means 'is smaller than'
> = means 'the same as'

a $0.7 > \frac{5}{10}$

b 50% ☐ 0.8

c $\frac{1}{10}$ ☐ 10%

d 30% ☐ $\frac{6}{10}$

e $\frac{8}{10}$ ☐ 80%

f 0.2 ☐ $\frac{1}{10}$

g 0.5 ☐ $\frac{8}{10}$

h 60% ☐ $\frac{3}{10}$

i 30% ☐ 0.3

j $\frac{7}{10}$ ☐ 0.7

k 1.0 ☐ 80%

l 0.6 ☐ 70%

m 0.4 ☐ $\frac{5}{10}$

n 50% ☐ 0.5

o $\frac{3}{10}$ ☐ 20%

N2.6 Finding tenths of amounts

Access

This spread provides access to the Year 7 objective:
▸ Divide numbers by 10 (38)

Lesson Plan

Mental starter

Show a function machine (**R7**) with operation ×10

Give students a two-digit number to input. They give the output.

Progress to giving the output (a multiple of 10) and students calculating the input.

Introductory activity

Refer to the mental starter. Recap what happens to a number when it is multiplied by 10. Use **R4** to show that the digits move to the next highest place.

Discuss how students found the input from the output. Emphasise that division is the inverse of multiplication.

Discuss what happens when you divide a number by 10.

Write the output and input on **R4**. Emphasise that the digits move to the next lowest place.

Discuss more examples to build confidence.

Discuss how to find one tenth of 40. Link back to finding fractions of amounts (N2.4).

Emphasise that to find one tenth of an amount you divide by 10. Discuss what percentage is the same as one tenth (link to N2.5). Discuss how to find 10% of £30.

Plenary

Discuss questions 4c and 5b, finding 20%. Encourage students to explain their strategies.

Extend to consider 20% of £60.

Homework

▸ Give students 10 values of which they must find 10%. Extend each answer to give 20% of each amount.
▸ Springboard 7: Pages 424, 427.

Worksheet Answers

1 a 2 beads in each section
  b $\frac{1}{10}$ of 20 = 2; $\frac{7}{10}$ of 20 = 14; $\frac{2}{10}$ of 20 = 4;
     $\frac{8}{10}$ of 20 = 16; $\frac{4}{10}$ of 20 = 8; $\frac{5}{10}$ of 20 = 10;
     $\frac{10}{10}$ of 20 = 20
2 c 50%   3 a 6 parts shaded   b 12

Exercise Commentary

Coverage

The questions assess objectives on Framework (Y456) Page 33.

Useful resources

R4 – place value table
R7 – function machines
N2.6WS – provides support for weaker students.

Differentiation

▸ Question 1 focuses on dividing by 10.
▸ Questions 2 and 3 focus on finding 10% of an amount.
▸ Questions 4 and 5 extend to finding 20%.
Support tier: includes 25% and 75%.

Misconceptions

Students will often use 'add a zero' as the rule for multiplying by ten, creating difficulty in this move to dividing by 10. Encourage the use of a place value table (**R4**).

Some students struggle to extend finding 10% to finding 20%. Emphasise the relationship between one tenth and two tenths (2 lots of one tenth). Saying each fraction out loud can help understanding.

Links

Place value: Framework (Y456) Page 3.

Exercise Answers

1 a 9 kg   b 5 cm   c £7   d £10   e 15 m
  f 19 mm   g 321   h 75 g
2 a 4 kg   b 8 kg   c 2 kg   d 10 kg   e 4.5 kg
3 £4
4 a 12 cm   b 50 g   c 100 g
5 a 90   b 18

1 Here are 20 beads.

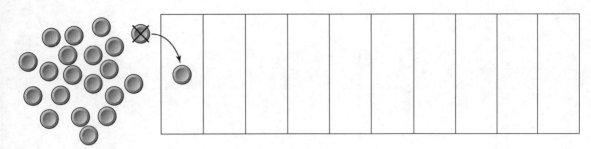

a Share the beads equally between the 10 sections.
Each section is a tenth.

b Use the drawing to link these calculations to their correct answers.
The first one is done for you.

$\frac{1}{10}$ of 20	14
$\frac{3}{10}$ of 20	16
$\frac{7}{10}$ of 20	20
$\frac{2}{10}$ of 20	2
$\frac{8}{10}$ of 20	10
$\frac{4}{10}$ of 20	8
$\frac{5}{10}$ of 20	6
$\frac{10}{10}$ of 20	4

2 This plank measures 10 cm.

10%

a Divide the plank into exactly 10% sections. The first one has been done for you.

b 10% of the plank has been shaded. Shade another 40%.

c How much of the plank is now shaded? Answer: _____%.

3 a Shade 60% of this rectangle.

b Use the diagram in question 1 to find 60% of 20.   Answer: _____.

Framework MATHS Scheme of work Year 7

N2 Fractions, decimals and percentages (6 hours)	Teaching objectives	Framework Maths resources	Other resources
Fractions, decimals and percentages, ratio and proportion (22–3)	Use fraction notation, including mixed numbers, and the vocabulary *numerator* and *denominator*.	7A Student Book: N2.1 7A Teacher's Book: N2.1WS, R24	
Fractions, decimals and percentages, ratio and proportion (22–3)	Recognise mixed numbers.	7A Student Book: N2.2 7A Teacher's Book: N2.2WS, R24	
Fractions, decimals and percentages, ratio and proportion (22–3)	Order a set of fractions such as 2, 2 3/4, 1 3/4, 2 1/2, 1 1/2.	7A Student Book: N2.2 7A Teacher's Book: N2.2WS, R24	
Fractions, decimals and percentages, ratio and proportion (24–5)	**Relate fractions to division**, and use division to find simple fractions of numbers and quantities.	7A Student Book: N2.3 7A Teacher's Book: N2.3WS, R24	
Fractions, decimals and percentages, ratio and proportion (28–9)	**Use decimal notation for tenths.**	7A Student Book: N2.4 7A Teacher's Book: N2.4WS, R4, R6, R19	
Fractions, decimals and percentages, ratio and proportion (30–1)	**Relate fractions to their decimal representations.**	7A Student Book: N2.4 7A Teacher's Book: N2.4WS, R4, R6, R19	
Measures (92–5)	Record estimates and readings from scales to a suitable degree of accuracy.	7A Student Book: N2.4 7A Teacher's Book: N2.4WS, R4, R6, R20	
Fractions, decimals and percentages, ratio and proportion (32–3)	Express one half, one quarter, three quarters, and tenths and hundredths, as percentages.	7A Student Book: N2.5 7A Teacher's Book: N2.5WS, R6	
Fractions, decimals and percentages, ratio and proportion (32–3)	Begin to understand percentage as the number of parts in every 100, and find simple percentages of small whole-number quantities (e.g. 25% of £8).	7A Student Book: N2.5, N2.6 7A Teacher's Book: N2.5WS, N2.6WS, R6	
Place value, ordering and rounding (6–7)	**Divide any positive integer by 10 or 100 and understand the effect**	7A Student Book: N2.6 7A Teacher's Book: N2.6WS, R4	
Problems involving 'real life', money and measures (82–9)	Use all four operations to solve simple word problems including finding simple percentages.	7A Student Book: N2.3–N2.6	

Access

Overview

This unit aims to assess students' understanding of data and probability from primary school, and lay the basis for later work. It introduces the averages mean, median and mode and aims to ensure that all students are confident with the mode.

In the spreads on probability, students are introduced to fraction notation and the probability scale, but an intuitive idea of chance is sufficient at this stage.

Spreads D1.1, D1.4 and D1.6 form the focus of the unit.

Framework references

The unit covers objectives on Framework (Y456) Pages 113, 115, 117.

Introduction

Ask students for their favourite current Top 10 single, recording the results in a tally chart on the board. Ask students to decide which is the most popular among the class. Discuss how the Top 10 is compiled and how the number 1 single is decided upon. Emphasise that this is an everyday example of where the most popular item has to be found.

Use the Check in activity to find out how confident students are in ordering positive numbers.

Check in activity

Write on the board: 13, 7, 4, 32, 27. Discuss:
▸ Which is biggest?
▸ Which is smallest?

Ask students to arrange the numbers in order of size, starting with the smallest. Use a number line (**R6**) to demonstrate that larger numbers are to the right on the number line.

Discuss '7 is bigger than 10 because 7 is bigger than 1 and 0'.

Useful resources

Worksheets
D1.1WS – the mode
D1.3WS – levelling
D1.5WS – describing chance

OHPs
D1.2OHP – data sets
D1.4OHP – probability table
D1.6OHP – probability scale and spinner

General resources
R6 – number lines
R9 – coordinate axes for a bar chart
R11 – tally chart
R21 – multiplication table
Multilink cubes
Bags or boxes
Letter cards: M A T H S
Coins

Springboard 7 pages
152–155, 252–256, 258–260, 301–304, 327

Differentiation – spanning the bridge

Spread	Bridge to the Support tier
D1.1	Progress Support tier students to consider the median of a set of data, extending to where the data set has an even number of values. Emphasise that there can be more than one modal value, but only one median value.
D1.2	Progress support tier students to consider the mean of a set of data. Commonly, this is the average they will be familiar with from Primary school.
D1.3	Progress Support tier students to consider situations where an average would be helpful. Discuss data collection, and recording data introducing statistical diagrams as a way of communicating not only averages, but other information collected. Link to the mode and take time to discuss scales, frequency and totals of different charts.
D1.4	Progress to introduce the probability scale to Support tier students. Extend also to consider calculating probabilities, and writing them as fractions.
D1.5	Both tiers consider calculating probabilities in this lesson. Progress Support tier students to consider the formal formula for calculating probabilities, emphasising keywords: **outcome** and **event**.
D1.6	Discuss with Support tier students what they would expect if they would expect if they threw a dice 60 times. Introduce keyword **fair**, and discuss the difference between theory and real life. Introduce the formula for experimental probability, and demonstrate its use as test of fairness.

D1.1 The mode

Access

This spread provides access to the Year 7 objective:
▸ Find the mode of a small set of discrete data (256)

Lesson Plan

Mental starter

Look at a collection of shapes (use the diagram in Students' book).

▸ How many squares?
▸ How many triangles?
▸ Which two shapes have equal numbers?

Introductory activity

Refer to the mental starter. Discuss which is the most common shape in the collection.

Emphasise that this is the mode, and discuss whether students have met the mode before.

Record the students' shoe sizes in a tally chart (**R11**). Emphasise the strategy of collecting tallies in groups of 5.

Discuss which is the most common shoe size, and why this information would be important (shoe shops would be interested). Emphasise that this is the modal shoe size.

Discuss what a bar chart of this information would look like. Draw one on **R9**.

Discuss what would be special about the bar representing the modal shoe size.

Discuss whether there can be more than one mode.

Plenary

Show this set of data: 3, 4, 3, 5, 4, 6, 5, 7

Tell students: 'Jotinder says the modal values here are 3 and 5'.

Discuss whether Jotinder is right or wrong.

Encourage students to give reasons for their answers.

Homework

▸ Find the modal hair colour and eye colour of a group of people.
▸ Springboard 7: Pages 152, 153, 154, 155.

Exercise Commentary

Coverage

The questions assess objectives on Framework (Y456) Page 117.

Useful resources

R9 – coordinate axes for a bar chart.
R11 – tally chart
D1.1WS – provides support for weaker students.

Differentiation

▸ Question 1 involves finding the mode for categorical data.
▸ Questions 2 and 3 focus on finding the mode for numerical data.
▸ Questions 4 and 5 involve reading the mode from charts.

Support tier: also includes the median.

Misconceptions

Students may confuse the mode with the frequency, for example giving the mode in question 1b as 11 rather than yellow. Encourage them to think about the original question – is the modal **colour** 11 or yellow?

Emphasise that the mode is a value from the data.

Students may make errors when counting the values. Encourage accuracy over speed, and suggest ordering the data first to see which value occurs most.

Links

Organising data: Framework (Y456) Page 115.

Exercise Answers

1 a Square b Yellow   2 a 5 b 28 c 8
3 7   4 a Blue b Clair   5 Maths

Worksheet Answers

1 b 10 c 14 d 27
2 a ⅲ ⅲ ⅲⅲ b ⅲ ⅲ ⅲⅲ ⅲⅲ ⅲ
  c ⅲ ⅲ ⅲ d ⅲ ⅲ ⅲ ⅲ ⅲ ⅲⅲ
3 a Frequencies: 5, 6, 7, 2 b Heights: 5, 6, 7, 2
  c Brown

1 How much does each 'tally' show?
The first is done for you.

a ⵊⵊ || = 7   b ⵊⵊ ⵊⵊ = ___   c ⵊⵊ ⵊⵊ |||| = ___   d ⵊⵊ ⵊⵊ || = ___

ⵊⵊ ⵊⵊ ⵊⵊ

2 Show these numbers as a tally.

a 9 = _____   b 12 = _____

c 15 = _____   d 23 = _____

3 Class 7M do a survey of hair colour in their class.

Brown	Red	Brown	Black	Blond	Brown	Blond
Black	Blond	Brown	Black	Black	Brown	
Blond	Brown	Brown	Red	Blond	Black	Blond

a Complete this tally of the data.

b Complete this bar chart using the data from the tally chart.

Colour	Tally	Frequency
Black	ⵊⵊ	5
Blond		
Brown		
Red		

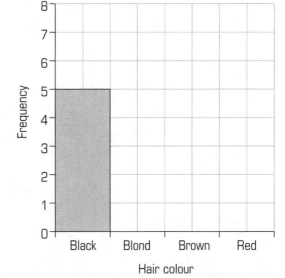

c The mode is the biggest group.
What is the modal hair colour?

Answer: _____ .

D1.2 What's in the middle?

Access

This spread provides access to the Year 7 objective:
▶ Find the median of a small set of discrete data (258)

Lesson Plan

Mental starter

Call out two numbers, say 13 and 17.

Students give the number exactly halfway between them (15). Encourage them to show their reasoning on a number line (**R6**).

Use different numbers – increasing the interval, and including halves (between 10 and 11 is 10.5)

Introductory activity

Introduce this scenario: a photographer is coming to do a shoot based around the average student in this class.

Discuss which student he would be interested in – the middle height student.

Ask five students to arrange themselves in height order.

Discuss how to identify the middle one.

Emphasise that you can remove one student from each end (highest and lowest) until only the middle student remains. Explain that the middle student is called the median.

Discuss what would happen if another person joined the group (to make an even number) and link to the starter activity.

Emphasise the approach: order the data and find the middle value. **D1.2OHP** provides more data sets for discussion.

Plenary

Show an even number of values with one decimal place: 4.3, 4.7, 5.2, 3.1, 3.1, 6.1

Encourage students to order the values, and find the median.

▶ What is the modal value?

Homework

▶ Record the shoe sizes of 10 people.
  Find the modal shoe size and the median shoe size. Write a sentence to explain which average a shoe shop would be interested in, and why.

▶ Springboard 7: Pages 301, 302, 303, 304.

Exercise Commentary

Coverage

The questions assess objectives on Framework (Y456) Pages 115 and 117.

Useful resources

R6 – number lines

D1.2OHP – data sets

Differentiation

▶ Questions 1–4 focus on finding middle values.

▶ Question 5 focuses on finding the median from an even number of values.

▶ Question 6 involves finding the median and mode.

Support tier: focuses on the mean. D1.1 focuses on the mean and median of larger data sets.

Misconceptions

Students often forget to order the data before finding the middle value. Remind them of the photographer scenario to prompt understanding and the need for order. Use questioning to explore this misconception – 'If the values are written in a different order, is the middle value the same?'

Links

Mental calculation: Framework (Y456) Pages 40–47.

Exercise Answers

1 a 6
  b 30
2 4, 4, 5, 7, 7, 8, 8; middle shoe size = 6
3 a 3, 4, 5, 7, 8; 5; middle value = 5
  b 3, 3, 9, 10, 12; middle value = 9
  c 2, 5, 5, 7, 9, 12, 18; middle value = 7
  d 6, 8, 18, 19, 20, 23, 29; middle value = 19
4 a 7 b 8
  c 40 d 15
5 £9
6 a 18 b 19

Name	Roy	Sarah	Ali	Vikki	Tom
Age	9 years	18 years	16 years	13 years	15 years
Weight	43 kg	60 kg	41 kg	65 kg	30 kg
Height	122 cm	182 cm	169 cm	165 cm	135 cm

£80   £30   £25   £85   £20   £50

D1.3 Levelling

Access

This spread provides access to the Year 7 objective
▸ Calculate the mean for a small set of discrete data (256)

Lesson Plan

Mental starter

Call out four numbers, all under 10.

Encourage students to add them mentally and give the total.

Repeat with different sets of numbers, increasing to strings of five.

Introductory activity

Introduce this scenario:

▸ Four children want to make some extra money, so they wash cars for their neighbours.

▸ Each child works equally hard, but they receive different amounts of money: £2, £3, £6, £9 (a total of £20).

▸ One child is happy. Which one?

Discuss what the other children will probably be thinking – that this is not fair.

Discuss what would be fair. Emphasise that it would be fair to share the total money **equally**. Emphasise that this **fair** amount as the **mean**, and we find it by dividing the **total** equally.

Model the scenario using towers of multilink cubes. Emphasise that you level the towers to find the mean.

Use the shoe size example in the Students' book to emphasise the method.

Plenary

Discuss solutions to the exercises, and encourage students to explain what the mean is for each question. For example in question 1a 'the mean number of boxes is 4'.

Homework

▸ Design a poster for how to find the mode, median and mean of a set of data. Give a set of values to use as an example: 7, 3, 5, 1, 4, 1, 6, 3, 9, 1

▸ Springboard 7: Page 327.

Exercise Commentary

Coverage

The questions assess objectives on Framework (Y456) Page 117.

Useful resources

Multilink cubes

R21 – multiplication table

D1.3WS – provides support for weaker students.

Differentiation

▸ Question 1 involves levelling.

▸ Questions 2–5 focus on calculating the mean.

▸ Question 6 involves finding all three averages for a larger set of data.

Support tier: focuses interpreting diagrams. D1.2 focuses on finding the mean of more complex data, including decimal values.

Misconceptions

This material prepares the ground for later work on averages. It is not likely that students will understand all the steps at this stage, but emphasising the idea of levelling will help them later.

Ensure that less confident students have access to multilink cubes and a multiplication grid (**R21**) to help with divisions.

Links

Adding several numbers: Framework (Y456) Page 43.

Exercise Answers

1 a 4　b 2　c 3　d 6　　　2 4　　　3 £5
4 6　　　5 3　　　　6 a 7　b 6　c 6

Worksheet Answers

1 a 3　b 4　c 3　d 4
2 a 5　b 3　c 3　d 5

1 Level out each tower of cubes to make equal height towers. This is the mean.
Use multilink cubes. The first has been started for you.

a

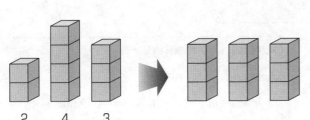

2   4   3

Mean = ___

b

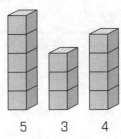

5   3   4

Mean = ___

c

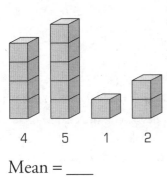

4   5   1   2

Mean = ___

d

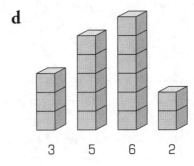

3   5   6   2

Mean = ___

2 How many items would each person have if they were shared out equally?

a

_____ coins

b

_____ cards

c

_____ pencils

d

_____ sweets

D1.4 Introducing chance

Access

This spread provides access to the Year 7 objective:
▶ Use vocabulary and ideas of probability, drawing on experience (276)

Lesson Plan

Mental starter

Show students how many of each colour cube you have. Place the cubes in a bag.

Ask students which colour they think you will pull out of the bag.

Pull one out of the bag – how many were right?

Repeat.

Introductory activity

Introduce the keywords **certain** and **impossible**.

Ask for an example of something that is certain to happen.

Ask for an example of something that is impossible. Refer to the mental starter. Discuss the meaning of keywords **likely** and **unlikely**.

Ask which word describes the following events:

▶ A dog will have kittens
▶ You will get homework today
▶ A coin will land on heads.

Discuss **equal chance** and ask for other examples of events that have an equal chance.

List all the events discussed under the appropriate headings in the table on **D1.4OHP**.

Plenary

Discuss question 4a.

Ask students to model it by putting the same combination of cubes into a bag and choosing one.

Discuss whether the outcome is what they expected.

Emphasise that any of the outcomes are possible but they are not all likely.

Homework

▶ Give five examples of certain events, and five examples of impossible events.
▶ Springboard 7: Pages 252, 253, 254.

Exercise Commentary

Coverage

The questions assess objectives on Framework (Y456) Page 113.

Useful resources

D1.4OHP – table from the Students' book and bags of coloured balls

Multilink cubes and bags or boxes

Differentiation

▶ Questions 1 and 2 focus on informal ideas of chance.
▶ Question 3 involves using the language of chance.
▶ Question 4 involves describing the chance of an event.

Support tier: focuses on the probability scale.

Misconceptions

Students will almost certainly have an intuitive idea about probability, but it is important to ensure that everyone understands the meanings of **certain** and **impossible** as a basis to build key vocabulary from.

Links

Comparing: Framework (Y456) Page 9.

Exercise Answers

1 a B
  b A
2 a C
  b A

3

Impossible	Unlikely	Equal chance	Likely	Certain
b	f	c	a	d
e	g		h	j
	i			

4 a No chance   b Certain
  c Likely   d Certain
  e Equal chance   f Unlikely

Impossible	Poor chance	Equal chance	Good chance	Certain

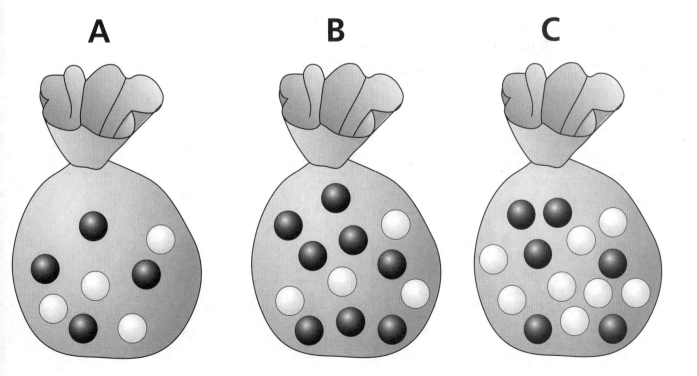

A   B   C

D1.5 Describing chance

Access

This spread provides access to the Year 7 objective:
▸ Use vocabulary and ideas of probability, drawing on experience (276)

Lesson Plan

Mental starter

Show students 5 balls – 1 red, 4 blue, then place the balls in a bag.

Ask students which colour they think you will pull out of the bag. Encourage them to explain their reasoning.

Pull a ball out of the bag. How many were right?

Discuss what changes when you add another ball to the bag.

How many red balls would you have to add to have an equal chance of picking red or blue?

Introductory activity

Recap the keywords from D1.4.

Refer to the mental starter. Ask students to be more precise about which colour ball they were expecting to be pulled out.

Discuss whether they can put a value on it.

Link to work on fractions (N2.1). The total outcomes form the denominator.

Emphasise that it is important to know how many outcomes there are in total, and then think about how many times the red *could* come up.

Place the letters MATHS in a bag.

Discuss how many letters in total could be pulled out.

How many of them are the letter S?

Plenary

Show equal numbers of blue and red cubes.

Give students the scenario: 'John says Jane is more likely to pick a red cube than a blue.'

Discuss whether this is correct.

Homework

▸ The letters CHANCE are placed in a bag.
  Find the chance of each letter being pulled out.

▸ Springboard 7: Pages 258, 259, 260.

Exercise Commentary

Coverage

The questions assess objectives on the Primary Framework (Y456) Page 113.

Useful resources

D1.5WS – provides further practice of the key ideas.

Multilink cubes and bags or boxes

Letter cards: MATHS

Coins

Differentiation

▸ Question 1 involves describing probabilities.

▸ Questions 2 and 3 focus on probabilities as fractions.

▸ Question 4 involves more than one successful outcome.

Support tier: extends to the probability of an event not happening.

Misconceptions

Students may feel uncomfortable with the move to fractions. Emphasise that it is quicker to write a fraction, but accept that many students will not be able to grasp this concept until a later stage.

Emphasise that the denominator is the total number of outcomes and the numerator shows the possible successful ones.

Links

Fractions: Primary Framework Page 23.

Exercise Answers

1 a 4 or $\frac{1}{4}$ b 6 or $\frac{1}{6}$ c 10 or $\frac{1}{10}$
2 a $\frac{1}{4}$ b $\frac{1}{6}$ c $\frac{1}{9}$
3 a $\frac{1}{12}$ b $\frac{1}{16}$ c $\frac{1}{4}$ d $\frac{1}{6}$
5 a $\frac{2}{6}$ b $\frac{3}{12}$ c $\frac{2}{5}$ d $\frac{5}{8}$ e $\frac{3}{10}$

Worksheet Answers

There are no unique answers in this game.

When you spin two coins, there are three ways they can land.

 or 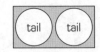 or

Follow these steps to see if you can guess which way will come up!
You will need two coins.

1 Guess a result – two heads, two tails or a head and a tail.
You can write: HH, TT or HT.

2 Spin two coins.

3 If the guess is correct follow the tick (✓) to the next level.
If not, follow the cross (✗).

4 Repeat until you reach the bottom level. This shows your percentage
of correct guesses.

You can play the game with other students – take it in turns to guess and use a different colour to mark your results.

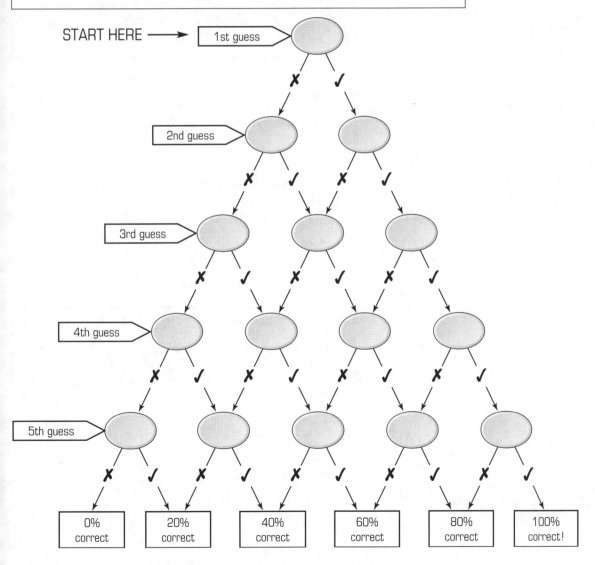

D1.6 The probability scale

Access

This spread provides access to the Year 7 objective:
▸ Understand and use the probability scale from 0 to 1 (278)

Lesson Plan

Mental starter

Assign a number to each student, starting with 1.

Ask number 5 to stand up.

Discuss the likelihood of a stranger being able to pick number 5 out of the class. Encourage use of fractions. Repeat for other numbers.

Introductory activity

Refer to the mental starter. Emphasise that fractions are **part of a whole**.

Using a number line from 0 to 1 (**R6**) ask students to estimate fractions of the way along the line ($\frac{1}{2}$, $\frac{1}{4}$, $\frac{1}{3}$, etc).

Emphasise the need to split the line into equal parts.

Introduce the probability scale on top of the number line.

Label impossible as 0, and certain as 1 and discuss why.

Discuss where likely and unlikely should go – linking to impossible and certain.

Label equal chance, $\frac{1}{2}$ in the middle of the number line. Use the example in the Students' book to discuss the total number of outcomes for flipping a coin and the chance of it landing on heads.

Show the spinner on **D1.6OHP** with one third red. Discuss the chance of it landing on red, and discuss where this would be on on the probability scale.

Plenary

Discuss where the chance of different events is on the probability scale:
▸ You will see a pig flying on your way home from school.
▸ You will have a birthday within 365 days.
▸ It will rain tomorrow.

Homework

▸ Place 10 events of students' choosing on a probability scale.
▸ Springboard 7: Pages 255, 256.

Exercise Commentary

Coverage

The questions assess objectives on Framework (Y456) Page 113.

Useful resources

R6 – number lines

D1.6OHP – probability scale and spinner

Differentiation

▸ Question 1 focuses on writing probabilities as fractions.
▸ Question 2 links informal understanding of probability to the probability scale.
▸ Question 3 focuses on placing an event on a probability scale.

Support tier: focuses on calcualting experimental probabilities.

Misconceptions

Students may have difficulty linking two fractional representations together in question 2 – one within a circle, and the other on a number line. Encourage students to think intuitively about the approximate fraction and likelihood in both cases.

Links

Fractions: Framework (Y456) Page 23.

Exercise Answers

1 a 0.3, $\frac{3}{10}$ b 0.7, $\frac{7}{10}$ c 0, $\frac{0}{10}$
2 a R b U c P d Q e T f S
3 a Impossible b Certain c Equal chance

Impossible	Likely	Equal chance	Unlikely	Certain

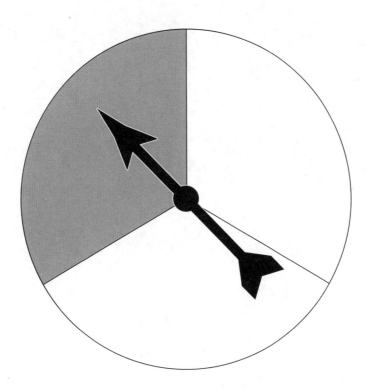

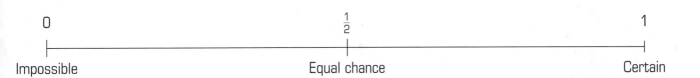

0                                      $\frac{1}{2}$ 1

Impossible   Equal chance   Certain

Framework MATHS — Scheme of work — Year 7

D1 Data and probability (6 hours)

	Teaching objectives	Framework Maths resources	Other resources
Organising and interpreting data (114–17)	Solve a problem by interpreting data in tables, charts, graphs and diagrams	7A Student Book: D1.1 7A Teacher's Book: D1.1WS, R9, R11	
Organising and interpreting data (116–17)	Find the mode of a set of data.	7A Student Book: D1.1 7A Teacher's Book: D1.1WS, R9, R11	
Place value, ordering and rounding (8–9)	Order a set of integers.	7A Student Book: D1.2 7A Teacher's Book: D1.2OHP, R6	
Organising and interpreting data (116–17)	Begin to find the median of a set of data.	7A Student Book: D1.2 7A Teacher's Book: D1.2OHP, R6	
Mental calculation strategies (+ and –) (42–3)	Add several numbers.	7A Student Book: D1.3 7A Teacher's Book: D1.3WS, R21	
Organising and interpreting data (112–13)	Discuss the chance or likelihood of particular events.	7A Student Book: D1.4, D1.5 7A Teacher's Book: D1.4OHP, D1.5WS	
Organising and interpreting data (112–13)	Begin to use words to describe probability	7A Student Book: D1.6 7A Teacher's Book: D1.6OHP, R6	

Access

Overview

This unit aims to introduce students to the idea of using letters to stand for numbers. The focus is on using letters to describe situations that can be solved intuitively. Many students find the use of letters difficult to grasp so this unit is designed to help build confidence. It may be unsuitable for weaker students.

Spreads A2.1, A2.4 and A2.5 form the focus of the unit.

Framework references

The unit covers objectives on Framework (Y456) Page 81.

Useful resources

Worksheets
A2.1WS – using letters
A2.2WS – adding and subtracting with symbols
A2.3WS – solving algebra problems
A2.4WS – symbols and values
A2.5WS – substitution

General resources
R17 – 100 square
Multilink cubes
Dice

Springboard 7 page
327

Introduction

Ask this question:

▶ There are 20 students in a class, and the teacher collects in 15 pieces of homework. How many students still have to hand in their homework?

Emphasise that you 'find missing numbers' like this in everyday life.

Check in activity

Write three numbers connected by addition and subtraction on the board, say 14, 5 and 19.

Ask students to make a calculation connecting all the numbers.

Highlight all four possible calculations.

Repeat with other sets of three numbers.

Differentiation – spanning the bridge

Spread	Bridge to the Support tier
A2.1	Extend Support tier students to consider multiplying unknown values and the algebraic convention $d + d + d + d + d = 5 \times d = 5d$, highlighting the difference between the multiplication operator and the letter x.
A2.2	Extend Support tier students to consider mathematical expressions for written sentences. Take time to discuss the difference between 5 subtract an unknown number, and an unknown number subtract 5.
A2.3	Extend the Support tier students to simplify expressions with two unknowns, or combining numbers and letters.
A2.4	Progress Support tier students to consider the difference between the use of a letter to represent an unknown, and the use of a letter to represent a **variable**. Link to work on expressions, and model substituting different numbers into various expressions. Recap on conventions of algebra (in particular, division and multiplication notation).
A2.5	Extend Support tier to substituting into a formula. Differentiate between evaluating an expression given a value, and substituting into a formula to find an unknown value. Emphasise that a formula links two or more different variables. Use real-life examples to gain confidence, e.g. number of minutes = 60 × number of hours.

Access

This spread provides access to the Year 7 objective:
▸ Use letter symbols to write expressions in meaningful contexts (112)

Lesson Plan

Mental starter

Show a 100 square (**R17**).

Ask for patterns, for example: when you move down a row you add 10.

Direct students to a number, say 34. Hide the number below it and ask students to give the number and their reasoning. Repeat, changing start number, and hidden square – to the left, to the right, up one square, etc.

Introductory activity

Refer to the mental starter, and discuss the patterns you have identified.

Discuss how to explain patterns: **whenever you move down one square you add ten**.

Emphasise that we use algebra to describe these patterns quickly.

Encourage students to pick a letter to represent a number from the grid to demonstrate that any can be used.

Discuss how to describe the square underneath, and to the left, and to the right.

Use the context in the Students' book with multilink cubes in a bag instead of marbles. Discuss the examples.

Emphasise the notation for the four operations, especially division ($\frac{n}{2}$).

Plenary

Discuss what answers would look like if in question 3 there had been x flowers in the field. The answer to question 3a would be $2 \times x$. Explain that in algebra we do not use the multiplication sign, to avoid this confusion with the letter x.

Homework

▸ Students imagine they are standing on number 26 on the 100 square and write directions to get to 36, 45, 16, 76, etc.

Exercise Commentary

Coverage

The questions assess objectives on Framework (Y456) Page 81.

Useful resources

R17 – 100 square

Multilink cubes

A2.1WS – provides support for weaker students.

Differentiation

▸ Question 1 involves all four operations.
▸ Questions 2 and 3 involve all four operations and different symbols.
▸ Question 4 involves students choosing their own symbols.

Support tier: focuses on writing simple algebraic expressions.

Misconceptions

In question 1, students may confuse the order of the subtraction, writing $10 - n$ instead of $n - 10$.

Encourage students to use numerical examples to check their expressions.

Links

Checking results: Framework (Y456) Page 73.

Exercise Answers

1 a $n - 10$ b $n - 4$ c $n - 20$ d $\frac{n}{2}$ e n
2 $b + 4$
3 a $2 \times c$ or $2c$ b $\frac{c}{4}$ c $c + 50$
4 a $n + 2$ b $n + 5$

Worksheet Answers

1 No
2 a $t + 4$ b $t + 10$
3 a $n + 8$ b $n + 20$

1 Josh keeps some of his marbles in a bag.

Can you tell exactly how many marbles are in Josh's bag, without guessing?

Circle the correct answer: Yes   or   No

2 Josh uses t to stand for the number of marbles in his bag.
He has t marbles in the bag and another 4 marbles.

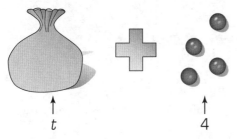

a How many marbles does Josh have altogether?
Circle the correct answer.

$t - 4$ marbles $t + 4$ marbles $4 - t$ marbles

b Josh won 6 more marbles.
How many marbles does he now have altogether?
Circle the correct answer.

$t + 4$ marbles   10 marbles $t + 10$ marbles   2 marbles

3 a These parcels weigh n kilograms altogether.
The small parcel to the side weighs 8 kilograms.

Add the small parcel to the big pile.
What is the total weight?
Circle the correct answer.

$n + 8$ $n - 8$ $8 - n$ $n8$

b Add another parcel weighing 12 kilograms to the pile.
What is the new total weight?
Circle the correct answer.

$n + 12$ 12   20 $n + 20$

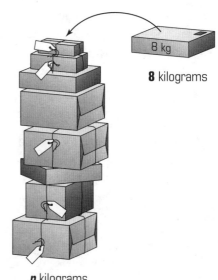

8 kg

8 kilograms

n kilograms

A2.2 Adding and subtracting with symbols

Access

This spread provides access to the Year 7 objective:
▸ Simplify linear expressions by collecting like terms (116)

Lesson Plan

Mental starter

Show a number pyramid with three numbers in the top layer.

Encourage students to add together two numbers to give the 'brick' below. Students calculate mentally, and give only one answer, the final layer.

Repeat with different numbers, and/or different values missing from the pyramid.

Introductory activity

Ask students for a different way of writing
5 + 5 + 5 + 5.

Emphasise that writing 5 × 4 is **simpler**.

Introduce a scenario:

▸ John has 2 tubes of sweets, each containing x sweets. Demonstrate that he has $2 \times x$ (2 lots of an unknown number) sweets and emphasise the convention that leads to $2x$.

▸ Jane has 3 tubes of sweets ($3x$).

Discuss how to find the total number of sweets:

John's sweets + Jane's sweets

$2x$ $+ 3x$

Encourage students to collect together the like terms.

Return to the number pyramid from the mental starter and include unknowns. Discuss each step to help students gain confidence.

Plenary

Discuss answers for question 4, which extends to subtracting like terms.

Show a number pyramid that includes numbers and letters, say 3, $4a$, $5a$, and work down the pyramid as a class. Emphasise that you can collect the a's together, but not the numbers.

Homework

▸ Complete a number pyramid with top five bricks:
$2a$, $3a$, $4a$, $5a$, $6a$

Exercise Commentary

Coverage

The questions assess objectives on Framework (Y456) Page 81.

Useful resources

R17 – 100 square

A2.2WS – provides support for weaker pupils.

Differentiation

▸ Question 1 involves numbers only.

▸ Questions 2 and 3 involve adding and subtracting like terms.

▸ Question 4 focuses on subtracting like terms.

Support tier: focuses on writing algebraic expressions. A2.3 focuses on collecting like terms.

Misconceptions

Some students will ignore the subtraction of terms and will simply add all the numbers together. Encourage students to read each question out loud, and direct them to work from left to right.

Links

Adding several numbers: Framework (Y456) Page 43.

Exercise Answers

1 a 3, 1, 4; 4, 5; 9   b 2, 6, 3; 8, 9; 17
   c 4, 2, 5; 6, 7; 13
2 a $3a$, a, $4a$; $4a$, $5a$; $9a$ b $2b$, $6b$, $3b$; $8b$, $9b$; $17b$
   c $4y$, $2y$, $5y$; $6y$, $7y$; $13y$ d $3x$, $4x$, $6x$; $7x$, $10x$; $17x$
   e $5t$, $3t$, $4t$; $8t$, $7t$; $15t$ f $6h$, $7h$, $2h$; $13h$, $9h$; $23h$
3 a $9m$ b $9t$ c $12n$ d $14p$ e $20h$ f $19b$
   g $22r$ h $25k$
4 a $2m$ b $8c$ c $4f$ d $7p$ e $9d$ f $6b$ g $5e$
   h $11v$

Worksheet Answers

1 22, 39   2 70, 50, 120   3 10, 40, 70
4 $a + 5$ 5 $a + 4$, $a + 4$, $2a + 8$
6 $n + 5$, $n + 6$, $2n + 11$

Number towers

Add the numbers in two boxes next to each other
to get the number in the box below.

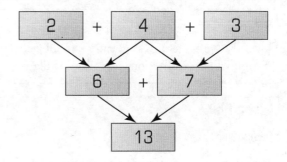

Complete these towers.

1
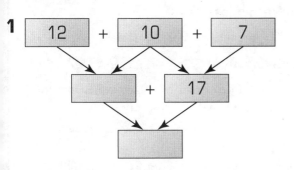

2
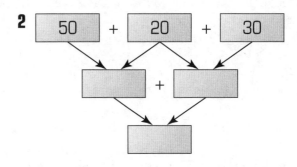

3
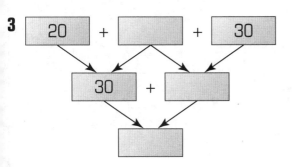

4
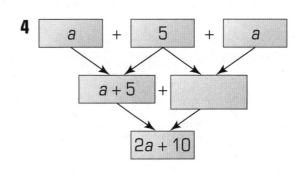

5
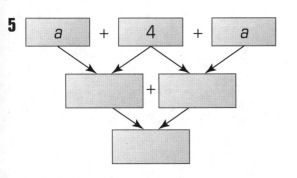

6
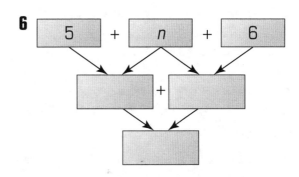

A2.3 Solving algebra problems

Access

This spread provides access to the Year 7 objective:
▶ Simplify linear expressions by collecting like terms (116)

Lesson Plan

Mental starter

Give students a string of one-digit numbers: 7, 5, 2, 3
Students mentally add, and give the total.

Repeat, increasing to longer strings, and to include some two-digit numbers.

Introductory activity

Recap the conventions of algebra by asking for the meaning of $3x$, $4p$, and so on. Emphasise that $3x$ means 3 lots of x.

Give students an expression, say $3p + 4p$ and discuss how to simplify it.

Draw a rectangle on the board with dimensions in centimetres and discuss how to calculate the perimeter. Emphasise that it is the total length around the outside of a shape and link to addition.

Draw a rectangle with width twice the length.

Explain that the dimensions are unknown, but that the width is 2 times the length. Encourage students to choose a symbol for the length (x). Discuss the value of the width ($x + x$, or $2x$ cm). Label the dimensions.

Encourage students to give an expression for the perimeter of this shape by adding the dimensions. Discuss how to simplify their expression.

Plenary

Draw a rectangle with width x cm and height y cm.

Ask students to calculate the perimeter.
Use this as an opportunity to reinforce collecting *like terms*.

Progress to an L-shape with one dimension missing, which can be calculated from the other dimensions.

Homework

▶ Find as many sets of dimensions as possible for a rectangle with perimeter $24y$ cm.
For example: $10y \times 2y$.

Exercise Commentary

Coverage

The questions assess objectives on Framework (Y456) Page 81.

Useful resources

A2.3WS – provides support for weaker students.

Differentiation

▶ Question 1 focuses on simplifying expressions for the perimeter of shapes.

▶ Question 2 involves ordering lengths based upon simplified expressions.

▶ Question 3 progresses to forming and simplifying expressions including subtraction of like terms.

Support tier: focuses on simplifying more complex expressions.

Misconceptions

Students tend to ignore the letters of like terms altogether, for example, in question 1a they write 4 cm, not $4x$ cm. Remind them that $2x$ means 2 lots of x, and encourage them to think about each term of the expression in this way.

Links

Perimeter: Framework (Y567) Page 97.

Exercise Answers

1 a $4x$ cm b $8y$ cm c $20x$ cm d $12a$ cm
  e $23n$ cm
2 a $16a$ cm b $11a$ cm c $13a$ cm d Blue
3 a $8x$ b $14x$

Worksheet Answers

1 a 6 cm + 6 cm + 6 cm = 18 cm or 3 × 6 cm = 18 cm
  b 5 cm + 5 cm + 5 cm + 5 cm = 20 cm
     or 4 × 5 cm = 20 cm
2 a $3x$ cm b $5a$ cm c $6h$ cm

The perimeter of a shape is the total distance around the edge.

This triangle has sides of 4 cm.
Its perimeter is 4 cm + 4 cm + 4 cm = 12 cm
You can say: 3×4 cm = 12 cm.

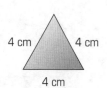

1 Find the perimeter of these shapes.

a

The perimeter is:

___ cm + ___ cm + ___ cm = ___ cm

Or:

___ × ___ cm = ___ cm

b

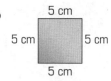

The perimeter is:

___ cm + ___ cm + ___ cm + ___ cm

= ___ cm

Or:

___ × ___ cm = ___ cm

2 In these questions the lengths of each side are written in symbols.
You can add them just like numbers.
Find the perimeter of each shape.

a

The perimeter is:

_____

= _____ cm

Or:

___ × ___ cm = _____ cm

b

The perimeter is:

_____

= _____ cm

Or:

___ × ___ cm = _____ cm

c

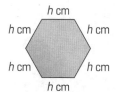

The perimeter is: _____ = _____ cm

Or: ___ × ___ cm = = _____ cm

A2.4 Symbols and values

Access

This spread provides access to the year 7 objective:
▸ Know that algebraic conventions follow the same conventions and order as arithmetic operations (114)

Lesson Plan

Mental starter

Tell students: I have a number, I add 4, the answer is 7. What was the number?

Continue with different clues and operations.

Introductory activity

Give students three numbers related by addition: 13, 17, 30. Ask for a calculation that links the three numbers: $13 + 17 = 30$.

Encourage students to offer new calculations, including subtractions, until you have all four possible combinations. Repeat with three more numbers. Emphasise that addition and subtraction are linked.

Refer to the mental starter. Discuss how to write each of the problems as an expression: $n + 4 = 7$. Encourage students to link the answer (3) with the inverse calculation: $7 - 4$.

Work through the examples in the Students' book. Encourage students to use algebra and to check answers by substituting.

Plenary

Discuss question 3. Encourage students to form expressions for each situation, highlighting different calculations based around the same question. For example: 3a could lead to $£10 + 5 = a$, or $a - 5 = 10$.

Homework

▸ Write situations to fit the equations in question 1. For example: $e + 4 = 7$ could be 'John adds £4 to his piggy bank. When he counts his money, he has £7. How much did he start with?'
▸ Springboard 7: Page 327.

Worksheet Answers

1 a 5 kg   b 12 kg   c 30 kg   d 80 kg   e 140 kg
   f 25 kg, 25 kg
2 b $x = 3$ c $t = 5$ d $r = 6$ e $f = 6$ f $p = 7$
   g $k = 14$ h $h = 25$
3 a 3, $x + 3$, $x + 15$ b 5

Exercise Commentary

Coverage

The questions assess objectives on Framework (Y456) Page 81.

Useful resources

A2.4WS – provides support for weaker students.

Differentiation

▸ Questions 1 and 2 involve solving simple equations involving addition and subtraction.
▸ Question 3 focuses on forming algebraic expressions to describe real-life situations.
▸ Question 4 involves solving equations.

Support tier: focuses on substitution.

Misconceptions

Students often feel uncomfortable with calculations that include letters. Encourage them to say the calculation out loud, substituting the letter with the word 'something'.

Question 3 may cause problems for weaker students. They are likely to be capable of solving the problem, but may not be able to write the algebraic expressions. Emphasise that the unknown will be represented by a letter. Students could work in pairs to devise and discuss each expression.

Links

The relationship between addition and subtraction: Framework (Y456) Page 43.

Exercise Answers

1 a $c = 3$ b $d = 4$ c $t = 1$ d $h = 4$ e $p = 0$
   f $b = 4$ g $g = 10$ h $u = 5$ i $v = 5$ j $a = 8$
   k $s = 4$ l $y = 5$ m $f = 8$ n $j = 25$ o $h = 15$
2 a $h = 11$ b $d = 11$ c $k = 18$ d $c = 9$ e $p = 7$
   f $g = 10$ g $t = 25$ h $j = 30$ i $m = 28$ j $u = 20$
   k $g = 37$ l $f = 60$ m $j = 15$ n $y = 2$ o $a = 20$
3 a $m - 5 = 10$ b $30 + w = 45$ c $30 + p = 55$
   d $30 - c = 14$
4 a $m = 15$, $w = 15$, $p = 25$, $c = 6$

1 Work out the missing weights of the parcels on these scales and write them on.

a

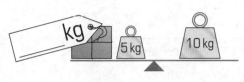

b

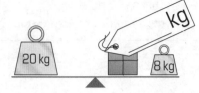

c

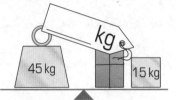

d

e

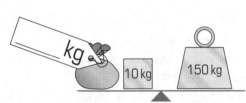

f

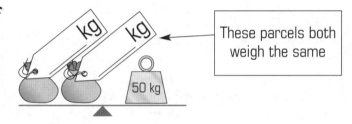

These parcels both weigh the same

2 Find the value of each letter.
The first one is done for you.

a $a + 8 = 16$

    $a = 16 - 8$

    $a = 8$

b $x + 9 = 12$

    $x = 12 - 9$

    $x = \underline{\ \ \ }$

c $15 + t = 20$

    $t = 20 - \underline{\ \ \ }$

    $t = \underline{\ \ \ }$

d $r + 7 = 13$

    $r = \underline{\ \ \ } - \underline{\ \ \ }$

    $r = \underline{\ \ \ }$

e $f + 9 = 15$

    $f = \underline{\ \ \ } - \underline{\ \ \ }$

    $f = \underline{\ \ \ }$

f $15 + p = 22$

    $p = \underline{\ \ \ } - \underline{\ \ \ }$

    $p = \underline{\ \ \ }$

g $7 + k = 21$

    $k = \underline{\ \ \ } - \underline{\ \ \ }$

    $k = \underline{\ \ \ }$

h $h + 10 = 35$

    $h = \underline{\ \ \ } - \underline{\ \ \ }$

    $h = \underline{\ \ \ }$

3 In this number tower, you add two boxes to give the number in the box below.

a Fill in the missing values.

b The value of the last box is 20.
What is the value of x?

    $x + \underline{\ \ \ \ \ \ \ \ \ \ } = 20$

    $x = \underline{\ \ \ \ }$

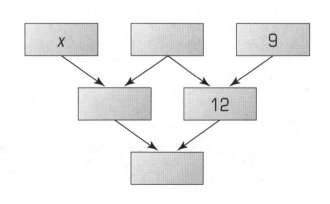

A2.5 Substitution

Access

This spread provides access to the Year 7 objective:
▸ Substitute positive integers into simple linear expressions (138)

Lesson Plan

Mental starter

Show an expression: $d + 4$.

Throw a dice, and ask students to **substitute** the dice value into the expression. The 'answerer' gets to throw the dice next.

Change the expression to include subtractions and multiplications to match the confidence of the group.

Introductory activity

Refer to the mental starter. Emphasise that students were **substituting** a value into an expression.

Introduce the doughnut box sizes, from the Students' book example, using an OHP of **A2.5WS**. Show students a written sentence: 1 medium box + 2 extra doughnuts gives 8 doughnuts.

Discuss a *mathematical sentence* that says the same things: $m + 2 = 8$.

Move to expressions like $m + 3$.

▸ What does m stand for?
▸ How many doughnuts in total?
▸ How many small boxes would contain the same amount?

Plenary

Work through how to write 2 small boxes and 1 extra doughnut (recapping that $2 \times s$ is the same as $2s$). Progress to substituting values into expressions with two variables: $2m + s$.

Homework

▸ Find different ways of ordering 7 doughnuts and write sentences or equations for the orders (for example $s + 4 = 7$, $m + 1 = 7$). Repeat for 16, 30 etc.

Worksheet Answers

1 4 doughnuts	2 1 doughnut
3 9 doughnuts	4 5 doughnuts
5 3 doughnuts	6 7 doughnuts
7 6 doughnuts	8 9 doughnuts

Exercise Commentary

Coverage

The questions assess objectives on Framework (Y456) Page 81.

Useful resources

Dice

A2.5WS – provides support for weaker students.

Differentiation

▸ Questions 1 and 2 focus on substituting single values into simple expressions.
▸ Questions 3–5 focus on more than one value and develop into using letters.
▸ Questions 6–8 focus on multiplying substituted values.

Support tier: focuses on substitution of a variable into two-step expressions.

Misconceptions

Most students will substitute without too many difficulties, and the dice game at the start provides a chance to practise this intuitive skill in a fun way.

In the plenary activity, some students may misinterpret $2s$ (where $s = 3$) to be 23. Encourage students to think of $2s$ as 2 lots of s.

Links

Mental calculations: Framework (Y456) Page 41.

Exercise Answers

1 a 6   b 18   c 50
2 2
3 a 12   b 7
4 a 7   b 6   c 11   d 11   e 15   f 12   g 19   h 2
  i 19
5 a 9   b 15   c 12   d 40   e 60   f 60   g 100
  h 36
6 Yes

Small boxes hold
3 doughnuts.

Medium boxes hold
6 doughnuts.

Large boxes hold
10 doughnuts.

You can use symbols to represent the numbers of doughnuts in each box:

$s = 3$ $m = 6$ $l = 10$

For a small box and two extra doughnuts:

$s + 2$ means $3 + 2$

so $s + 2 = 5$

1 | Draw $s + 1$ doughnuts:

2 | Draw $s - 2$ doughnuts:

3 | Draw $m + 3$ doughnuts:

4 | Draw $m - 1$ doughnuts:

5 | Draw $m - 3$ doughnuts:

6 | Draw $l - 3$ doughnuts:

7 | Draw $s + s$ doughnuts:

8 | Draw $s + m$ doughnuts:

Framework MATHS Scheme of work

A2 Using symbols (5 hours)	Teaching objectives	Framework Maths resources	Other resources
Reasoning and generalising about numbers or shapes (80–1)	Explain a generalised relationship in words and using symbols	7A Student Book: A2.1 - A2.5 7A Teacher's Book: A2.1WS, A2.2WS, A2.3WS, A2.4WS, A2.5WS, R17	
Problems involving 'real life', money and measures (82–9)	Use all four operations to solve simple word problems.	7A Student Book: A2.3 - A2.5 7A Teacher's Book: A2.3WS, A2.4WS, A2.5WS	

Note: this unit uses letter symbols which is beyond the scope of the Y456 Framework. However, the simple approach taken should help students gain confidence in using symbols to help lay the foundation for later algebra work.

Access

Overview

The first spread in this unit aims to consolidate students' understanding of times shown on analogue and digital clocks, and how to convert between them. The following two spreads introduce and practise reading and plotting coordinates in the first quadrant.

Spreads S2.1 and S2.2 form the focus of the unit.

Framework references

The unit covers objectives on Framework (Y456) Pages 99, 101, 109.

Useful resources

Worksheets
S2.1WS – time
S2.2WS – reading coordinates
S2.3WS – coordinates and shapes

General resources
R8 – coordinate grid
R9 – axes in a single quadrant
R14 – special triangles
R15 – special quadrilaterals
R20 – analogue clock

Springboard 7 pages
180, 276, 278

Introduction

Discuss why you need clocks and time in order to make arrangements to meet up with other people. Refer to the school timetable and the fixed times in it, such as registration, break, lunch, home times. Discuss other everyday examples.

Check in activity

Show students different times on an analogue clock (**R20**) and ask them to say the time.

Ask them to draw clock hands to show different times.

Differentiation – spanning the bridge

Spread	Bridge to the Support tier
S2.1	Support and Access students can work alongside one another in this lesson as both tiers focus on conversion between analogue and digital clocks. Support tier would benefit from some discussion about the link between the analogue clock and angles: half turn = 180°, quarter turn = 90°, full turn = 360°.
S2.2	The two tiers cover entirely different topics in this lesson. However Support tier students will benefit from a quick revision of coordinates as this is the focus for S2.3. Progress Support tier students to consider parallel and perpendicular sides of shapes, and formal notation used.
S2.3	Use Support tier students to elicit key language and properties of shapes during the starter activity, extending to different types of triangles. This emphasis on shape properties is required for the Support tier exercises, but essentially both groups of students cover similar matter.

S2.1 Time

Access

This spread provides access to the Year 7 objective:
▸ Use units to measure, calculate and solve problems involving time (228)

Lesson Plan

Mental starter

Tell students: a TV programme starts at (08.30) and ends at (09.15).

▸ How long does the programme last?

Repeat with different start and end times, progressing to hours and minutes.

Introductory activity

Refer to the mental starter. Discuss minutes in an hour, seconds in a minute. Progress to hours in a day, days in a week, weeks in a month, months in a year, days in year.

Ask students what they usually are doing at 8.30. Emphasise that 8.30 could be morning or evening and discuss how to distinguish: am and pm. Discuss how to show 8.30 on an analogue clock (**R20**).

Discuss a digital clock and how it distinguishes between morning and evening. Emphasise that instead of returning to 1 at 1 pm, the digital clock continues to 13. Use the scale in the Students' book to illustrate this.

Ask students digital/analogue conversion questions:

▸ Is 14.00 this morning or afternoon? What would an analogue clock read?
▸ How would a digital clock show 3.15 pm?

Discuss conversion strategies.

Plenary

Refer to the mental starter. Give students a start time and an end time (pm), using the 24-hour clock. Encourage students to give the length of TV programme, and explain their method.

Homework

▸ Complete a timetable of a typical day, using the 24-hour clock.
▸ Springboard 7: Page 180.

Exercise Commentary

Coverage

The questions assess objectives on Framework (Y456) Pages 99 and 101.

Useful resources

R20 – analogue clock

S2.1WS – provides further practice of the key ideas.

Differentiation

▸ Question 1 focuses on using appropriate units of time.
▸ Questions 2 and 3 focus on converting between 12-hour and 24-hour times.
▸ Question 4 involves multiple calculations converting between units of time.

Support tier: focuses on 24-hour and 12-hour times, and extends to angles between clock hands.

Misconceptions

Students may write time as 1800 pm, confusing the 12- and 24-hour clocks. Emphasise during the introductory activity we use that one *or* the other, and with the 24-hour clock am or pm is unnecessary.

Some students will add 10 instead of 12 to the analogue time. Encourage them to use the scale in the Students' book. Use adding 10 to 1 pm to make 11 pm as an example to challenge this misconception.

Links

Mental calculations: Framework (Y546) Page 41.

Exercise Answers

1 a seconds b years c hours d weeks
  e seconds f minutes
2 a Bath b 1 pm c Breakfast d Work
  e Washes f Watching TV g 11 pm
3 a A or D b E c D or A d B e C

Worksheet Answers

2 4 o'clock, 6:15, 9:30, 3:05, 8:45   4 a 09:30 b 08:00 c 20:00 d 14:30 e 01:30 f 23:00
5 a 9 am b 4 pm c 3:31 am d 9:35 pm e 11:32 am f 11:36 pm

1 Put hands on each clock to show the time.

9 o'clock	half past one	7:15	quarter to five	five past six

   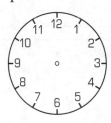 

2 What times are shown on these clocks?

_____   _____   _____   _____   _____

This scale will help you convert between 12 and 24-hour times.

00.00 01.00 02.00 03.00 04.00 05.00 06.00 07.00 08.00 09.00 10.00 11.00 12.00 13.00 14.00 15.00 16.00 17.00 18.00 19.00 20.00 21.00 22.00 23.00 00.00

12   1 am 2 am 3 am 4 am 5 am 6 am 7 am 8 am 9 am 10 am 11 am   12   1 pm 2 pm 3 pm 4 pm 5 pm 6 pm 7 pm 8 pm 9 pm 10 pm 11 pm   12

Midnight   Midday   Midnight

am times   **pm times**

---

3 Put hands on each clock to show these 24-hour times. Use the scale to help you.

07:30	10:00	13:30	16:45	23:30

4 Convert these 12-hour times to 24-hour times. Use the scale to help you.

    a 9.30 am → _____   **b** 8.00 am → _____   **c** 8.00 pm → _____

    d 2.30 pm → _____   **e** 1.30 am → _____   **f** 11.00 pm → _____

5 Convert these 24-hour times to 12-hour times. Use the scale to help you.

    a 09:00 hrs → _____   **b** 16:00 hrs → _____   **c** 03:31 hrs → _____

    d 21:35 hrs → _____   **e** 11:32 hrs → _____   **f** 23:36 hrs → _____

S2.2 Reading coordinates

Access

This spread provides access to the Year 7 objective:
▸ Read and plot points using coordinates in all four quadrants (218)

Lesson Plan

Mental starter

Show a right-angled triangle (**R14**). Discuss its angle and side properties.

Repeat for isosceles, scalene, equilateral triangles. Encourage use of the keywords: **acute**, **obtuse**, **equal**.

Introductory activity

Draw a cross on an OHP. Give students a blank piece of paper and challenge them to draw a cross in exactly the same position. Go around the class, with the OHP and demonstrate the difficulty in locating an **exact** position.

Look at the OHP again, this time with a coordinate grid (**R9**) behind it. Emphasise that coordinates can be used to determine an exact position on a coordinate grid.

Highlight the conventions of coordinates:

▸ The first number is how far **across** the position is
▸ The second number is how far **up** the position is.
▸ A comma separates the two numbers.
▸ You use brackets around the coordinates.

Discuss strategies for remembering which comes first – across or up.

Draw another cross, and ask for the coordinates. Progress to plotting points with given coordinates.

Plenary

Discuss question 1.

Discuss how you could describe a position to the left of the grid. Emphasise that the x-axis is similar to a number line, with negative numbers to the left. Show the negative x-axis on **R8** and ask for coordinates of points.

Homework

▸ Mark letters on a coordinate grid. Write the series of coordinates for different words.
▸ Springboard 7: Page 278.

Exercise Commentary

Coverage

The questions assess objectives on Framework (Y456) Page 109.

Useful resources

R8 – coordinate grid
R9 – axes in a single quadrant
R14 – special triangles
S2.2WS – provides further practice of the key ideas.

Differentiation

▸ Questions 1 and 2 require students to identify positions given coordinates.
▸ Question 3 focuses on writing coordinates.
▸ Question 4 extends to finding the midpoint.

Support tier: focuses on parallel and perpendicular lines.

Misconceptions

Many students will plot (y, x) instead of (x, y). Students may have developed strategies at primary level for remembering the order they could share these. The strategy: you walk **across** the hall, then **up** the stairs, is given in the Students' book.

Links

Perpendicular and parallel lines: Framework (Y456) Page 109.

Exercise Answers

1 a Hut b Windmill c Tower d Bridge e Skull
2 a Swamp b Fire Hill c Lost Wood d Lake
  e Island
3 a (3, 5) b (11, 2) c (1, 3) d (9, 4)
  e (7, 2) f H = (4, 1), K = (8, 5)
4 (6, 3)

Worksheet Answers

2 Parker's Farm   3 Ruin   4 Amber Lake   5 Swamp   6 Red Hill

Franco goes on a journey. Here is a map of the area.

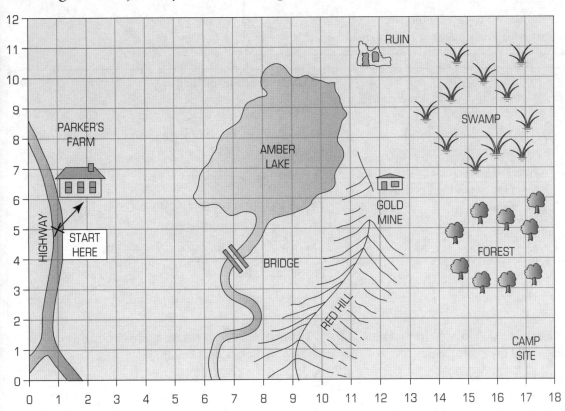

1 Plot the points and join them on the map to show Franco's journey.

(1, 5) (3, 7) (8, 11) (11, 10) (11, 8) (13, 7)

(14, 5) (14, 3) (15, 2) (17, 1)

> Remember, you go **across** first, then **up**.

2 What will Franco see on his left at (3, 7)? _____

3 What will Franco see on his right at (11, 10)? _____

4 What will Franco see on his left at (11, 10)? _____

5 What will Franco see on his right at (13, 7)? _____

6 What will Franco see on his left at (15, 2)? _____

7 Plot a shorter route from the Highway (1, 5) to the Camp Site (17, 1). Draw the new route on the map, and write the coordinates here.

_____

_____

S2.3 Coordinates and shapes

Access

This spread provides access to the Year 7 objective:
▸ Read and plot points using coordinates in all four quadrants (218)

Lesson Plan

Mental starter

Show a square (**R15**). Discuss its angle and side properties, and any misconceptions that arise.

Repeat for other quadrilaterals – rectangles, parallelograms, etc. Encourage use of the keywords: **parallel**, **perpendicular**, **equal**

Introductory activity

Recap coordinates from S2.2.

Choose students to plot points (4, 5), (6, 1) (1, 2) on a coordinate grid (**R9**). Demonstrate how to join these points to make a triangle.

Draw three crosses on the grid: (2, 4), (6, 4), (6, 1). Encourage students to read the coordinates.

Look at the example of the points on a line in the Students' book. Emphasise that the **across** coordinate is increasing by 2, the **up** coordinate is increasing by 1. Encourage students to give the next two coordinate pairs. Plot them on a grid to confirm that they are on the line.

Plenary

Mark the points (4, 4) and (8, 4) on a grid (**R9**). Ask students for coordinates of a third point to complete a triangle. Progress to creating an **isosceles triangle**, and a **right-angled triangle**.

Homework

▸ Plot the points of a square, rectangle, and right-angled triangle on a coordinate grid, labelling each point with its coordinate.
▸ Springboard 7: Page 276.

Worksheet Answers

1 a A (1, 2)   B (2, 4)   C (4, 2)
  b P (2, 4)   Q (6, 6)   R (6, 2)
2 c A kite

Exercise Commentary

Coverage

The questions assess objectives on Framework (Y456) Page 109.

Useful resources

R9 – axes in a single quadrant
R15 – special quadrilaterals
S2.3WS – provides support for weaker students.

Differentiation

▸ Questions 1 and 2 focus on reading coordinates from a grid.
▸ Question 3 involves drawing a coordinate grid and plotting points to create shapes.
▸ Question 4 focuses on plotting a pattern of coordinates.

Support tier: focuses on using geometrical properties to identify missing coordinates.

Misconceptions

Some students find it difficult to draw axes accurately (question 3). Encourage them to copy the axes given. Highlight the equal intervals between numbers, and that each axis starts from 0.

Links

Properties of shapes: Framework (Y456) Page 103.

Exercise Answers

1 a R = (1, 5); S = (8, 3); T = (3, 1)
  b J = (6, 4); K = (3, 0); M = (3, 5)
2 A = (3, 7); B = (14, 7); C = (9, 5); D = (16, 1);
  E = (9, 2); F = (2, 1)
3 a Triangle
  b Trapezium
  c Pentagon
  d Hexagon
4 a (8, 6)   (9, 7)   (10, 8)

1 a Write the coordinates of the points A, B and C.

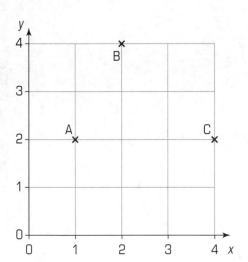

A(____, ____) B(____, ____)

C(____, ____)

b Write the coordinates of the points P, Q and R.

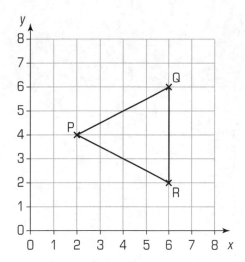

P(____, ____) Q(____, ____)

R(____, ____)

2 a Plot these points on this grid.
(5, 3)   (5, 6)   (5, 9)   (1, 6)   (14, 6)

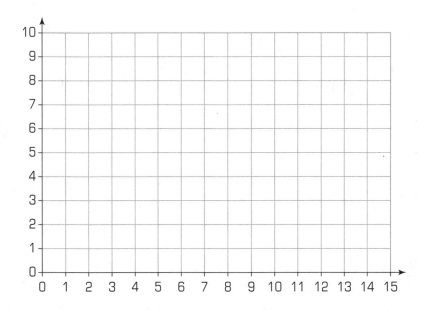

b Join all the points together with straight lines.

c What shape have you drawn? _____

Framework MATHS   Scheme of work   Year 7

S2 Angles and shapes (3 hours)	Teaching objectives	Framework Maths resources		Other resources
Measures (98–101)	Use units of time; read the time on a 24-hour digital clock and use 24-hour clock notation.	7A Student Book:	S2.1	
		7A Teacher's Book:	S2.1WS, R20	
Shape and space (102–3)	Classify triangles.	7A Student Book:	S2.2	
		7A Teacher's Book:	R8, R9, R14	
Shape and space (108–9)	Recognise positions and directions. Read and plot coordinates in the first quadrant.	7A Student Book:	S2.2, S2.3	
		7A Teacher's Book:	S2.2WS, S2.3WS, R8 R9, R14, R15	
Shape and space (102–3)	Recognise properties of rectangles.	7A Student Book:	S2.3	
		7A Teacher's Book:	S2.3WS, R9, R15	
Reasoning and generalising about numbers or shapes (78–9)	Solve mathematical problems or puzzles, recognise and explain patterns and relationships, generalise and predict.	7A Student Book:	S2.1–S2.3	

Access

Overview

The aim of this unit is to develop students' skills in sorting and organising raw data and representing sorted discrete data in Carroll diagrams, Venn diagrams, pictograms and bar charts. They will also interpret data shown in these types of charts and diagrams.

Spreads D2.1, D2.3 and D2.4 form the focus of the unit.

Framework references

The unit covers objectives on Framework (Y456) Pages 115 and 117.

Introduction

Discuss criteria for sorting people in everyday life: for example by packed lunch or school meals, method of transport to school, distance travelled to school, number of siblings in school.

Discuss when it might be useful to sort people in this way.

Check in activity

Ask students whether they have a pet. Record the number of hands shown. Discuss how to get more detailed information about students' pets (different types).

Write each type of pet on A4 paper: cat, dog, etc. Choose one student with that pet to hold up that piece of paper. Ask students to line up behind the correct label.

Discuss where students with more than one type of pet should stand and the overlaps between categories.

Useful resources

Worksheets
D2.1WS – sorting
D2.4WS – displaying data

OHPs
D2.2OHP – Carroll and Venn diagrams
D2.3OHP – favourite vegetables
D2.5OHP – interpreting diagrams

General resources
R6 – number lines
R11 – tally chart
R14 – triangles
R15 – quadrilaterals
R16 – 3-D shapes
Triangles and quadrilaterals cut from different colours of card

Springboard 7 pages
145, 154, 312, 401

Differentiation – spanning the bridge

Spread	Bridge to the Support tier
D2.1	The two tiers differ quite dramatically during this topic. Progress Support tier students to discuss the reason for sorting, as a way of organising information to tell something. Extend to a discussion on the types of data available, and ways of getting data (surveys). Move to discussion based around the Maypole High School problem – why might there be a problem/how could 'proper' information be collected about this problem?
D2.2	Progress by discussing what questions might have been asked to generate the information in the Caroll diagram. Develop to discuss different types of questions: **open**, **closed**, and the advantages and disadvantages of each approach. Discussion on biased and irrelevant questions and possible improvements will be beneficial.
D2.3	Extend Support tier students to discuss the difference between discrete and continuous data, and look at a frequency table of grouped data intervals.
D2.4	Progress to demonstrate a bar chart and a bar line chart of the data for Support tier students.
D2.5	A greater emphasis should be placed on the scale of diagrams for Support tier students, as this is fundamental to their interpretation of diagrams. Dual bar charts will need discussing, and also total frequency from bar charts. Support students would benefit from discussing pie charts prior to attempting the exercises.

D2.1 Sorting

Access

This spread provides access to the Year 7 objective:
▸ Plan how to collect and organise small sets of data (252)

Lesson Plan

Mental starter

Show a selection of triangles, quadrilaterals and 3-D shapes on **R14**, **R15** and **R16**, one at a time.

Encourage students to name the shapes and discuss their properties: parallel, quadrilateral, equal, etc.

Introductory activity

Show students a selection of triangles and quadrilaterals cut from different coloured cards. Discuss how to group the shapes into two different groups. Choose students to demonstrate, for example by colour, by number of sides.

Show a Carroll diagram. Discuss how to label each column (shape), and each row (colour). Emphasise that this diagram enables you to group according to shape *and* colour.

Discuss how to place each shape.

Discuss how to label a Venn diagram.

Highlight that the main two categories are unconnected – shape and colour. Emphasise the overlap and discuss how to place the shapes, including any outside the circles.

Link each part of the Venn diagram with the corresponding part in the Carroll diagram.

Plenary

Discuss how to draw a Venn diagram to show multiples of 4 and multiples of 3 up to 30.

Homework

▸ Draw a Venn diagram to show multiples of 2 and multiples of 3 up to 30.
▸ Springboard 7: Page 312.

Exercise Commentary

Coverage

The questions assess objectives on Framework (Y456) Page 117.

Useful resources

D2.1WS – provides support for weaker students.

R14, **R15** and **R16** – special triangles, quadrilaterals and 3-D shapes.

Triangles and quadrilaterals cut from coloured card.

Differentiation

▸ Question 1 focuses on sorting into two groups.
▸ Questions 2–4 focus on Carroll and Venn diagrams.
▸ Question 5 focuses on drawing a Carroll diagram from a Venn diagram.

Support tier: focuses on identifying issues for a survey.

Misconceptions

In the Venn diagrams students may place a shape in the first category it fits in.

Encourage them to check each of the categories before making their final choice.

Students should be familiar with the names of different shapes. Use the starter activity to reinforce the shapes and names they will be using.

Links

Shapes: Framework (Y456) Pages 102–3.

Exercise Answers

1

	Red	Not red
	5	4

2

	Small	Not small
Yellow	2	2
Not yellow	3	2

Worksheet Answers

1 Colours: blue, green, brown, yellow, purple   Names: Emily, Ann, James, John, Alfie
  Tools: hammer, hack-saw, drill, spade, pliers   Countries: France, Canada, China, Egypt, Pakistan
2 Odd and straight: 1, 7   Odd and curved: 3, 5, 9   Even and straight: 4   Even and curved: 2, 6, 8

88

1 Sort these 20 words onto the four lists.

hammer	*France*	*Emily*	*blue*	*Ann*	*Canada*
hack-saw	*green*	*brown*	*James*	*China*	*yellow*	*John*
drill	*Egypt*	*purple*	*Alfie*	*spade*	*Pakistan*	*pliers*

Colours	Names	Tools	Countries
_____	_____	_____	_____
_____	_____	_____	_____
_____	_____	_____	_____
_____	_____	_____	_____
_____	_____	_____	_____

2 Sort the numbers 1–9 onto this Carroll diagram.

1 2 3
4 5 6
7 8 9

	Straight lines only	Has curved lines
Odd number		
Even number		

3 Sort the shapes onto the Venn diagram.

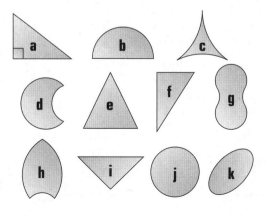

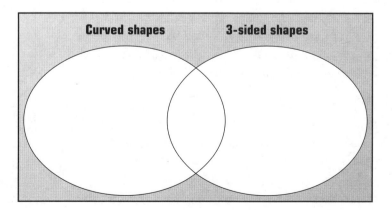

Curved shapes   3-sided shapes

D2.2 Reading diagrams

Lesson Plan

Mental starter

Explain to the class that in an alien world, only certain numbers exist.

Ask students to call out numbers.

Write them in a circle on the board if they exist (say, multiples of 3), and outside the circle if they don't.

Encourage students to guess the rule.

Introductory activity

Discuss the Carroll diagram from the Students' book (on **D2.2OHP**).

Recap the use of a sorting diagram, and how it sorts according to two categories, gender *and* vehicle. Ask questions based on the diagram: for example, how many cars were not driven by men?

Encourage students to explain where the information is from.

Discuss the Venn diagram from the Students' book (and plenary D2.1), shown on **D2.2OHP**.

Ask students how many numbers were multiples of 4. Emphasise that this includes the overlap.

Discuss what the overlap indicates (multiples of 3 *and* 4). Discuss whether these numbers have anything else in common (multiples of 12).

Discuss the frequency table in the Students' book (on **D2.2OHP**) and the questions in the example. Ask students for statements based upon the table.

Plenary

Show students the Venn diagram with three circles (multiples of 3, 5 and 7) on **D2.2OHP**.

Encourage students to discuss which values are placed incorrectly, and where they should be placed.

Homework

▸ Complete a frequency table of the tutor groups' favourite colours, and prepare questions based upon it to ask the class.
▸ Springboard 7: Page 154.

Exercise Commentary

Coverage

The questions assess objectives on Framework (Y456) Page 117.

Useful resources

D2.2OHP – diagrams from the Students' book and Venn diagram for the plenary.

Differentiation

▸ Questions 1 and 2 focus on interpreting Venn and Carroll diagrams.
▸ Question 3 focuses on a frequency table.
▸ Question 4 focuses on finding the total frequency.

Support tier: focuses on writing questions for a questionnaire.

Misconceptions

In question 1, reading the Carroll diagram, students may be tempted to consider only the first correct category they come across. However, sometimes more than one category must be considered. This is addressed in the introductory activity, but it might also be useful for students to work in pairs and discuss their answers.

Links

Multiples: Framework (Y456) Page 19.

Exercise Answers

1 a holly, yew, fir, pine, cedar
  b fir, pine, cedar
  c rowan, elder, hawthorn, oak, beech
  d rowan, elder, hawthorn
  e holly, yew
2 600, should be in the centre
3 a toast
  b cereal
  c 18
  d kippers (only one person)
4 150

	Car	Not car
Driven by men	3	4
Not driven by men	7	5

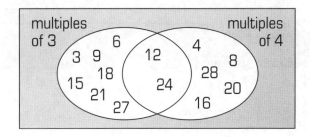

Colour	Votes
Red	5
Green	10
Blue	8
Orange	2
Purple	3

For plenary

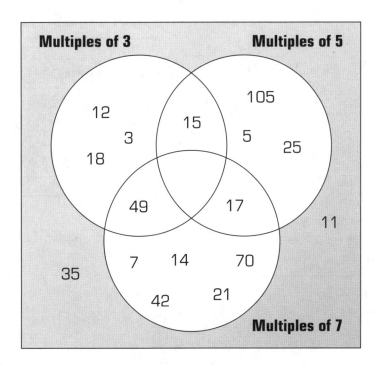

D2.3 Organising data

Access

This spread provides access to the Year 7 objective:
▸ Construct frequency tables for sets of data (252)

Lesson Plan

Mental starter

As a class, count up in 4s from 0.

Count down from 48.

Repeat, counting up and then down in 5s.

Discuss which was easiest to count in: 4s or 5s.

Introductory activity

Ask students for their favourite colour, and write them randomly on the board. Ask which is the most popular. Emphasise that it is difficult to see, and ask students for suggestions of how to organise the data.

Show the tally chart (**R11**), and demonstrate how to work through the data, tallying each result and crossing them off as you go.

Emphasise that we group tallies into 5s. Link with the mental starter, and ease of counting.

Discuss how to count the tallies to complete the frequency column. Highlight the **frequency** as the number of times the value appears.

Ask, which is the modal colour? Discuss who might be interested in this information. (Clothes designers, paint manufacturers)

Plenary

Show the vegetables frequency table on **D2.3OHP**.

Ask students to complete the missing values.

Encourage students to add the frequencies to find the total and spot the mistake.

(One 'peas' has been missed.) Highlight this as a checking procedure.

Homework

▸ Record the colour of 30 cars on the way home, and organise their data in a frequency table (**R11**).
▸ Springboard 7: Page 401.

Exercise Commentary

Coverage

The questions assess objectives on Framework (Y456) Page 115.

Useful resources

R11 – blank tally chart

D2.3OHP – favourite vegetables for plenary

Differentiation

▸ Question 1 focuses on completing a frequency table.
▸ Questions 2 and 3 involve tallying results in a frequency table.
▸ Question 4 focuses on designing a frequency table.

Support tier: includes sets of continuous data.

Misconceptions

Tallying items will be difficult for some students. Encourage them to work from left to right when tallying, and to cross off each value once it has been recorded in the tally.

Links

Ordering: Framework (Y456) Page 9.

Exercise Answers

1

Watersport	Water-skiing	Sailing	Surfing	Swimming
Frequency	126	239	142	625

2 Frequencies: 7, 6, 4, 8
3 Frequencies: 4, 13, 7, 3, 2
4 Frequencies: 4, 12, 7, 20, 1

Cabbage	Peas	Lettuce	Beans	Carrot	Beans
Carrot	Cabbage	Carrot	Cabbage	Beans	Carrot
Peas	Carrot	Peas	Cabbage	Peas	Peas
Lettuce	Peas	Carrot	Lettuce	Peas	Cabbage
Peas	Beans	Beans	Carrot	Lettuce	Beans

Vegetable	Tally	Frequency
Cabbage		5
Carrot	ǁǁǁ ǁ	
Peas	ǁǁǁ ǁ	7
Lettuce	ǁǁǁ	
Beans		6

D2.4 Displaying data

Access

This spread provides access to the Year 7 objective:
▸ Construct graphs and diagrams to represent data (262–264)

Lesson Plan

Mental starter

Give students a number, say 38.

Ask whether it is nearer 0 or 100? 0 or 50? 30 or 40? 35 or 40? Numbers lines (**R6**) may be useful. Repeat for other integers, progressing to 1dp numbers, such as 5.8.

Introductory activity

Show students a picture from a book or magazine and ask them to tell you as much as they can about what it shows. Emphasise that a picture can give lots of information immediately. In Maths, charts, tables and graphs give a picture of information.

Discuss the first pictogram from the Students' book. Which was the most/least popular fruit? Emphasise that a pictogram uses pictures to represent numbers. Highlight that one banana represents one person.

Discuss the frequency table in the Students' book. Emphasise that the numbers are larger. Is reasonable to draw one picture for each unit? Highlight that in this pictogram, one picture represents two items and this is shown on the **key**.

Ask spot questions on the data to build confidence.

Plenary

Discuss question 4 and the symbols students used.

Discuss a title for the pictogram, and highlight that without this the pictogram could mean something completely different.

Homework

▸ Represent the information on car colours from D2.3 on a pictogram.

Worksheet Answers

2 Frequencies: 6, 3, 2, 8, 5
4 6   5 Red   6 Purple

Exercise Commentary

Coverage

The questions assess objectives on Framework (Y456) Page 115.

Useful resources

R6 – number lines

D2.4WS – provides support for weaker students.

Differentiation

▸ Questions 1 and 2 focus on simple pictograms.
▸ Question 3 involves using a key.
▸ Question 4 focuses on designing a pictogram.

Support tier: includes pie charts, bar charts and bar-line charts.

Misconceptions

Students assume that one picture always represents one unit. Refer them back to the key for each question.

Students may not draw the pictures uniformly, or with equal intervals. Encourage students to compare their pictograms with a partner to invite discussion around this point.

Links

Reading scales: Framework (Y456) Page 95.

Exercise Answers

1 Girls: 6 symbols   Boys: 8 symbols
2 Real tree: 9 symbols
  False tree: 11 symbols
  No tree: 4 symbols
3 January: 1 symbol; February: 4 symbols;
  March: 4 symbols; April: 3 symbols;
  May: 4 symbols; June: $5\frac{1}{2}$ symbols
4 Edinburgh: 3 symbols; London: 4 symbols;
  Malaga: 6 symbols; Paris: 3 symbols;
  Orlando: 5 symbols

Class 7P call out their favourite colours for a survey.

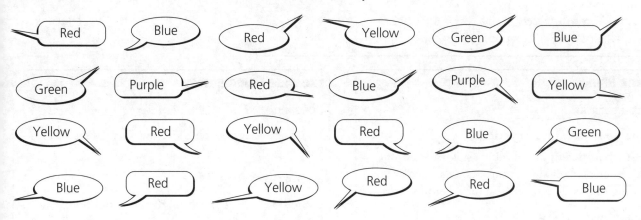

1 Tally the data from this survey into this table.

2 Write the totals in the frequency column.

Colour	Tally	Frequency
Blue		
Green		
Purple		
Red		
Yellow		

3 Complete this pictogram to show this data.
Use ☺ to represent one person.

4 How many students called out Blue?

_____

5 What was the most popular colour?

_____

6 What was the least popular colour?

_____

Favourite colour

Blue	
Green	
Purple	
Red	
Yellow	
	Number of students

Key: ☺ = _____

D2.5 Interpreting data

Access

This spread provides access to the Year 7 objective:
▶ Interpret diagrams and graphs (268)

Lesson Plan

Mental starter

Show a ×5 function machine (**R7**).

Give students the input value and ask for the output value. Progress to giving the output and students providing the input. Repeat with different functions.

Introductory activity

Recap the use of diagrams to represent information. Discuss the pictogram in the Students' book (shown on **D2.5OHP**).

Tell students that 'John' thinks 3 people said their favourite drink was blackcurrant, and encourage students to explain why this is wrong. Highlight the key indicating one picture represents 5 people.

Ask spot questions:
▶ How many people said milkshake?
▶ How many people were asked in total?

Discuss who might be interested in this information: the caretaker, a parent, the person in charge of the school tuck shop?

Discuss the bar chart shown in the Students' book (**D2.5OHP**).

Ask students how many people liked 'Mix'.

Highlight the scale on the vertical axis.

Discuss how many people were asked in total, and what numbers your would expect if you asked twice as many people.

Plenary

Show a pie chart representing information on favourite break-time snacks of year 7's. (**D2.5OHP**).

Emphasise that this is another way of displaying information. Ask students which was the most/least popular snack, and encourage students to give statements about the information.

Homework

▶ Create five questions (and answers) based on a given bar chart.
▶ Springboard 7: Page 145.

Exercise Commentary

Coverage

The questions assess objectives on Framework (Y456) Page 115.

Useful resources

D2.5OHP – diagrams from the Students' book, and for the plenary

Differentiation

▶ Questions 1 and 2 focus on simple pictograms and bar charts.
▶ Question 3 involves comparing charts using scales on axes.
▶ Question 4 focuses on finding the total frequency from a bar chart.

Support tier: includes a wide variety of charts, including pie charts.

Misconceptions

In question 4 students may think the two bar charts represent two different groups of people. Working in pairs, and careful discussion of the information before approaching the question will help to remedy this problem.

Use of scale can cause problems, and students should be directed to make sure they understand the scale before they start to answer a question.

Links

Scales: Framework (Y456) Page 95.

Exercise Answers

1 a 2   b 25   c 42
2 a 7   b 2   c 13   d 3
3 a 40   b 30   c 20   d 25
4 130

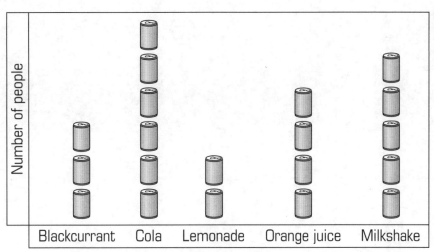

Key: = 5 people

Favourite drink

The scale goes up in 2s.

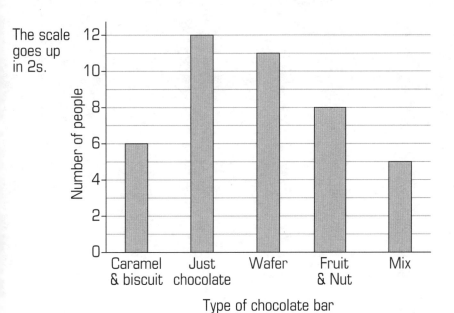

Type of chocolate bar

Favourite break-time snack

D2 Handling data (5 hours)	Teaching objectives	Framework Maths resources	Other resources
Organising and interpreting data (114–17)	Solve a problem by organising and representing data in Venn and Carroll diagrams	7A Student Book: D2.1 7A Teacher's Book: D2.1WS, R14, R15, R16	
Organising and interpreting data (114–17)	Solve a problem by interpreting data in Venn and Carroll diagrams.	7A Student Book: D2.2 7A Teacher's Book: D2.2OHP	
Organising and interpreting data (114–17)	Solve a problem by organising and representing data in frequency diagrams	7A Student Book: D2.3 7A Teacher's Book: D2.3OHP, R11	
Organising and interpreting data (114–17)	Solve a problem by organising and representing data in pictograms	7A Student Book: D2.4 7A Teacher's Book: D2.4WS, R6	
Organising and interpreting data (114–17)	Solve a problem by interpreting data in pictograms and bar charts.	7A Student Book: D2.5 7A Teacher's Book: D2.5OHP	

Access

Overview

This unit aims to develop multiplication and division using mental methods and jottings. Multiplying and dividing by 10 and 100 is introduced and used to convert between metric measures. The link between multiplication and division is emphasised.

Spreads N3.1, N3.2, N3.4, N3.6 and N3.7 form the focus of the unit.

Framework references

The unit covers objectives on Framework (Y456) Pages 7, 13, 61, 63, 67, 91

Introduction

Discuss everyday examples of when it is important to give accurate measurements, such as a recipe. Compare with other examples when accuracy is not required, for example, the number of people living in a town.

Check in activity

Ask two students to stand at the front of the class, one holding a card saying 10 and one 20.

Give students numbers between 10 and 20 and ask them to stand next to whichever of 10 or 20 their number is closer to. Repeat for different intervals of 10.

Useful resources

Worksheets
N3.2WS – mental multiplication
N3.3WS – multiplying decimals by 10
N3.4WS – dividing by 10
N3.5WS – number and measure
N3.6WS – multiplying by partitioning
N3.7WS – division on a number line
N3.8WS – more division ideas
N3.1OHP – number lines

General resources
R4 – place value tables
R6 – number lines
R7 – function machines
R19 – ruler
R21 – multiplication table
Ruler, metre rule
Dice
Coin

Springboard 7 pages
72, 116, 120, 215, 220, 253, 338, 347

Differentiation – spanning the bridge

Spread	Bridge to the Support tier
N3.1	Progress to discuss rules for multiplication and division by 10 and 100 using a place value table. Extend to work problems, discussing which operation to use in different situations. Link to conversion between metric units (mm to cm to m to km).
N3.2	There is little link between the tiers in this lesson but Support tier students will benefit from the discussion on mental multiplication strategies. Progress from this to give Support students string calculations (+ first, then ×) to first calculate mentally and then using a calculator. This will provide the opportunity to introduce the order of operations.
N3.3	Progress Support tier students to the idea of doubling and halving to help with more complex calculations (in particular × by 8). Combine this with the idea of multiplying by 10 to help with calculations like 13×5 (× 10 and then halve).
N3.4	There is a little link between the tiers in this lesson but Support tier students will benefit from a recap on dividing by 10. Progress to consider partitioning more complex numbers. Discuss strategies for multiplying by 9 and by 11. Demonstrate breaking more complex calculations into easier ones to help: $13 \times 19 = (13 \times 10) + (13 \times 10) - 13$. Emphasise multiplication as 'lots of'.
N3.5	Support tier should recap number and measure with Access students. Progress to using the grid method to multiply HTU by U and TU by TU, linking back to N3.4.
N3.6	Support tier students have covered multiplying partitioning but would benefit from recapping. Progress to consider division of numbers using the repeated subtraction method (use and analogy of dealing 24 cards amongst 4 people). Progress to subtracting chunks of the number (focusing on chunks of 10).
N3.7	Extend Support tier students to consider the repeated subtraction method of division where there are remainders. Extend to the repeated subtraction of chunks of 10.
N3.8	Discuss with Support tier students when you might use a calculator rather than a mental or written method. Recap the order of operations. Illustrate the use of brackets on a scientific calculator, and using memory keys, and highlight the importance of estimating first.

N3.1 Rounding numbers

Lesson Plan

Mental starter

Write a large group of integers, including some multiples of 10 and 100 on the board.

Explain 'tens' as multiples of 10, and give an example. Explain 'hundreds' as multiples of 100.

Invite students to come to the board, and circle a 'ten' in red or a 'hundred' in blue.

Introductory activity

Ask students how long it takes to get to school. Highlight that this time is not an exact value. It has been rounded to the nearest minute, or 5 minutes.

Refer to the mental starter.
▸ Which two tens is 38 between?
▸ Which is it nearer?

Show the interval between 30 and 40 on a number line (**N3.1OHP**). Ask students which numbers are nearer 30 than 40, and vice versa.

Emphasise that when the unit is less than 5, it is nearer 30, and when the unit is bigger than 5 it is nearer 40.

Explain that when the digit is 5 the number is halfway. **N3.1OHP** provides more examples for practice. Emphasise that you round halfway numbers **up**.

Repeat for 230, with a number line from 200 to 300.

Discuss which digit helps to decide whether a number is closer to 200 or 300. Emphasise that the tens digit helps you decide. Emphasise that ten digits less than 5 means **round down**, 5 or above means **round up**.

Plenary

Round £438 to the nearest 100, and to the nearest 10.

Extend to rounding numbers with 1dp to the nearest integer using **N3.1OHP**.

Homework

▸ Give students five integer numbers to round to the nearest 10 and the nearest 100.
▸ Springboard 7: Page 347.

Exercise Commentary

Coverage

The questions assess objectives on Framework (Y456) Page 13.

Useful resources

R4 – place value tables
R6 – number lines
N3.1OHP – number lines

Differentiation

▸ Question 1 focuses on numbers between 0 and 10.
▸ Questions 2, 3 and 5 focus on rounding to 10 or 100.
▸ Question 4 focuses on numbers between 0 and 100.

Support tier: focuses on multiplying and dividing by 10 or 100.

Misconceptions

Students often experience difficulties in correctly identifying the decider digit to help round up or down. Encourage students to first decide on the two numbers the value is between, and write these on a blank number line (**R6**). A place value table (**R4**) can also help students to look at the number in a structured way.

Links

Approximating: Framework (Y456) Page 73.

Exercise Answers

1 a start b finish c finish d start e start
  f finish g finish h start i start j start
2 a 0 b £10 c £10 d £10 e 0
3 a £30 b £20 c £30 d £40 e £40
  f £40 g £60 h £80 i £70 j £90
  k £30 l £20 m £90 n £100
4 a start b finish c finish d start e start
  f finish g finish h finish
5 a 100 km b 300 km c 500 km d 300 km
  e 400 km f 200 km g 300 km h 100 km
  i 100 km j 100 km k 500 km

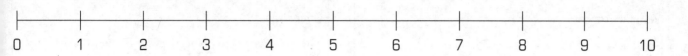

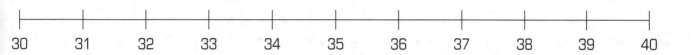

N3.2 Mental multiplication

■■■■

Access

This spread provides access to the Year 7 objective:
▸ Consolidate the rapid recall of number facts (88)

Lesson Plan

Mental starter

Show a ×2 function machine (**R7**).

Give an input, and ask for the output. Repeat with other one-digit and two-digit integers.

Introductory activity

Refer to the mental starter and discuss partitioning more complicated numbers like 27, into 20 and 7, and doubling each part. Highlight that **doubling** is the same as **multiplying by 2**

Highlight the 2, 4, 8 times tables in the multiplication square (**R21**) and ask students to describe the patterns.

Emphasise that the 4 times table is double the 2 times table, and the 8 times table is double again.

Discuss strategies for multiplying a number by 4.

Highlight that 2×4 is the same as 2×2 doubled and work through the calculation [8].

Repeat for 32×4 – ask students to calculate mentally and hold up the answer on a piece of scrap paper.

Extend to calculating 14×8, using the same methods, emphasising that this is $14 \times 2 \times 2 \times 2$.

Ask students how they could calculate 13×6 using a double. Highlight that to multiply by 6 you double the 3 times table.

Plenary

Repeat the mental starter for the operation × 4.

Give students the output for a × 2 function machine and discuss how to find the input by halving. Extend to giving the output for × 4 machine.

Homework

▸ Students draw a bubble with ×2 written in it. They write 20 numbers with their doubles (e.g. 46→92) leading out from the bubble.
▸ Springboard 7: Page 215.

Exercise Commentary

Coverage

The questions assess objectives on Framework (Y456) Page 61.

Useful resources

R7 – function machines
R21 – multiplication square
N3.2WS – provides support for weaker students.

Differentiation

▸ Questions 1 and 2 focus on doubling.
▸ Questions 3 and 4 focus on using doubling to develop times tables.
▸ Questions 5–7 focus on using doubling to multiply by 4, 6 and 8.

Support tier: focuses on the order of operations.

Misconceptions

Encourage students to use jottings to keep track of how many times they have doubled a number. A model is given in the Students' book.

Links

Multiplication facts: Framework (Y456) Page 59.

Exercise Answers

1 a £10 b £6 c £20 d 14 kg e £16
  f 18 m g £40 h 100 m
2 a side a = 4 cm, double side a = 8 cm
  b side b = 2 cm, double side b = 4 cm
  c side c = 3 cm, double side c = 6 cm
3 6 times table: 6, 12, 18, 24, 30, 36, 42, 48, 54, 60
4 10 times table: 10, 20, 30, 40, 50, 60, 70, 80, 90, 100
5 a 88 b 48 c 128 d 60 e 56 f 64
6 a 90 b 84 c 120 d 180 e 186 f 126
7 a 104 b 120 c 128 d 160 e 168 f 248

Worksheet Answers

1 a 8 b 12 c 14   2 Clockwise from top: 140, 10, 100, 12, 120, 18, 180, 14
3 Double: 2, 6, 12, 14, 16, 20, 40, 100   × 10: 20, 60, 120, 140, 160, 200, 400, 1000

N3.2WS Name:

....

1 Double these numbers. Write your answers in the boxes.

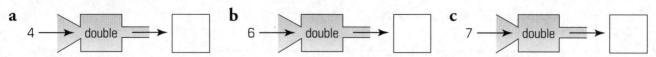

a 4 → double → ☐   **b** 6 → double → ☐   **c** 7 → double → ☐

2 Double each of the numbers in the 'arrow' boxes.
Write your answers in the circles.

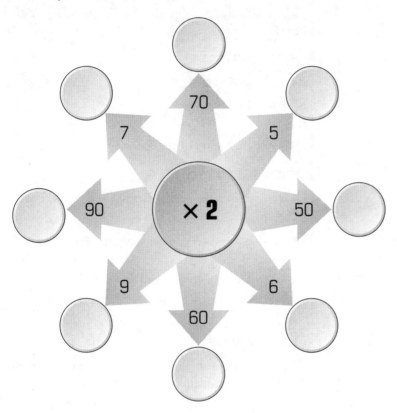

3 Multiply the numbers in these boxes by 20.
First double them, then multiply by 10.

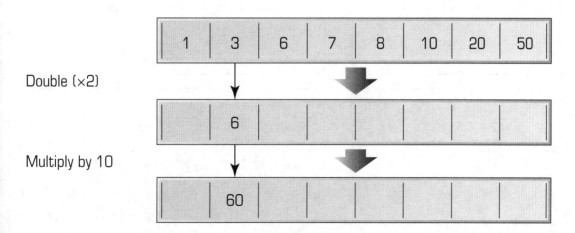

| 1 | 3 | 6 | 7 | 8 | 10 | 20 | 50 |

Double (×2)

| | 6 | | | | | | |

Multiply by 10

| | 60 | | | | | | |

Access

This spread provides access to the Year 7 objective:
▸ Multiply and divide integers by 10, 100 and 1000 and explain the effect (38)

Lesson Plan

Mental starter

Show a ×10 function machine (**R7**).

Give an input, and ask for the output.

Repeat with other one-digit and two-digit integers.

Introductory activity

Show the Th, H, T and U columns on a place value table (**R4**). Write 435 in the table, and ask students for the number of hundreds, tens and units.

Show a ruler (**R19**). Ask students how we can divide a unit. Highlight the ten divisions for each unit on the ruler; each interval is one tenth of a centimetre.

Show the tenths column on the place value table. Emphasise that ten tenths make one unit, ten units make one ten, etc. Practise writing decimal values.

Highlight that multiplying by 10 means moving each digit to the next highest column in the place value table.

Plenary

Refer to question 5. Give students a time for 10 laps, and ask for the time for 1 lap. Discuss the methods used. Highlight that division that is the inverse/opposite of multiplication.

Homework

▸ Give students a simple picture made of straight lines. Ask them to measure and label each length to the nearest millimetre, writing the measurements in cm.
▸ Springboard 7: Page 116.

Exercise Commentary

Coverage

The questions assess objectives on Framework (Y456) Page 7.

Useful resources

R4 – place value table

R7 – function machines

R19 – ruler

N3.3WS – provides further practice of the key ideas.

Differentiation

▸ Questions 1 and 2 focus on place value in decimals.
▸ Questions 3–5 focus on multiplying decimals by 10.
▸ Question 6 involves recognising upper and lower bands.

Support tier: focuses on mental methods for multiplication. N3.1 focuses on multiplying and dividing by 10.

Misconceptions

Students may continue to add a zero for multiplying by 10. Encourage students to use a place value table to demonstrate each digit moving to the next highest place, and to think carefully about what adding a zero does to a decimal number (it indicates no hundredths and does not change the number). Also encourage students to use estimation: 3.2×10 is approximately 3×10 which is 30, so the answer must be close to this.

Links

Measures: Framework (Y456) Page 91.

Worksheet Answers

2 a 25　b 52　c 70　d 127　e 209　f 80

Exercise Answers

1 a 1.5 cm　b 4.8 cm　c 6.4 cm　d 7.6 cm
2 a 9 tenths　b seven　c twenty　d two　e 3 tenths
　f two　g five hundred　h twenty　i 6 tenths
3 a 58　b 27　c 71　d 99　e 33　f 43
4 a 152　b 123　c 111　d 139　e 183　f 242
5 Mat, 36 minutes; Claire, 29 minutes; Sarah, 101 minutes; Dinesh, 133 minutes; Lizzie, 45 minutes
6 a 60 and 70　b 20 and 30　c 130 and 140
　d 190 and 200

1 Draw lines of these lengths on the rulers.

a 3.4 cm

b 6.7 cm

c 9.1 cm

2 When you multiply a number by 10 you move the digits one place to the left.

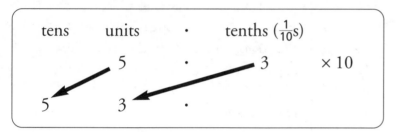

Multiply these numbers by 10. Write your answers in the table.

	calculation	hundreds	tens	units	•	tenths ($\frac{1}{10}$s)
a				2	•	5
	2.5 × 10 =				•	
b				5	•	2
	5.2 × 10 =				•	
c				7	•	0
	7.0 × 10 =				•	
d					•	
	12.7 × 10 =				•	
e					•	
	20.9 × 10 =				•	
f					•	
	0.8 × 10 =				•	

N3.4 Dividing whole numbers by 10

Access

This spread provides access to the Year 7 objective:
▸ Multiply and divide integers by 10, 100 and 1000 and explain the effect (38)

Lesson Plan

Mental starter

Show a ×10 function machine (**R7**).

Give an input and ask for the output. Repeat with other one-digit and two-digit integers, extending to decimals to 1 dp.

Introductory activity

Write a list of integers on the board. Ask students to use their calculators to divide each number by 10. Record the answers on the board.

Look at the results and encourage students to devise a rule for dividing by 10. It may be helpful to show the numbers on (**R4**).

Emphasise that the rule is: to divide by 10, move the digits to the next lowest place. Give some examples for practice.

Recap the rule for multiplying by 10. Compare with the rule for dividing. Emphasise that dividing is the opposite (inverse) of multiplying.

Briefly look at an application of dividing by 10. How could you split a 250 cm piece of string into 10 equal pieces?

Plenary

Discuss strategies for remembering to move digits to the next highest place for multiplying by 10, and moving to the next lowest place when dividing by 10.

Homework

▸ Design a poster to explain what happens when you multiply or divide a number by 10.
▸ Springboard 7: Page 72.

Worksheet Answers

1 9	2 3	3 5	4 12	5 17
6 23	7 54	8 86	9 49	10 80

Exercise Commentary

Coverage

The questions assess objectives on Framework (Y456) Page 7.

Useful resources

R4 – place value table
R7 – function machine
N3.4WS – provides support for weaker students.

Differentiation

▸ Question 1 involves dividing whole numbers by 10.
▸ Questions 2 and 3 involve dividing by 10 in context.
▸ Questions 5 and 6 include decimal answers.

Support tier: focuses on partitioning. N3.1 focuses on multiplying and dividing by 10 and 100.

Misconceptions

Students are often confused when the answer is a decimal. Highlight that decimals are used in money, and in measurements. Encourage them to use a place value table (**R4**) to gain confidence in each digit moving to the next lowest place. Encourage students to estimate first.

Links

Decimal notation: Framework (Y456) Page 29.

Exercise Answers

1 a 6 b 8 c 5 d 4 e 2 f 10 g 12 h 17
  i 19 j 21 k 36 l 40
2 a 6 b 11 c 22 d 48
3 a £5 b £6 c £9 d £15 e £18 f £30
  g £50 h £70 i £75 j £78
4 a 5.6 b 2.3 c 1.5 d 4.6
5 a £1.80 b £4.20 c £7.90 d £7.20 e £8.00
  f £4.50

When you divide a number by 10, you move the digits one place to the right.

hundreds	tens	units	
3	2	0	÷ 10
	3	2	

Divide these numbers by 10. Move the digits one place to the right.
The first one is done for you.

	calculation	hundreds	tens	units
1			9	0
	90 ÷ 10 =			9
2			3	0
	30 ÷ 10 =			
3				
	50 ÷ 10 =			
4				
	120 ÷ 10 =			
5				
	170 ÷ 10 =			
6				
	230 ÷ 10 =			
7				
	540 ÷ 10 =			
8				
	860 ÷ 10 =			
9				
	490 ÷ 10 =			
10				
	800 ÷ 10 =			

N3.5 Number and measure

Access

This spread provides access to the Year 7 objective:
▸ Convert between metric units (230)

Lesson Plan

Mental starter

Show a ×10 function machine (**R7**).

Give an input and ask for the output. Extend to giving the output, and asking for the input. Highlight division as the opposite of multiplication.

Introductory activity

Refer to the mental starter to recap how to multiply by 10. Extend to multiplying by 100 by asking simple ×100 calculations: 3 × 100, 7 × 100. Use a place value table (**R4**) to demonstrate how multiplying by 100 moves the digits up two higher places. Progress to a decimal to show that 'adding two zeros' does not work.

Ask students how many millimetres are in a centimetre. Weaker students could use a ruler or **R19**. Emphasise that for **every** centimetre, there are 10 millimetres. Ask how many millimetres in 3 cm. Highlight that to convert cm to mm you multiply by 10. Demonstrate 3 × 10 on a place value table (**R4**), showing how to add the **zero place holder** in the units column.

Repeat for cm in a metre (×100) (weaker students can use a metre rule). Extend to number of cm in 1.9 m.

Recap the method for dividing by 10. Ask students to suggest the method for dividing by 100. Confirm using a place value table (**R4**).

Plenary

Discuss how to calculate the number of millimetres in 1.8 metres. Encourage students to suggest conversion to centimetres, then to millimetres. Ask for shortcuts: How many millimetres in one metre?

Homework

▸ Further calculations involving multiplication and division by 10 and 100.
▸ Springboard 7: Page 120.

Worksheet Answers

1 a 70   b 150   c 230   d 470   e 560   f 980
2 a 40 mm, 50 mm, 70 mm, 80 mm
   b 5 cm, 8 cm, 9 cm   c 200 cm, 800 cm
3 a <   b >   c >   d <   e >   f <

Exercise Commentary

Coverage

The questions assess objectives on Framework (Y456) Page 91.

Useful resources

R4 – place value table
R7 – function machine
R19 – ruler
N3.5WS – provides practice of the key ideas.
Ruler, metre rule

Differentiation

▸ Question 1 focuses on multiplying by 10.
▸ Questions 2, 3 and 5 involve converting from large to small units.
▸ Questions 4, 6 and 7 involve converting from small to large units.

Support tier: focuses on written multiplication, N3.1 focuses on converting a wider range of measures.

Misconceptions

Students may find it difficult identify the correct operation to use in conversion questions, especially in questions 6 and 7. Encourage students to estimate the size first, to give them a sense of the size of the answer. Rulers and metre rules can be a good support.

Links

Multiplying and dividing by 10, 100, 1000: Framework (Y456) Page 7.

Exercise Answers

1 a 50   b 90   c 60   d 80   e 130   f 150   g 210
   h 320
2 a 40 mm   b 20 mm   c 70 mm   d 10 mm
   e 50 mm   f 100 mm
3 length = 40 mm, width = 30 mm, height = 20 mm
4 11 cm
5 a 400 mm   b 800 mm   c 600 mm   d 200 mm
   e 700 mm   f 1000 mm
6 a 2 m   b 4 m   c 8 m   d 3 m   e 6 m   f 1 m

1 Multiply these numbers by 10:

a   7 × 10 = _____

b   15 × 10 = _____

c   23 × 10 = _____

d   47 × 10 = _____

e   56 × 10 = _____

f   98 × 10 = _____

2 Rewrite these measurements in centimetres or millimetres.

> 10 mm = 1 cm   100 cm = 1 m

Do not try to measure the drawings, they are not accurate.

a
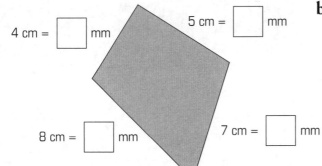

4 cm = ☐ mm   5 cm = ☐ mm

8 cm = ☐ mm   7 cm = ☐ mm

b
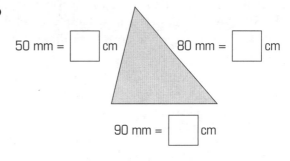

50 mm = ☐ cm   80 mm = ☐ cm

90 mm = ☐ cm

c
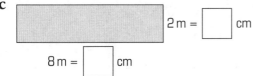

2 m = ☐ cm

8 m = ☐ cm

3 Use these signs, > or <, between the pairs of measurements to make these statements true.

a 60 mm   ☐   7 cm

b 2 m   ☐   120 cm

c 250 mm   ☐   20 cm

d 3 m   ☐   400 m

e 5 m   ☐   60 cm

f 34 mm   ☐   5 cm

N3.6 Multiplying by partitioning

Access

This spread provides access to the Year 7 objective:
▸ Consolidate and extend mental methods of calculation (96)

Lesson Plan

Mental starter

Give a starting number between 1 and 10.

Students take turns to roll two dice and add the scores together. They multiply the start number by this total. (**R21** may be helpful). Repeat with different start numbers.

Introductory activity

Give students a number, say 438. Ask how many hundreds, tens and units there are.

Introduce the keyword **partition** and explain that it means split into **parts**. Demonstrate on a place value table (**R4**) that 438 can be partitioned into 400, 30 and 8. Give students two-digit numbers to partition into tens and units.

Discuss what the calculation 16×9 means: 16 lots of 9. Ask students to partition the 'more complicated' number (16). Emphasise that 16 lots of 9 is the same as 10 lots of 9 and 6 lots of 9.

Encourage students to use jottings:
$10 \times 9 = 90$ $6 \times 9 = 54$ $54 + 90 = 144$.

Repeat for 13×6 (shown in the Students' book)

Extend to 23×7. Model jotting of 20×7 as $2 \times 10 \times 7$.

Link to multiplying by 10, and doubling strategies.

Plenary

Ask students multiplication questions orally, to extend the technique of mental partitioning and multiplying. Keep to two-digit numbers between 11 and 19.

Homework

▸ Students carry out five multiplying by partitioning calculations then write a word problem to fit each one.
▸ Springboard 7: Page 220.

Exercise Commentary

Coverage

The questions assess objectives on Framework (Y456) Page 63.

Useful resources

R4 – place value table
R21 – multiplication table
N3.6WS – provides support for weaker students.

Differentiation

▸ Questions 1 and 2 focus on simple multiplications.
▸ Questions 3 and 4 involve partitioning TU numbers.
▸ Questions 5–7 involve using partitioning.

Support tier: focuses on written division. N3.4 focuses on partitioning in real-life contexts.

Misconceptions

A multiplication square (**R21**) will be useful for students with weak times tables.

Students may lose track of where they are in the partitioning process. Encourage them to use jottings. They may also forget to add the multiplied parts at the end. Refer students back to the original calculation.

Links

Multiplication facts: Framework (Y456) Page 59.

1 Complete these calculations.

a $2 \times 4 =$ _____   b $3 \times 6 =$ _____   c $5 \times 6 =$ _____

d $8 \times 7 =$ _____   e $5 \times 4 =$ _____   f $6 \times 8 =$ _____

g _____ $\times 4 = 16$ h $3 \times$ _____ $= 24$ i _____ $\times 4 = 36$

2 Split up these numbers into tens and units.

a 16 is the same as $\boxed{10}$ + $\boxed{}$ b 11 is the same as $\boxed{10}$ + $\boxed{}$

c 19 is the same as $\boxed{10}$ + $\boxed{}$ d 13 is the same as $\boxed{10}$ + $\boxed{}$

3 Fill in the boxes to multiply these numbers.

a 16×4 16 is $\boxed{10}$ + $\boxed{}$

$10 \times 4 = \boxed{}$

$6 \times 4 = \boxed{}$

So $16 \times 4 = \boxed{40}$ + $\boxed{}$

$= \boxed{}$

b 19×3 19 is $\boxed{}$ + $\boxed{9}$

$10 \times 3 = \boxed{}$

$9 \times 3 = \boxed{}$

So $19 \times 3 = \boxed{}$ + $\boxed{}$

$= \boxed{}$

c 15×7 15 is $\boxed{10}$ + $\boxed{}$

$10 \times 7 = \boxed{}$

$5 \times 7 = \boxed{}$

So $15 \times 7 = \boxed{}$ + $\boxed{}$

$= \boxed{}$

d 14×4 14 is $\boxed{}$ + $\boxed{}$

$10 \times 4 = \boxed{}$

$4 \times 4 = \boxed{}$

So $14 \times 4 = \boxed{}$ + $\boxed{}$

$= \boxed{}$

N3.7 Division on a number line

Access

This spread provides access to the Year 7 objective:
▸ Consolidate and extend mental methods of calculation (96)

Lesson Plan

Mental starter

Show a multiplication square on the OHP (**R21**).

Ask students a multiplication question, say 4 × 6. Encourage students to give another calculation that links these three numbers (6 × 4, 24 divided by 6, 24 divided by 4). Extend to questions based around division.

Introductory activity

Refer to the mental starter, and highlight the connection between multiplication and division. Emphasise that if you know the multiplication fact, you also know the division fact.

Look at the calculation 5 + 5 + 5 + 5. Discuss a better way of writing it: 5 × 4. Highlight that multiplication is like repeated addition, and division is repeated subtraction.

Discuss how to work out 28 ÷ 4.

Demonstrate repeated subtraction (jumping) of 4 from 28 on a number line (**R6**), and then counting the number of jumps. Emphasise the multiplication fact to support this (what times 4 makes 28?)

Repeat with 32 ÷ 8, progressing to 48 ÷ 16.

Plenary

Choose four students and explain that you are going to deal out 20 cards between them.

Ask students for the calculation we need to do to work out how many cards each will have.

Deal one card each, and ask students how many you have left. Repeat, until all the cards have been dealt, recording how many cards are left after each deal.

Link this repeated subtraction to the division calculations.

Homework

▸ Complete a multiplication square with values missing, using multiplication and division facts.

▸ Springboard 7: Page 253.

Exercise Commentary

Coverage

The questions assess objectives on Framework (Y456) Page 63.

Useful resources

R6 – number lines

R21 – multiplication table

N3.7WS – provides support for weaker students.

Differentiation

▸ Question 1 involves simple divisions.
▸ Questions 2–4 focus on TU ÷ U.
▸ Questions 5 and 6 extend to two-digit divisors.

Support tier: focuses on dividing with remainders.

Misconceptions

Students find division more difficult than multiplication. Emphasise the link between division and multiplication. Weaker students may need a multiplication square. Encourage the use of a number line to keep track of the number of jumps made.

In question 6 students may order the values incorrectly in their calculation, causing problems. Encourage them to estimate an answer before doing the calculation.

Links

Multiplication facts: Framework (Y456) Page 59.

Exercise Answers

1 a 3 b 3 c 9 d 2 e 3 f 4 g 13 h 8
  i 4 j 14 k 5 l 11
2 a 7 b 10
3 12
4 a 4 b 6 c 7 d 5 e 3 f 11 g 13 h 15
  i 17 j 12
5 a 3 b 3 c 5 d 4
6 4

Worksheet Answers

1 8   2 8   3 9   4 5   5 12

Use these number lines to work out these divisions.
The number lines are marked to help you.

1 $32 \div 4 =$ ☐

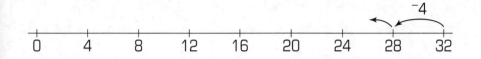

Jump backwards until you reach 0

2 $40 \div 5 =$ ☐

3 $27 \div 3 =$ ☐

Be careful where you start.

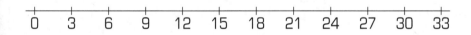

4 $25 \div 5 =$ ☐

Write your own numbers on the line.
Count down in 5s.

5 $48 \div 4 =$ ☐

Write your own numbers on the line.
Start at 48 and count down in 4s.

N3.8 More division ideas

Access

This spread provides access to the Year 7 objective:
▶ Consolidate and extend mental methods of calculation (96)

Lesson Plan

Mental starter

Give students a two-digit number. Flip a coin: heads for 'half' or tails for 'double'.

Students do the calculation. The first to answer correctly flips the coin next time.

Introductory activity

Recap division as repeated subtraction, with $36 \div 9$ on a jotted number line – starting at 36, with repeated jumps of 9 towards 0.

Link this to a more formal written method with each subtraction on a new line as in the Students' book. Emphasise that you keep subtracting until you reach zero. Highlight that you count the rows to find out how many subtractions you have done.

Work through $20 \div 5$ as a class. Ask students to use this to derive another fact: $40 \div 5 = ?$ Highlight that 40 is double 20, so, you can double the answer.

Write $20 \div 5 = 4$ in a circle in the centre of the board. Write $40 \div 5 = 8$ on a 'leg' from the circle. Ask students for other facts they can find from this one, writing each as a 'leg' from the related fact.

Emphasise that:
▶ If you double the start number, you double the answer.
▶ If you halve the start number, you halve the answer.
▶ If you double the **divisor**, you are dividing by more, so the answer gets smaller – it halves.
▶ If you halve the divisor, you are dividing by less, so the answer gets bigger – it doubles.

Plenary

Discuss question 7.

Write the calculation $96 \div 12 = 8$ in a circle. Ask for further calculations derived from this one (based on halving or doubling).

Homework

▶ Derive as many calculations as possible from a given calculation by doubling or halving.
▶ Springboard 7: Page 338.

Exercise Commentary

Coverage

The questions assess objectives on Framework (Y456) Page 67.

Useful resources

A coin

N3.8WS – provides further practice of the key ideas.

Differentiation

▶ Question 1 practises recall of division facts.
▶ Questions 2–4 focus on division using doubling and halving.
▶ Questions 5–7 use repeated subtraction.

Support tier: focuses on calculator methods.

Misconceptions

In questions 3, where the divisor is doubled, students may double the answer instead of halving it. Emphasise that it is being divided into a larger number of parts, so each part will have a smaller value. Students should be encouraged to estimate the answer first, to help them to decide whether to double or halve the answer. It may be beneficial for them to discuss this work in pairs.

Links

Multiplication facts: Framework (Y456) Page 59.

Exercise Answers

1 a 8   b 8   c 5   d 4   e 5   f 8   g 9   h 8
 i 7   j 7
2 a 16   b 12   c 6   d 8   e 6   f 14
3 a 4   b 3   c 3   d 3   e 3   f 5
4 a 8   b 16   c 32
5 a 7   b 7   c 9   d 8   e 8   f 5   g 5   h 8
6 a 3   b 7   c 9   d 4   e 8   f 5   g 5   h 7
7 8

Worksheet Answers

1 18   2 19   3 18   4 14   5 12   6 12   7 16
8 18   9 18   10 14   11 14   12 18

Use this multiplication table to help you to divide by doubling.

▶ The number in the circle is **half** the first number in the calculation.

▶ Fill in the circles and complete the 'halve it' sums.

▶ **Double** the answers in the squares, and write them in the triangles.

▶ This is the answer to the calculation.

×	1	2	3	4	5	6	7	8	9	10
1	1	2	3	4	5	6	7	8	9	10
2	2	4	6	8	10	12	14	16	18	20
3	3	6	9	12	15	18	21	24	27	30
4	4	8	12	16	20	24	28	32	36	40
5	5	10	15	20	25	30	35	40	45	50
6	6	12	18	24	30	36	42	48	54	60
7	7	14	21	28	35	42	49	56	63	70
8	8	16	24	32	40	48	56	64	72	80
9	9	18	27	36	45	54	63	72	81	90
10	10	20	30	40	50	60	70	80	90	100

	calculation	halve it			double it	
1	$54 \div 3$	27	$\div 3 =$	9	$54 \div 3 =$	18
2	$90 \div 5$	45	$\div 5 =$		$90 \div 5 =$	
3	$126 \div 7$	63	$\div 7 =$		$126 \div 7 =$	
4	$84 \div 6$		$\div 6 =$		$84 \div 6 =$	
5	$108 \div 9$		$\div 9 =$		$108 \div 9 =$	
6	$96 \div 8$		$\div 8 =$		$96 \div 8 =$	
7	$96 \div 6$		$\div 6 =$		$96 \div 6 =$	
8	$72 \div 4$		$\div 4 =$		$72 \div 4 =$	
9	$36 \div 2$		$\div 2 =$		$36 \div 2 =$	
10	$126 \div 9$		$\div 9 =$		$126 \div 9 =$	
11	$98 \div 7$		$\div 7 =$		$98 \div 7 =$	
12	$144 \div 8$		$\div 8 =$		$144 \div 8 =$	

Framework MATHS   Scheme of work   Year 7

N3 Multiplication and division (6 hours)

	Teaching objectives	Framework Maths resources	Other resources
Place value, ordering and rounding (10–13)	Round any integer to the nearest 10 or 100.	7A Student Book: N3.1 7A Teacher's Book: N3.1OHP, R4, R6	
Mental calculation strategies (× and ÷) (60–1)	Use doubling and halving, starting from known facts.	7A Student Book: N3.2, N3.8 7A Teacher's Book: N3.2WS, N3.8WS, R7, R21	
Place value, ordering and rounding (6–7)	Multiply decimals mentally by 10 or 100 and explain the effect	7A Student Book: N3.3, N3.5 7A Teacher's Book: N3.3WS, N3.5WS, R4, R7, R19	
Fractions, decimals and percentages, ratio and proportion (28–9)	Use decimal notation for tenths.	7A Student Book: N3.3, N3.5 7A Teacher's Book: N3.3WS, N3.5WS, R4, R7, R19	
Place value, ordering and rounding (6–7)	Divide any positive integer by 10 and understand the effect	7A Student Book: N3.4 7A Teacher's Book: N3.4WS, R4, R7	
Measures (90–1)	Convert larger to smaller units.	7A Student Book: N3.5 7A Teacher's Book: N3.5WS, R4, R7, R19	
Mental calculation strategies (× and ÷) (62–3)	Partition (e.g. 47 × 6 = (40 × 6) + (7 × 6)).	7A Student Book: N3.6 7A Teacher's Book: N3.6WS, R4, R21	
Pencil and paper procedures (× and ÷) (66–9)	Develop and refine written methods for TU × U, TU ÷ U.	7A Student Book: N3.6, N3.7 7A Teacher's Book: N3.6WS, N3.7WS, R4, R6, R21	
Pencil and paper procedures (× and ÷) (66–9)	Use informal pencil and paper methods to support, record or explain multiplications and divisions.	7A Student Book: N3.6, N3.7, N3.8 7A Teacher's Book: N3.6WS, N3.7WS, N3.8WS, R4, R6, R21	
Making decisions (74–5)	Choose and use appropriate number operations to solve problems, and appropriate ways of calculating: mental, mental with jottings, written methods, calculator.	7A Student Book: N3.2 - N3.8	
Problems involving 'real life', money and measures (82–9)	Use all four operations to solve simple word problems.	7A Student Book: N3.2–N3.8	

Access

© Oxford University Press 2004 for use within purchaser's institution

116

Overview

The first three spreads of this unit aim to develop students' understanding of factors, multiples, primes and square numbers. The last three spreads focus on representing simple functions and generating coordinates using mapping diagrams, and plotting their graphs.

Spreads A3.1, A3.2, A3.3 and A3.4 form the focus of the unit.

Framework references

The unit covers objectives on Framework (Y456) Pages 19, 21, 61, 109

Useful resources

Worksheets
A3.1WS – factors
A3.2WS – multiples
A3.4WS – multiplication mappings
A3.5WS – plotting pairs

OHPs
A3.3OHP – square numbers
A3.6OHP – chains and posts

General resources
R7 – function machines
R9 – coordinate axes
R17 – hundred square
R21 – multiplication square
4×4 squared grid
Counters

Springboard 7 pages
47, 280, 306, 307, 316, 395

Introduction

Discuss patterns found in everyday life, for example the numbers of eggs in 1, 2, 3 boxes, the numbers of rewritable CDs (bought in packs of 5) in 1, 2, 3 boxes. Emphasise that you use these patterns to work out problems such as: if I need 12 CDs, how many packs should I buy?

Check in activity

Give a start number, say 4 and a rule, say 'add 6'. Go around the class, each student giving the next term in the sequence. Repeat for different start numbers and rules (extending to subtraction, doubling and halving).

Encourage students to describe patterns in the sequences.

▸ Are all the numbers even/odd?

▸ Are all the numbers are multiples of something?

Differentiation – spanning the bridge

Spread	Bridge to the Support tier
A3.1	Extend Support tier students to consider prime numbers and understand the definition – only two factors: itself and 1.
A3.2	Discuss the visual representation of factors (as length and width of a rectangle) and link to work on Area. Emphasise that two equal factors define a square number. Demonstrate the different factors of 10 as rectangles (5×2 and 1×10) and of 7 – to recap definition of a prime.
A3.3	Extend Support tier students to consider numerical squares (a square number from $n \times n$) and progress to triangular numbers.
A3.4	The two tiers can work side by side in this spread, although greater emphasis should be placed on keywords **input** and **output** for Support tier students and they need to understand that a '$\times p$' function machine will produce multiples of p as output values.
A3.5	The Support tier extends in this spread through completion of a mapping diagram from a function machine, generating the coordinate pairs and drawing the graph. Each of these aspects is covered during the Access introductory activity, but the Support tier students will work through the steps with little help.
A3.6	Extend Support tier to recording input and output values in a table of values, and generating coordinate pairs from this table as opposed to a mapping diagram.

A3.1 Factors

Access

This spread provides access to the Year 7 objective:
▸ Recognise and use factors (52)

Lesson Plan

Mental starter

Show students a 4 × 4 grid, with squares numbered 1 to 16. Ask students to give a multiplication that leads to one of the numbers. For example, for 12, students could give 1 × 12 or 2 × 6 or 3 × 4. Encourage students to find all possible multiplications for each number.

Introductory activity

Refer to the mental starter. List all the possible multiplications that give 12.

Demonstrate how 12 counters can be displayed in
▸ 1 row of 12
▸ 2 **equal rows** of 6
▸ 4 **equal** rows of 3, with none left over.

Highlight the pairs of numbers as **factor pairs** and individual numbers as **factors**. Define **factors** of a number as the numbers that multiply together to make it.

Emphasise that if you double the number of rows, you **halve** the number of counters in each row.

Repeat for 28: list all the possible multiplications and arrange 28 counters in different rectangles. List the factors of 28. Highlight doubling 7 to 14, so halving 4 to 2.

Discuss when 2 would be a factor – when the number is even.

Plenary

Discuss the factors of 21, 24 and 13. Highlight 13 as a **prime number** since it only has two factors, 13 and 1. Ask students if they can think of any more prime numbers.

Challenge students to find a number with three factors (for example, 9).

Homework

▸ Find 10 prime numbers under 30, by looking for numbers that have only two factors.
▸ Springboard 7: Page 316.

Exercise Commentary

Coverage

The questions assess objectives on Framework (Y456) Pages 21 and 61.

Useful resources

Counters

4 × 4 grid with squares numbered 1 to 16

A3.1WS – provides support for weaker students.

Differentiation

▸ Questions 1–3 focus on arranging counters to find factors.
▸ Question 4 focuses on finding factors using a multiplication table.
▸ Question 5 involves halving and doubling.

Support tier: focuses on factors and primes.

Misconceptions

This work depends heavily on recall of multiplication and division facts, and weaker students will need a multiplication square. Many students will forget to list $1 \times n$ as a multiplication. Students can be encouraged to start at this point, especially with the counter work – one long row – before moving on.

Links

Multiplication facts: Framework (Y456) Page 59.

Exercise Answers

1 b $1 \times 6, 6 \times 1, 3 \times 2, 2 \times 3$ 2 1, 2, 4, 8
3 a $1 \times 20, 2 \times 10, 4 \times 5, 5 \times 4, 10 \times 2, 20 \times 1$
   b 1, 2, 4, 5, 10, 20; 20
4 a 1, 3, 9   b 1, 3, 5, 15   c 1, 2, 4, 8, 16
  d 1, 2, 3, 6, 9, 18   e 1, 3, 7, 21
  f 1, 5, 25   g 1, 3, 9, 27
5 a 1, 2, 3, 5, 6, 10, 15, 30
  b 1, 2, 3, 4, 6, 9, 12, 18, 36
  c 1, 2, 4, 8, 16, 32   d 1, 2, 4, 8, 10, 20, 40
  e 1, 2, 4, 7, 14, 28   f 1, 2, 5, 10, 25, 50

Worksheet Answers

1 b 1, 2, 3, 4, 6, 12   2 b 1, 2, 3, 6, 9, 18

You can arrange these 10 counters into two rectangle patterns.

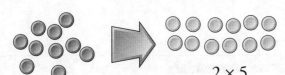

2×5 or 10×1

$10 = 2 \times 5$ and 1×10
1, 2, 5 and 10 are **factors** of 10.

1 a Arrange these 12 counters into three different rectangle patterns on this grid:

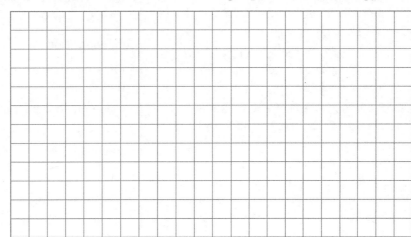

b List all the factors of 12: _____

2 a There are 18 counters here.
Draw rectangle patterns to list all the factors of 18.

There are three different
rectangle patterns.

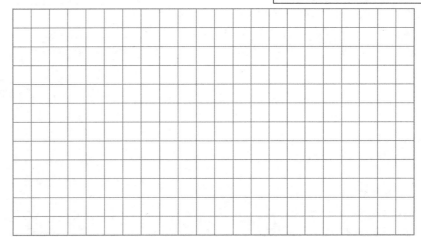

b List all the factors of 18: _____

A3.2 Multiples

Access

This spread provides access to the Year 7 objective:
- Recognise and use multiples (52)

Lesson Plan

Mental starter

Start at zero and choose students to count up in steps of 4. Write the numbers on the board.

Repeat for counting up in 6s.

Introductory activity

Refer to the mental starter. Recap the keywords **sequence** and **term** from A1. Ask students for the rule for the sequence 0, 4, 8, ...

Discuss what the numbers from the 4s sequence have in common. Highlight that they are all in the 4 times table (see **R21**). Introduce the key word **multiple**.

Ask students for a multiple of 5. Write all multiples given in a circle around a central '5'. Highlight that any number in the 5 times table is a multiple of 5.

Encourage students to give complex calculations (×10, ×100) and to use doubling/halving strategies to find further multiples of 5. Highlight that 5 is a **factor** of each of these numbers.

Ask students spot questions to gain confidence:
- A multiple of 8
- A factor of 12

Plenary

Discuss question 5.

Discuss the meaning of the question (link to wording in question 3), and how multiple and factor are opposite of one another – factors multiply to make multiples. Multiples divide to make factors.

Homework

- Shade the multiples of 3 in one colour, 5 in another, 7 in another, etc on a 100 square (**R17**).
- Springboard 7: Pages 306 and 307.

Worksheet Answers

1 12, 15, 60, 9, 18, 33, 36, 21
2 120, 150, 600, 90, 180, 330, 360, 210

Exercise Commentary

Coverage

The questions assess objectives on Framework (Y456) Page 19.

Useful resources

R17 – 100 square
R21 – multiplication square
A3.2WS – provides support for weaker students.

Differentiation

- Question 1 focuses on finding multiples by multiplying.
- Question 2 focuses on listing multiples.
- Questions 3–5 involve factors.

Support tier: includes identifying square numbers from their factors.

Misconceptions

Students may become confused with the latter questions, which require them to move between factors and multiples. Encourage them to refer back to a reference example – 3 and 4 are factors of 12; 12 is a multiple of 3 and 4.

Links

Multiplication facts: Framework (Y456) Page 59.

Exercise Answers

1 a 16, 20, 40, 12, 24, 36, 48, 28
  b Multiples of 3: 12, 15, 30, 9, 18, 27, 36, 21
     Multiples of 6: 24, 30, 60, 18, 36, 54, 72, 42
  c Double
2 a 2, 4, 6, 8, 10, 12, 14, 16, 18, 20, 22, 24, 26, 28, 30
  b 3, 6, 9, 12, 15, 18, 21, 24, 27, 30
  c 6, 12, 18, 24, 30
3 a 4 b 24
4 1, 2, 3, 4, 6, 8, 12, 24
5 3

1 Multiply the numbers in the arrow boxes by 3.
Write your answers in the circles.

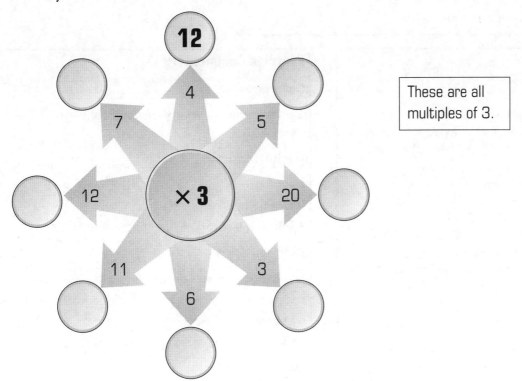

These are all multiples of 3.

2 Use question 1 to help you multiply each number by 30.
Write your answers in the circles.

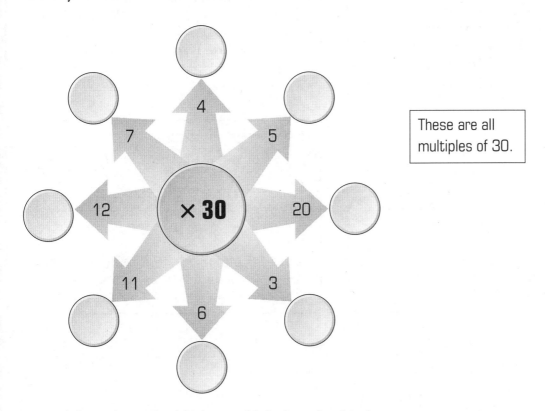

These are all multiples of 30.

A3.3 Square numbers

Access

This spread provides access to the Year 7 objective:
▸ Recognise squares of numbers 1 to 12 (56)

Lesson Plan

Mental starter

Draw a bubble, and explain that 3 belongs in it (write it in the bubble), but 4 does not. Go around the class asking for suggestions of numbers. Write the prime numbers in the bubble, and non-primes outside. Discuss which numbers belong. What is the rule?

Introductory activity

Recap the factors of 12, by listing all the possible multiplication questions. Emphasise that 12 counters can be arranged in 1 row of 12, 2 **equal rows** of 6, 4 **equal** rows of 3 and relate these to the factor pairs (on **A3.3OHP**).

Discuss the factors of 4.

Show that 4 counters can be arranged into a 1 × 4 rectangle and a 2 × 2 square. List the factor pairs. Emphasise that 4 has two **equal factors** and is a **square number**.

Challenge students to work in pairs, to find another square number using counters.

Discuss what makes a square – highlight equal length and height, and link to **equal factors**. Demonstrate that 9 is a square number, as it makes a square of height 3, and base 3 (on **A3.3OHP**). Link to area.

Highlight 1 and 4 in the multiplication square (**R21**). Ask students what they think the next square number will be.

Plenary

Show a Venn diagram of prime numbers and square numbers. Choose students to write a number somewhere in the diagram. Discuss whether any numbers will belong in the overlapping section.

Homework

▸ Design a poster to explain square numbers.
▸ Springboard 7: Page 47.

Exercise Commentary

Coverage

The questions assess objectives on Framework (Y456) Page 21.

Useful resources

Counters

R21 – multiplication square

A3.3OHP – factors of 12 and square numbers.

Differentiation

▸ Question 1 focuses on arranging square patterns.
▸ Questions 2 and 3 focus on finding square numbers.
▸ Question 4 focuses on finding factors.

Support tier: includes squares and triangular numbers.

Misconceptions

Weaker students will need access to a multiplication square (**R21**). Many students will forget to list 1 and n as the factors of n in question 4. Encourage them always to start from this point.

Links

Multiplication facts: Framework (Y456) Page 59.

Exercise Answers

1 a Yes b No c No d No e Yes f Yes
  g Yes h No
2 1, 4, 9, 16, 25, 36, 49, 64, 81, 100
3 a Square b Not square c Square d Not square
  e Not square f Square g Not square
  h Not square i Square
4 a 1, 2 b 1, 2, 4 c 1, 2, 5, 10 d 1, 2, 4, 8, 16
  e 1, 2, 3, 5, 6, 10, 15, 30 f 1, 2, 3, 4, 6, 8, 12, 24
  g 1, 5, 7, 35 h 1, 2, 4, 5, 8, 10, 20, 40

$12 = 1 \times 12$

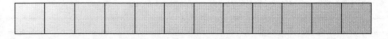

$12 = 2 \times 6$

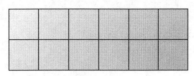

$12 = 4 \times 3$

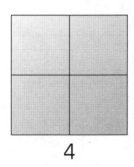

1

4

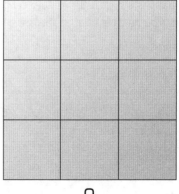

9

A3.4 Multiplication mappings

Access

This spread provides access to the Year 7 objective:
▸ Express simple functions using symbols (160)

Lesson Plan

Mental starter

Show three function machines, ×2, ×3, ×4 (**R7**).

Give an input, and point to a machine. Students give the output.

Move through the machines with different inputs, and writing inputs and outputs on either side of the machine.

Introductory activity

Refer to the mental starter. Discuss what the outputs for each machine have in common (**multiples**).

Refer to the Comptons' Miracle Food example in the Students' book. Discuss the relationship between the plant height before, and the plant height after. Highlight that the height of each plant has **doubled**, and, linking to the mental starter, that this means multiply by 2.

Refer back to the ×2 function machine. Write the inputs and outputs linked with arrows as a **mapping**.

Ask students questions about the mapping, with various input values:
▸ A plant starts at 8 metres.
  What will its height be after Compton's Miracle Food?

Show students a mapping for the function ×4. Ask what the relationship is between an input and its output; and check that this works for all values given.

Plenary

Discuss question 4.

Write the mappings from blue to red and discuss the relationship from blue to red, and from red to blue, highlighting division as the opposite of multiplication.

Homework

▸ Find ten outputs for each of ten multiplicative function machines.
▸ Springboard 7: Pages 306 and 307.

Exercise Commentary

Coverage

The questions assess objectives on Framework (Y456) Page 61.

Useful resources

R7 – function machines
R21 – multiplication square
A3.4WS – provides support for weaker students.

Differentiation

▸ Question 1 focuses on doubling.
▸ Questions 2 and 3 focus on finding the operation in the mapping.
▸ Question 4 involves a real-life context.

Support tier: uses function machines to generate multiples.

Misconceptions

Weaker students may need access to a multiplication square (**R21**). Many will find this work straightforward. Encourage students to check that their rule for the relationships works for all the values given. This will be important at a later date, when identifying more complex functions.

Links

Multiplication facts: Framework (Y456) Page 59.

Exercise Answers

1 a 30; 6, 12, 50
2 a ×3 **b** ×5
3 a $\frac{1}{2}$, 2; 1, 4; $1\frac{1}{2}$, 6 **b** ×4
4 a ×3 **b** 12

Worksheet Answers

1 a +4 **b** ×2 **c** −2 **d** ×4 **e** ÷2 **f** ÷3
2 a 2 cm, 8 cm **b** ×4

The relationship between the **before** and **after** numbers is add 2:

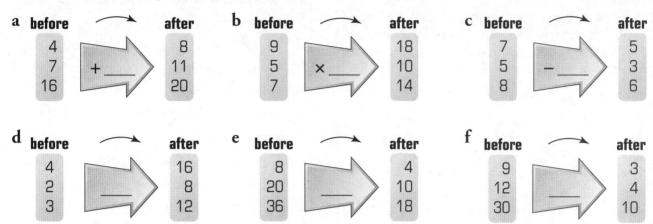

1 Write the relationship between the **before** and **after** numbers.

a before → after
4   +___   8
7   11
16   20

b before → after
9   ×___   18
5   10
7   14

c before → after
7   −___   5
5   3
8   6

d before → after
4   ___   16
2   8
3   12

e before → after
8   ___   4
20   10
36   18

f before → after
9   ___   3
12   4
30   10

2 This drawing shows an ant and its enlargement in a microscope.

a Measure the lengths of the two images.

original length   = _____ cm

enlarged length = _____ cm

b What is the relationship that describes the enlargement?

Answer: _____.

A3.5 Plotting pairs

Access

This spread provides access to the Year 7 objective:
▸ Plot graphs of simple linear functions (164)

Lesson Plan

Mental starter

De-code

Show a set of axes in the first quadrant (**R9**), with the letters of the alphabet at various points. Demonstrate a word, say CAT, using only coordinates. Invite students to set a code for the class to work out.

Introductory activity

Refer to the mental starter. Recap ways of remembering the order of coordinates – share ideas such as you go into the lift before you go up. Refer back to the previous lesson, and Compton's Miracle Food.

Ask students for before and after values and write these as inputs and outputs of a ×2 function machine (**R7**). Emphasise that these pairs of numbers can be written as coordinates.

Invite students to come and plot the coordinates on a coordinate grid (**R9**).

Emphasise that there are also points in between the whole number values that also follow the pattern, and discuss how all the points can be joined.

Demonstrate how to find missing 'after' values using the graph. Emphasise the importance of starting on the 'before' axis.

Plenary

Refer back to the graph for Compton's Miracle Food. Give an 'after' height and discuss how to find the 'before' height from the graph.

Ask students a mixture of questions based upon the graph, and invite students to demonstrate their ideas on an OHP.

Homework

▸ Generate and plot the coordinates to produce a straight line for a ×5 function machine, in the first quadrant.
▸ Springboard 7: Page 395.

Exercise Commentary

Coverage

The questions assess objectives on Framework (Y456) Page 109.

Useful resources

R7 – function machines
R9 – coordinate axes
A3.5WS – provides support for weaker students.

Differentiation

▸ Question 1 focuses on reading values from a graph.
▸ Question 2 focuses on identifying a relationship from a graph.
▸ Question 3 involves predicting values from a graph.

Support tier: focuses on graphs of functions.

Misconceptions

Some students will plot (*y*, *x*). Encourage students to share ideas about how to remember the order – across the hall, up the stairs, etc.

Links

Multiples: Framework Page (Y456) 19.

Exercise Answers

1 a 9, 15   b 6 m   c 12 m
2 a 4, 8, 12, 16   b ×4
3 a 24 m   b 5 m

Worksheet Answers

1 a (0, 0)   (1, 2)   (2, 4)   (3, 6)   (5, 10)
   d ×2
   e 4, 12
2 a 0, 1, 2, 3
   b ÷2

1 a Write these mapping pairs as coordinates.

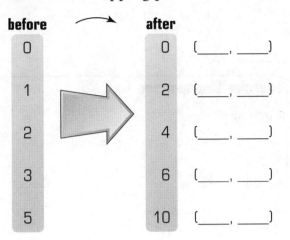

before → after

0 → 0 (____ , ____)

1 → 2 (____ , ____)

2 → 4 (____ , ____)

3 → 6 (____ , ____)

5 → 10 (____ , ____)

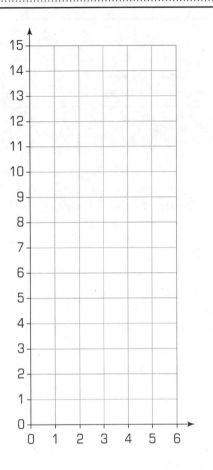

b Plot the points on this grid.

c Join the points with a straight line. Use a ruler.

d Write the rule that connects the **before** and **after** numbers.

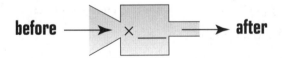

before ——→ × ____ ——→ after

e Fill in these mapping pairs from the graph:

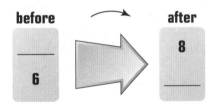

before → after

6 → 8

____ → ____

2 a Complete the mapping by filling in the **after** values from the graph.

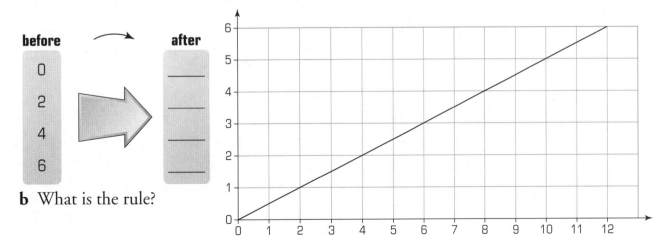

before → after

0 → ____

2 → ____

4 → ____

6 → ____

b What is the rule?

A3.6 Mappings and graphs

Access

This spread provides access to the Year 7 objective:
▸ Plot graphs of simple linear functions (164)

Lesson Plan

Mental starter

Show a set of axes in the first quadrant (**R9**), with the letters of the alphabet at various points. Spell a word or phrase, using only coordinates. Encourage students to identify the word from the coordinates given.

Introductory activity

Refer to the mental starter. Recap that for coordinates the first number indicates across, the second number indicates up. Highlight that:
▸ The horizontal axis is the *x*-axis, and the vertical axis is the *y*-axis.
▸ The lines are numbered, not the squares.
▸ The numbers start from zero, where the axes cross.
▸ The intervals between the numbers on the *x*-axis are always equal, and likewise on the *y*-axis.

Suggest *x* comes before *y* in alphabet as another strategy for remembering the order of coordinates.

Show a +4 function machine (**R7**).

Students generate outputs, given inputs 1, 2, 3, 4. Discuss how to use these numbers as coordinates. Invite students to plot the coordinates and join them with a straight line. Use pairs of values to highlight that the *y* number is 4 more than the *x* number.

Plenary

Discuss question 4. **A3.6OHP** shows the diagrams and coordinate grid from the Students' book.

Encourage students to calculate the number of posts for a given number of chains, and vice versa, and to identify the operations in the function machine.

Homework

▸ Ask students to generate outputs for given inputs of a +3 function machine, plot the coordinates and join them with a straight line.
▸ Springboard 7: Page 280.

Exercise Commentary

Coverage

The questions assess objectives on Framework (Y456) Page 109.

Useful resources

R7 – function machines
R9 – coordinate axes
A3.6 OHP – diagrams from question 4 in the Students' book for the plenary.

Differentiation

▸ Question 1 focuses on drawing axes accurately.
▸ Questions 2 and 3 focus on plotting points on a grid to make shapes.
▸ Question 4 involves generating coordinates and plotting the graph of a function.

Support tier: focuses on using a table of values.

Misconceptions

In question 4, the number of steps involved can be confusing. Encourage students to take their time, and work through each part carefully.

Weaker students will have difficulty drawing axes. Give them pre-prepared axes to enable them progress through the activities, if necessary.

Links

General statements: Framework (Y456) Page 81.

Exercise Answers

2 c Square
3 c 5
4 a 3, 4, 5
   b (1, 2) (2, 3) (3, 4) (4, 5) (5, 6)
   e Add 1 to number of chains.

 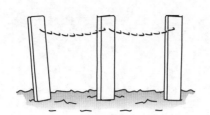 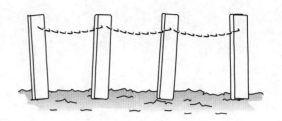

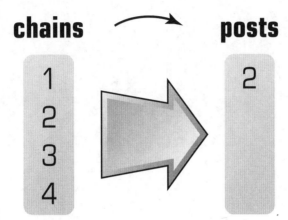

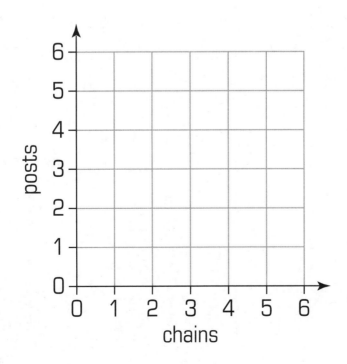

A3 Functions and graphs (6 hours)	Teaching objectives	Framework Maths resources	Other resources
Properties of numbers and number sequences (20–21)	Find all the pairs of factors of any number up to 100.	7A Student Book: A3.1 7A Teacher's Book: A3.1WS, R21	
Rapid recall of multiplication and division facts (58–9)	**Know by heart all multiplication facts up to 10 × 10.**	7A Student Book: A3.1 7A Teacher's Book: A3.1WS, R21	
Mental calculation strategies (× and ÷) (60–1)	Use doubling or halving, starting from known facts.	7A Student Book: A3.1, A3.4 7A Teacher's Book: A3.1WS, A3.4WS, R7, R21	
Properties of numbers and number sequences (18–19)	Recognise multiples of 6, 7, 8, 9, up to the 10th multiple.	7A Student Book: A3.2 7A Teacher's Book: A3.2WS, R17, R21	
Mental calculation strategies (× and ÷) (62–3)	Use the relationship between multiplication and division.	7A Student Book: A3.2 7A Teacher's Book: A3.2WS, R17, R21	
Properties of numbers and number sequences (20–21)	Know squares of numbers to at least 10 × 10.	7A Student Book: A3.3 7A Teacher's Book: A3.3OHP, R21	
Fractions, decimals and percentages, ratio and proportion (26–7)	Begin to use simple ideas of ratio and proportion.	7A Student Book: A3.4, A3.5 7A Teacher's Book: A3.4WS, A3.5WS, R7, R9, R21	
Shape and space (108–9)	Read and plot coordinates in the first quadrant.	7A Student Book: A3.5, A3.6 7A Teacher's Book: A3.5WS, A3.6OHP, R7, R9	
Properties of numbers and number sequences (16–17)	Recognise and extend number sequences.	7A Student Book: A3.6 7A Teacher's Book: A3.6OHP, R7, R9	
Reasoning and generalising about numbers or shapes (76–7)	Explain methods and reasoning, orally and in writing.	7A Student Book: A3.1–A3.6	
Reasoning and generalising about numbers or shapes (78–9)	Solve mathematical problems or puzzles, recognise and explain patterns and relationships, generalise and predict. Suggest extensions by asking 'What if...?'	7A Student Book: A3.1–A3.6	

Access

Overview

This unit aims to develop students' understanding of angle and properties of shapes. The focus is on describing, measuring and constructing angles, and recognising and labelling equal, parallel and perpendicular lines using conventional notation.

Spreads S3.1, S3.2 and S3.5 form the focus of the unit.

Framework references

The unit covers objectives on Framework (Y456) Pages 103, 109, 110, 111

Introduction

Discuss examples of triangles and quadrilaterals in the classroom and in pictures of buildings of different styles. Encourage students to suggest other real-life examples, for example kites, in tiling patterns.

Check in activity

Encourage students to sketch a shape with three sides. Discuss what you call a shape with three sides. Ask students to hold up their sketches and compare the different shapes. Emphasise that they are all triangles. Link 'tri' to three, as in other real-life examples such as tricycle, triathlon, triplets. Repeat for four-sided shapes, emphasising that they are all quadrilaterals. Link 'quad' to four, as in quad bikes, quadruplets.

Useful resources

Worksheets
S3.1WS – compass turns
S3.4WS – drawing angles
S3.5WS – parallel and perpendicular lines

OHPs
S3.2OHP – acute and obtuse angles
S3.3OHP – measuring angles

General resources
R12 – protractor
R14 – triangles
R15 – quadrilaterals
R20 – clock face
Protractors
Rulers
Dice

Springboard 7 pages
107, 455–461

Differentiation – spanning the bridge

Spread	Bridge to the Support tier
S3.1	Support tier students need to cover naming angles and using their understanding of different types of angles to correctly identify the scale to use when measuring with a protractor. Emphasise correct use of a protractor.
S3.2	Extend Support tier students to finding an angle based on the angle facts: (full turn = 360°, half turn/straight line = 180°, etc.
S3.3	Extend Support tier students to drawing angles. Use the introductory activity to highlight the important features – correct placement of protractor, using the appropriate scale. Encourage students to draw an estimate first.
S3.4	During the introductory activity, encourage Support tier students to estimate and measure the angles in a triangle. Progress to identifying a pattern of each students different triangles (e.g., they add up to approximately 180° every time). Progress to placing the angles of a triangle along a straight line to derive: angles in triangle are the same as angles on a straight line = 180°. Link with work on calculating angles (S3.2).
S3.5	Support tier have covered parallel and perpendicular lines in S2 and can be used to support weaker students during the introductory activity. Progress to recap work in S2 on flat and 3D shapes, and of nets as a 2D representation of 3D shapes. Highlight keywords: faces, edges and vertices. Model 2D representation on isometric paper.

S3.1 Compass turns

Access

This spread provides access to the Year 7 objective:
▸ Use angle measure (232)

Lesson Plan

Mental starter

Show a clock face (**R20**) with one hand pointing to 12.

Ask students where the hand will point after one full turn (12), after quarter of a turn (3 or 9), half a turn (6), three quarters of a turn (9 or 3).

Change the starting position and repeat.

Introductory activity

Discuss what students understand by the word 'angle'. Highlight an angle as a **measure of turn** and that it is measured in **degrees** written °.

Refer to the mental starter.

Discuss a full turn. Highlight that there are 360 degrees in a full turn.

Show a half turn. Highlight that it is half a full turn, and makes a straight line. Discuss how many degrees this is.

Show that a quarter turn makes a corner, and that this is 90°. Highlight the keyword **right angle**.

Discuss how to specify the direction of the turn. Emphasise the use of **clockwise** and **anticlockwise**.

Look at the compass in the Students' book. Ask questions based around angles and directions of a compass showing the turn at first.

I face North.
I turn 90°/quarter turn clockwise/ anticlockwise. What am I facing?
Emphasise the need for an angle and a direction.

Plenary

Ask students to stand up and face the front. Give instructions: Turn clockwise 90°. Turn half a turn anticlockwise, etc. Students who make mistakes sit down. The winner is the last one standing.

Homework

▸ Find ten times on a clock when the angle between the hands is **a** 90° **b** 180°.
▸ Springboard 7: Pages 455–461.

Exercise Commentary

Coverage

The questions assess objectives on Framework (Y456) Page 110.

Useful resources

R20 – clock face

S3.1WS – provides further practice of the key ideas.

Differentiation

▸ Question 1 focuses on compass directions.
▸ Questions 2 and 3 involve turning in degrees.
▸ Question 4 involves following a series of compass directions.

Support tier: focuses on measuring angles using a protractor.

Misconceptions

Students may equate clockwise as turning right, and anticlockwise as turning left, which can cause difficulties when turning from south to east (anticlockwise, but turn looks like a left turn). Encourage students always to refer back to an image of the clockface to identify the direction.

Students may believe there to be a left angle (turning the other way). Explain that a right angle means a turn of 90° in either direction.

Links

Recognising positions: Framework (Y456) Page 109.

Exercise Answers

1 **a** High Road **b** Museum **c** Station **d** East **e** North-east
2 **a** South **b** North
3 **a** North-east **b** North-west
4 Ray – swimming pool; Liz – cinema

Worksheet Answers

2 **a** West, South-east, South, East, South-west **b** East **c** North-east **d** North-west **e** East **f** South

1 Fill in the missing points on this compass.

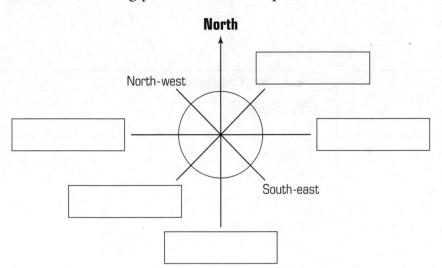

Choose your answers from this box:

South-west   East

North-east

South   West

2 a Fill in each new direction of this journey. Start at 'North'.

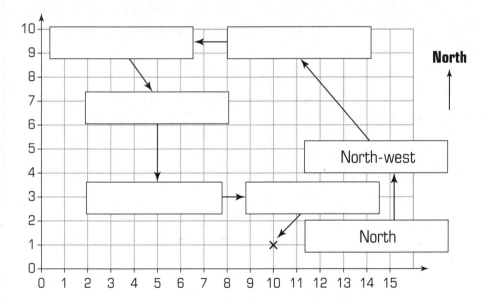

Start at X and follow these coordinates. Which direction are you going in?

b From (**10, 1**) to (**6, 1**) the direction of travel is _____.

c From (**6, 1**) to (**10, 5**) the direction of travel is _____.

d From (**10, 5**) to (**7, 8**) the direction of travel is _____.

e From (**7, 8**) to (**1, 8**) the direction of travel is _____.

f From (**1, 8**) to (**1, 3**) the direction of travel is _____.

S3.2 Angles

Access

This spread provides access to the Year 7 objective:
▸ Use angle measure (232)

Lesson Plan

Mental starter

Show a clock face (**R20**) with one hand pointing to 12. Move one hand through 90° clockwise. Highlight that this makes a right angle. Move the hand to 6 and highlight that this makes a straight line.

Move both hands to create different angles. Encourage students to say whether each angle is more than or less than a right angle/straight line.

Introductory activity

Recap that a right angle is 90° and a half turn is 180°.

Refer to the mental starter. Define, **acute** and **obtuse** angles as in the Students' book.

Show an acute angle on **S3.2OHP**. Emphasise that it is **less than** a right angle, and so must be **less than 90°**.

Show an obtuse angle on **S3.2OHP**. Emphasise that it is **more than** a right angle, and so must be more **than 90°**. It is **less than** 180°.

Show the angles from **S3.2OHP** one at a time. For each angle, two possible measurements are given. Discuss which is correct.

Plenary

Students write down four angles between 1° and 180° inclusive. Roll a dice. The score indicates:

1 Right angle   **2 and 4** Acute angle
3 and 5 Obtuse angle   **6** Half turn

Students cross off their angles accordingly. The first to cross all four angles wins.

Homework

▸ Name and draw a selection of angles (acute, obtuse, right and straight line).
▸ Springboard 7: Page 457.

Exercise Commentary

Coverage

The questions assess objectives on Framework (Y456) Page 111.

Useful resources

R20 – clock face

Dice

S3.2OHP – acute and obtuse angles to estimate.

Differentiation

▸ Question 1 focuses on classifying angles.
▸ Question 2 involves choosing the correct angle.
▸ Question 3 involves matching angles with degrees.

Support tier: focuses on calculating angles on a straight line.

Misconceptions

Students may consider one angle to be bigger than another if its arms are bigger. This is not directly addressed in the activities, but can be touched upon in informal discussion with students. Emphasise that an angle is a measure of turn.

Links

Properties of shapes: Framework (Y456) Page 103.

Exercise Answers

1 a Obtuse   **b** Right   **c** Acute   **d** Acute
    e Straight line   **f** Obtuse   **g** Right
    h Straight line
2 a 40°   **b** 120°   **c** 130°   **d** 35°   **e** 65°   **f** 115°
    g 95°   **h** 160°
3 a 90°   **b** 75°   **c** 155°   **d** 20°   **e** 180°   **f** 120°

15° or 150°?

30° or 130°?

45° or 145°?

40° or 120°?

60° or 100°?

160° or 70°?

80° or 170°?

S3.3 Measuring angles

Access

This spread provides access to the Year 7 objective:
▶ Use angle measure (232)

Lesson Plan

Mental starter

Show four triangles – right-angled, isosceles, equilateral and scalene (**R14**). Ask students to name each angle – recapping on the definitions of right/acute and obtuse.

Introductory activity

Sketch an acute angle (or use **S3.3OHP**) and ask if it is more than or less than 90°. Discuss an estimate, using 45° (half a right angle) as another reference point.

Demonstrate how to measure it exactly with a protractor (**R12**), highlighting in particular:
▶ The central cross of the protractor should be exactly on the point of the angle.
▶ The baseline of the protractor **must** line up with the angle baseline (link to use of a ruler)
▶ The angle should be within the scale of the protractor.
▶ There are two scales.

Encourage students to decide whether the angle is acute or obtuse before measuring so they know which scale to use. Discuss the examples on **S3.3OHP** using a protractor (**R12**).

Repeat for angles where the base line is not horizontal.

Emphasise that an angle stays the same, even if it is moved, and encourage students to move the page to help them measure easily.

Plenary

Discuss question 3. Emphasise that the two angles on a straight line must add to 180°.

Draw two angles on a straight line on the board or OHP. Choose a student to measure one angle. Discuss whether the other angle needs to be measured. As a class, calculate the missing angle.

Homework

▶ Estimate and then measure five angles.
▶ Springboard 7: Page 455.

Exercise Commentary

Coverage

The questions assess objectives on Framework (Y456) Page 111.

Useful resources

R12 – protractor
R14 – triangles
Protractors
S3.3OHP – angles to measure.

Differentiation

▶ Question 1 focuses on reading a protractor.
▶ Question 2 focuses on using a protractor to measure angles.
▶ Question 3 involves matching angles that add to 180°.

Support tier: focuses on drawing angles and triangles. S3.1 focuses on measuring angles.

Misconceptions

Students may find the protractor difficult to place. Emphasise the link with a ruler. Also encourage students to think about the baseline **turning**. An estimate will help students decide which scale to use.

Links

Properties of shapes: Framework (Y456) Page 103.

Exercise Answers

1 a 20°   b 50°
  c 65°   d 80°
  e 35°
2 a 40°   b 90°
  c 50°   d 110°
  e 35°   f 125°
3 a and f; b and d; c and h; d and b; e and g; f and a; g and e; h and c

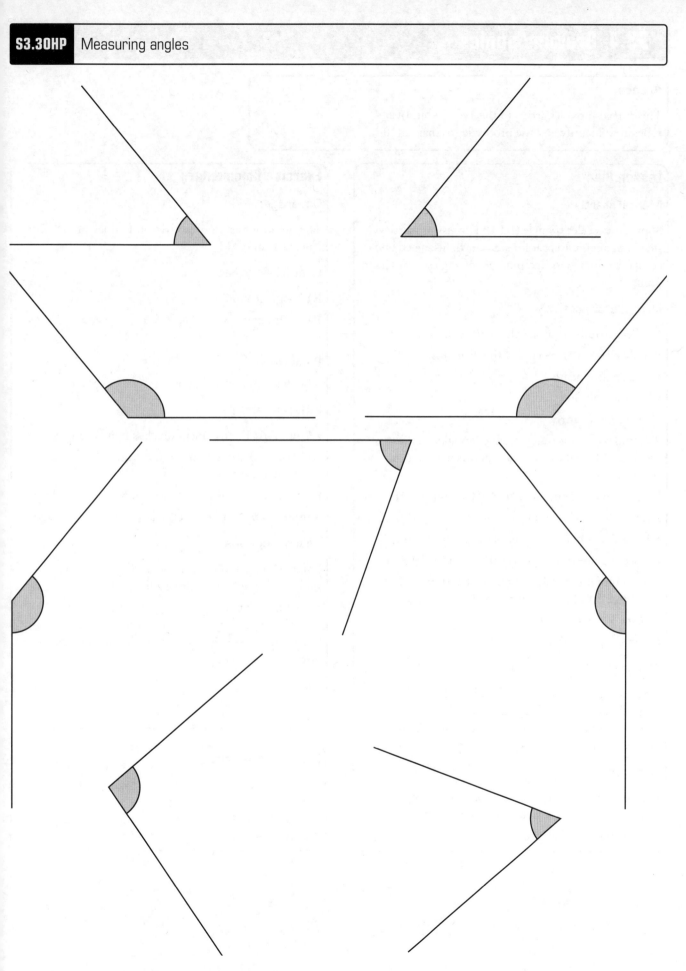

S3.4 Drawing angles

Access

This spread provides access to the Year 7 objective:
▸ Begin to identify and use properties of shapes (184)

Lesson Plan

Mental starter

Show an isosceles triangle (**R14**). Discuss properties – sides and angles. Repeat for scalene, right-angled and equilateral triangles. Recap names of angles – acute and obtuse.

Introductory activity

Challenge students to sketch an angle of 50°.

Highlight the main points of the diagrams:

▸ The angle is acute.
▸ Two straight lines.
▸ The point of **turn**.

Ask students to measure a partner's angle, and discuss accuracy. Make the distinction between estimating and constructing.

Discuss how to draw an angle of 50° using a protractor:

▸ Draw the baseline using a ruler.
▸ Put a dot at one end – this is the point of turn.
▸ Place the protractor cross at this point of turn.
▸ Read round the scale from 0 degrees (**not** 180°), through 10°, 20°, etc, to reach 50°.
▸ Mark 50° with a dot.
▸ Join the point of turn to the 50° dot.

Plenary

Discuss angles in the classroom. Highlight, in particular, doors and doorframes, windows and window frames. Discuss whether these have to be exactly 90 degrees and stress the accuracy required.

Homework

▸ Give students a sketch of a boat, with all lengths and angles labelled. Ask students to accurately construct.
▸ Springboard 7: Page 460.

Exercise Commentary

Coverage

The questions assess objectives on Framework (Y456) Pages 103 and 111.

Useful resources

R12 – protractor
R14 – triangles
Rulers
Protractors
S3.4WS – provides support for weaker students.

Differentiation

▸ Questions 1 and 2 focus on classifying triangles.
▸ Question 3 focuses on using a protractor to measure and angles accurately.
▸ Question 4 focuses on drawing angles accurately.

Support tier: focuses on calculating angles in triangles.

Misconceptions

Students may find the protractor difficult to place. Link to placing a ruler along a line.

Students may have difficulties choosing the correct scale. Encourage them to think of the turn of the base line from 0°, and also to estimate and name the angle prior to constructing it.

Links

Making shapes: Framework (Y456) Page 105.

Exercise Answers

1 a Isosceles b Equilateral c Right-angled
  d Equilateral
2 a Equilateral b Isosceles c Right-angled
3 a 40° b 130° c 125° d 55°

1 Draw these angles on this protractor.

a 100°   **b** 40°   **c** 140°
d 70°   **e** 120°

Label each angle. The first has been done for you.

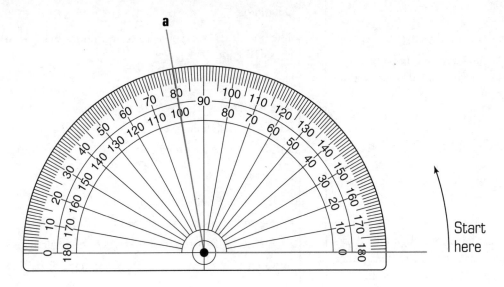

2 Use a protractor to draw these angles.
Place the cross on the dot.

a 50°   **b** 80°

c 130°   **d** 20°

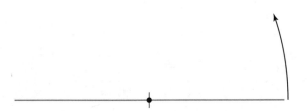

S3.5 Parallel and perpendicular lines

Access

This spread provides access to the Year 7 objective:
▸ Identify parallel and perpendicular lines (180)

Lesson Plan

Mental starter

Describe a triangle for students to identify:

I have three sides which are all equal. All my angles are equal, what am I? Repeat for right-angled, scalene and isosceles triangles (**R14**).

Introductory activity

Refer to mental starter, and explain that shapes have different **properties**. Show a square and a rectangle (**R15**), discuss common properties and how the shapes differ.

Label the lengths on three sides of the rectangle.

Discuss how to complete the labelling. Highlight that the two 'lengths' of the rectangle stay the same distance apart (height) throughout the shape. Introduce the notation for equal sides.

Define parallel lines, emphasising that they never meet and link to real-life examples – ladders/train tracks. Introduce parallel notation.

Show a rectangle and a parallelogram (**R15**).

Discuss common properties and how they differ. Label parallel and equal sides.

Introduce keyword **perpendicular** and how to mark perpendicular sides.

Plenary

Discuss question 4. Choose students to mark the shapes with the correct notation. Repeat the mental starter with quadrilaterals (**R15**).

Homework

▸ Label acute and obtuse angles; equal, parallel, perpendicular sides on quadrilaterals and triangles.
▸ Springboard 7: Page 107.

Exercise Commentary

Coverage

The questions assess objectives on Framework (Y456) Pages 103 and 109.

Useful resources

R14 – triangles
R15 – quadrilaterals
S3.5WS – provides further practice of the key ideas.

Differentiation

▸ Questions 1 and 2 focus on parallel lines.
▸ Question 3 focuses on perpendicular lines.
▸ Question 4 focuses on properties of quadrilaterals.
Support tier: focuses on 2-D representations of 3-D shapes.

Misconceptions

Students may struggle with the language of geometry, and should be encouraged to share ideas for remembering the terms. Ensure the terms and notation are displayed prominently in the class for students to refer to.

Links

Making shapes: Framework (Y456) Page 105.

Exercise Answers

1 a Parallel   b Not parallel   c Parallel
3 a, c, e

Worksheet Answers

1 Yes, they are parallel.

1 Use a ruler to check if lines A and B are parallel to each other.

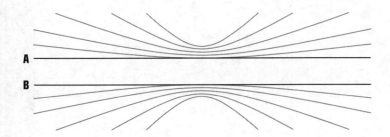

A

B

Are the lines parallel? _____

2 Draw a line parallel to line AB.
It should be 2 cm below line AB and 7 cm long.

A ————————————————————— B

3 Draw a line perpendicular to each of these lines.
A protractor has been drawn for you.

a   **b**

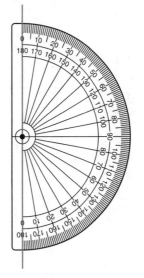

4 Draw a line perpendicular to line GH.

G ————————————————————————————————— H

Framework MATHS Scheme of work Year 7

S3 Triangles and quadrilaterals (6 hours)	Teaching objectives	Framework Maths resources	Other resources
Shape and space (110–11)	Make and measure clockwise and anticlockwise turns. Begin to know that angles are measured in degrees.	7A Student Book: S3.1 7A Teacher's Book: S3.1WS, R20	
Shape and space (110–11)	Identify, estimate and order acute and obtuse angles.	7A Student Book: S3.2 7A Teacher's Book: S3.2OHP, R20	
Shape and space (110–11)	Use a protractor to measure and draw acute and obtuse angles to the nearest 5°.	7A Student Book: S3.3, S3.4 7A Teacher's Book: S3.3OHP, S3.4WS, R12, R14	
Shape and space (102–3)	Classify triangles (isosceles, equilateral, scalene), using criteria such as equal sides, equal angles, lines of symmetry.	7A Student Book: S3.3, S3.4 7A Teacher's Book: S3.3OHP, S3.4WS, R12, R15	
Shape and space (102–3)	Recognise properties of rectangles.	7A Student Book: S3.5 7A Teacher's Book: S3.5WS. R14, R15	
Shape and space (108–9)	Recognise perpendicular and parallel lines.	7A Student Book: S3.5 7A Teacher's Book: S3.5WS. R14, R15	
Reasoning and generalising about numbers or shapes (80–1)	Make and investigate a general statement about familiar numbers or shapes by finding examples that satisfy it.	7A Student Book: S3.3 - S3.5	

Overview

The aim of this unit is to develop students' understanding of fractions, decimals and percentages, and their equivalence. The last spread introduces the concept of ratio.

Spreads N4.2, N4.4 and N4.5 form the focus of the unit.

Framework references

The unit covers objectives on Framework (Y456) Pages 19, 21, 61, 109

Introduction

Discuss examples of where fractions are used in daily life, for example 'half price sale', '8 out of 10 cats prefer … '. Discuss fractions that apply to the class. For example, 1 in 4 students owns a pet, half of the students come to school by bus.

Check in activity

Give each student a number ladder with five empty boxes (**R5**). Read out five numbers between 1 and 100. Students write each number in a box depending on whether they think it will be the biggest, or the smallest, etc. The aim is to write the numbers in order, with the smallest at the bottom. Repeat with numbers between 100 and 300, etc.

Useful resources

Worksheets
N4.1WS – fractions
N4.2WS – fractions and decimals
N4.4WS – percentage of amounts
N4.5WS – ratio

OHP
N4.3OHP – 100 grid and number line

General resources
R6 – number lines
R17 – 100 square
R21 – multiplication table
Multilink cubes – at least two colours
Counters

Springboard 7 pages
179, 193, 427, 432, 436, 437

Differentiation – spanning the bridge

Spread	Bridge to the Support tier
N4.1	Progress Support tier students to consider equivalent fractions of those in simplest form (multiplying), extending to finding a numerator of 100 to link with percentages. Focus on converting percentages to decimals and vice versa.
N4.2	Progress Support tier students to consider equivalence of percentages, fractions and decimals, in particular the equivalences of 50%, 10% and 25%. Progress to finding percentage of amounts using equivalent fractions.
N4.3	Progress Support tier students to finding percentages of amounts, developing to derive 5% and 2.5% from 10% and using these values to calculate more complex percentages of amounts.
N4.4	Support tier students have worked on finding percentage of amounts during N2.2 and N2.3, and the introductory activity can be used as a recap for these students. Progress to consider describing amounts as proportions of one another – expressing as a fraction, decimal and percentage.
N4.5	Extend the Support tier to combine ratio and proportion, and progress to solving problems where the total number of parts is increased (as in the plenary activity).

Access

This spread provides access to the Year 7 objective:
▸ Simplify fractions by cancellation (62)

Lesson Plan

Mental starter

Give a number and ask students to halve it. Develop to two-digit numbers. Discuss how to partition a number (for example 58 into 50 and 8) to ease halving.

Introductory activity

Shade a fraction on a grid (**R24**) and discuss its numerical representation. Emphasise that the numerator is how many parts are shaded and the denominator is the number of **equal parts**. Repeat for other fractions. Choose students to shade given fractions.

Refer to the mental starter. Discuss what operation you perform to halve any number. Link finding half to division by 2, **splitting into 2 equal parts**.

Discuss finding one third of an amount (say £24). Emphasise **splitting into 3 equal parts**, and link to division by 3.

Discuss shading half, one third and two thirds of a 4 × 6 rectangle (on **R24**). Repeat for $\frac{4}{6}$ (**splitting into 6 equal parts, and shading 4**). Use the diagrams to highlight the equivalence between two thirds and four sixths. Demonstrate dividing numerator and denominator of $\frac{4}{6}$ by the same number (2) to get $\frac{2}{3}$.

Plenary

Discuss question 6. Encourage students to suggest how the shaded parts could be placed in the diagram to show a more familiar representation of the simplified fraction (for example in question 6a shade the top row).

Homework

▸ Find the 'odd' fraction in a set of ten, where nine fractions are equivalent to $\frac{3}{4}$.
▸ Springboard 7: Page 179.

Exercise Commentary

Coverage

The questions assess objectives on Framework (Y456) Pages 23 and 25.

Useful resources

R21 – multiplication table
R24 – squared grid
N4.1WS – provides support for weaker students.

Differentiation

▸ Questions 1–3 focus on identifying fractions from pictorial representations.
▸ Questions 4 and 5 require students to calculate fractions of amounts.
▸ Question 6 focuses on simplifying fractions.

Support tier: focuses on equivalent fractions, decimals and percentages.

Misconceptions

Students find non-unitary fractions difficult to calculate, and may find question 5 a challenge. Encourage them to say each fraction out loud to highlight the denominator as the number of equal parts the shape needs to be split into.

Division may prove problematic for some students, and a multiplication table (**R21**) can be used for support. Simplifying fractions may be confusing. Encourage students to copy the pictorial representations and try 'moving' a shaded part to help them 'see' the simplified version and equivalence, as in the plenary activity.

Links

Division: Framework (Y456) Page 59.

Exercise Answers

1 a $4, \frac{1}{4}$ b $3, \frac{1}{3}$ c $10, \frac{1}{10}$ d $5, \frac{1}{5}$
2 a $\frac{1}{6}$ b $\frac{2}{5}$ c $\frac{7}{10}$ d $\frac{3}{8}$ 3 a $\frac{5}{6}$ b $\frac{2}{5}$ c $\frac{3}{10}$ d $\frac{3}{8}$
4 a 4 b 3 c 3 d 5 e 10 f 4 g 3 h 6
5 a 9 parts shaded b 10 parts shaded
   c 8 parts shaded d 3 parts shaded
6 a $\frac{1}{2}$ b $\frac{1}{4}$ c $\frac{1}{3}$ d $\frac{3}{4}$ e $\frac{1}{2}$ f $\frac{2}{3}$ g $\frac{1}{2}$ h $\frac{3}{4}$ i $\frac{1}{2}$
   j $\frac{1}{3}$ k $\frac{3}{4}$ l $\frac{1}{3}$

Worksheet Answers

1 a $\frac{2}{8}$ b $\frac{3}{8}$ c $\frac{4}{6}$ d $\frac{4}{7}$
2 a $\frac{1}{2}$ b $\frac{1}{3}$ c $\frac{1}{4}$ d $\frac{1}{2}$ e $\frac{1}{4}$ f $\frac{1}{5}$
3 a $\frac{1}{3}$ b $\frac{2}{5}$ c $\frac{1}{3}$ d $\frac{2}{5}$ e $\frac{1}{3}$ f $\frac{3}{8}$

1 What fraction of each shape is shaded?

a  _____

b 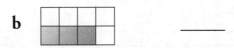 _____

c 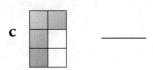 _____

d 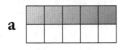 _____

2 Use the shapes to write these as a simpler fraction:

a $\dfrac{5}{10}$ or _____

b $\dfrac{3}{9}$ or _____

c $\dfrac{2}{8}$ or _____

d $\dfrac{10}{20}$ or _____

e $\dfrac{3}{12}$ or _____

f $\dfrac{2}{10}$ or _____

3

To simplify $\frac{6}{10}$ you divide top and bottom by the same number.

$$\overset{\div 2}{\underset{\div 2}{\dfrac{6}{10}}} = \dfrac{3}{5}$$ $\dfrac{6}{10}$ is the same as $\dfrac{3}{5}$.

Simplify these fractions.

a $\overset{\div 3}{\underset{\div 3}{\dfrac{3}{9}}} = \dfrac{}{3}$

b $\overset{\div 2}{\underset{\div 2}{\dfrac{4}{10}}} = \dfrac{}{5}$

c $\overset{\div 4}{\underset{\div 4}{\dfrac{4}{12}}} = \dfrac{}{}$

d $\overset{\div 3}{\underset{\div 3}{\dfrac{6}{15}}} = \dfrac{}{}$

e $\overset{\div 5}{\underset{\div 5}{\dfrac{5}{15}}} = \dfrac{}{}$

f $\overset{\div 2}{\underset{\div 2}{\dfrac{6}{16}}} = \dfrac{}{}$

N4.2 Fractions and decimals

Access

This spread provides access to the Year 7 objective:
▸ Convert fractions to decimals (64)

Lesson Plan

Mental starter

Give each student a number, say 10, 20, 30 or 40. Give a fraction question, say half of 60. Students stand up if their number is the answer.

Introductory activity

Use a number line from 0 to 10 (**R6**).

Mark an arrow on the number line and ask students to identify the number it is pointing at. Discuss how many whole numbers are between 0 and 10.

Show a number line from 0 to 1 (**R6**). Discuss what numbers describe values between whole numbers. Introduce **decimals** and link **dec** with **ten**. Label 0.1, 0.2 etc. below the line. Discuss the value of the ten equal intervals. Link to fractions to determine the name **tenths**. Label $\frac{1}{10}$, $\frac{2}{10}$ etc. above the line

Practise counting up and down (past the unit boundaries) in tenths. Discuss larger values, such as 2.7, 3.1 and mark them on a number line.

Use a blank number line from 0 to 0.1 (**R6**). Emphasise that each tenth can be split into ten again, which means the whole number has been split into a hundred – link with fractions and elicit keyword **hundredths**. Link to pounds and pence. Link decimals with two decimal places to fractions out of 100.

Plenary

Show a number line from 0 to 2 (**R6**). Choose students to place given tenths (for example 0.3, 4 tenths). Extend to hundredths.

Homework

▸ Place fractions and decimals on a 0–1 number line.
▸ Springboard 7: Page 432.

Exercise Commentary

Coverage

The questions assess objectives on Framework (Y456) Pages 29 and 31.

Useful resources

R6 – number lines

N4.2WS – provides further practice of the key ideas.

Differentiation

▸ Questions 1–4 focus on tenths as fractions and decimals.
▸ Questions 5–7 focus on hundredths.
▸ Questions 8–11 extend to ordering decimals.

Support tier: focuses on finding percentages of quantities.

Misconceptions

Students should be encouraged to draw diagrams to help compare fractions and decimals.

Ordering numbers can prove confusing to weaker students. Remind them to work from left to right, and to think about the place value of each digit in the number before beginning to order them. Hundredths can be particularly problematic. Encourage students to relate them to pounds and pence.

Links

Money: Framework (Y456) Page 84.

Worksheet Answers

1 b $\frac{3}{10}$ or 0.3   c $\frac{9}{10}$ or 0.9   d $\frac{1}{10}$ or 0.1   e $\frac{6}{10}$ or 0.6
  f $\frac{5}{10}$ or 0.5
3 b 0.1   c 0.16   d 0.25   e 0.65   f 0.4
4 b $\frac{15}{100}$ c $\frac{35}{100}$ d $\frac{80}{100}$ e $\frac{33}{100}$ f $\frac{90}{100}$

Exercise Answers

1 a 0.3   b 0.7   c 0.8   d 0.5
2 a 0.3   b 0.8   c 0.9   d 0.5
3 a $\frac{4}{10}$ b $\frac{7}{10}$ c $\frac{2}{10}$ d $\frac{6}{10}$ e 1 or $\frac{10}{10}$
4 a 0.6   b 0.2
5 a 0.35   b 0.85   c 0.55   d 0.92   e 0.16
6 a $\frac{39}{100}$ b $\frac{27}{100}$ c $\frac{76}{100}$ d $\frac{87}{100}$ e $\frac{54}{100}$
7 a 0.37   b 0.63   c 0.85
8 a 0.4, 1.5, 3.2, 4.3, 6.0   b 4.5, 5.2, 5.7, 6.2, 7.6
9 a $\frac{6}{10}$ b 6   c $\frac{6}{100}$ d $\frac{6}{10}$ e $\frac{6}{100}$
10 a 2.36, 3.89, 5.01, 6.72, 9.53
   b 3.75, 3.77, 5.51, 5.73, 7.35
11 For example 3.65

1 How much of each shape is shaded?
Give your answer as a fraction and a decimal.
The first is done for you.

a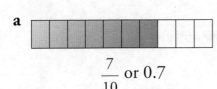

$\dfrac{7}{10}$ or 0.7

b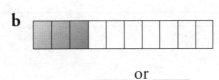

_____ or _____

c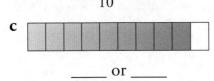

_____ or _____

d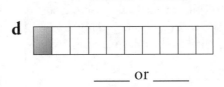

_____ or _____

e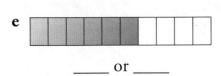

_____ or _____

f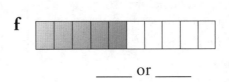

_____ or _____

2 Shade in these parts of this 10 × 10 square.
The first has been done for you.

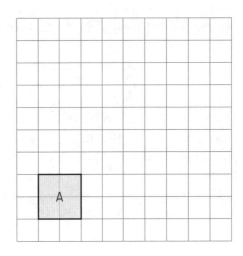

A $\dfrac{4}{100}$ or 0.04   **B** $\dfrac{7}{100}$ or 0.07

C $\dfrac{5}{100}$ or 0.05   **D** $\dfrac{10}{100}$ or 0.1

E $\dfrac{14}{100}$ or 0.14   **F** $\dfrac{17}{100}$ or 0.17

3 Write these fractions as decimals.
The first one is done for you.

a $\dfrac{6}{100}$ = 0.06   **b** $\dfrac{10}{100}$ = _____   **c** $\dfrac{16}{100}$ = _____

d $\dfrac{25}{100}$ = _____   **e** $\dfrac{65}{100}$ = _____   **f** $\dfrac{40}{100}$ = _____

4 Write these decimals as fractions.
The first one is done for you.

a 0.02 = $\dfrac{2}{100}$ **b** 0.15 = _____   **c** 0.35 = _____

d 0.80 = _____   **e** 0.33 = _____   **f** 0.90 = _____

Access

This spread provides access to the Year 7 objective:
▶ Recognise the equivalence of fractions, decimals and percentages (70)

Lesson Plan

Mental starter

Encourage students to write decimal values on paper. Choose six students and encourage them to line up in numerical order, according to their decimal values.

Introductory activity

Recap equivalent fractions and decimals.
▶ What decimal is equivalent to 3 tenths?
▶ What fraction is equivalent to 0.12?

Introduce **percentages**.

Emphasise that decimals are parts. Discuss the words 'per cent': meaning for every hundred out of 1 whole. Percentages are parts out of 100. Link to fractions with denominators of 100.

Use a 100 square (**R17**) to discuss equivalences: for example, 1 tenth/0.1/10% of the numbers are multiples of 10. Practise giving equivalents for shaded squares on a 100 grid (**N4.3OHP**).

Show a 0–1 number line (**R6**). Choose students to place different fractions/decimals percentages on the number line.

Discuss conversion between percentages and decimals using the number line on **N4.3OHP**.

Plenary

Discuss question 8. Emphasise that to compare numbers they must all be converted to the same type of number.

For each part, discuss which type to convert all the numbers to and why, before explaining which is the bigger number.

Homework

▶ Design a garden as in question 1, on a 100 square. Complete a table of fraction/decimal/percentages for the design.
▶ Springboard 7: Page 193.

Exercise Commentary

Coverage

The questions assess objectives on Framework (Y456) Page 33.

Useful resources

R6 – number lines
R17 – 100 square
N4.3OHP – 100 grid and number line.

Differentiation

▶ Question 1 focuses on understanding percentages.
▶ Questions 2–7 focus on converting between forms.
▶ Question 8 extends to comparing numbers.

Support tier: focuses on finding percentages of amounts. N4.1 focuses on equivalent fractions, decimals and percentages.

Misconceptions

Students will have difficulty converting fractions where the denominator is not 100 (questions 2, 3 and 7). Provide 100 squares (**R17**), and encourage students to shade the fraction given to see the equivalent fraction with denominator 100.

Links

Multiplying and dividing by 100: Framework (Y456) Page 7.

Exercise Answers

1 a Lawn: 39%, $\frac{39}{100}$, 0.39; Pond: 4%, $\frac{4}{100}$, 0.04; Vegetables: 21%, $\frac{21}{100}$, 0.21; Flowers: 24%, $\frac{24}{100}$, 0.24
2 a $\frac{6}{10}$ b 0.6 c 60%
3 a $\frac{3}{4}$ b 0.75 c 75%
4 a 0.35 b 0.61 c 0.27 d 0.83 e 0.97
5 a 28% b 78% c 43% d 55% e 82%
6 a $\frac{60}{100}$ b $\frac{47}{100}$ c $\frac{18}{100}$ d $\frac{94}{100}$ e $\frac{50}{100}$
7 a 37% b 95% c 50% d 25% e 10%
8 a 0.6 b $\frac{3}{4}$ c 0.21

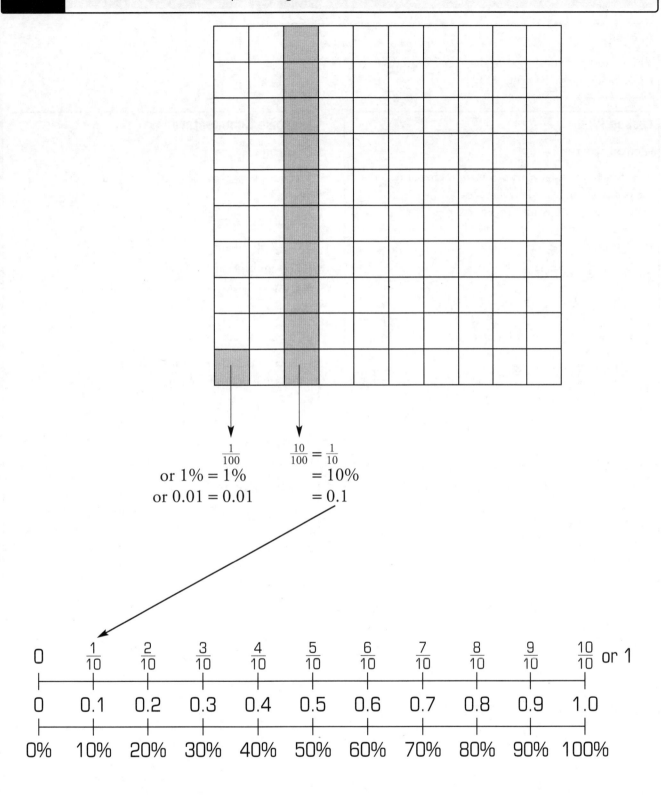

$$\frac{1}{100}$$

$$\frac{10}{100} = \frac{1}{10}$$

or 1% = 1%   = 10%

or 0.01 = 0.01   = 0.1

N4.4 Percentage of amounts

Access

This spread provides access to the Year 7 objective:
▶ Calculate simple percentages (72)

Lesson Plan

Mental starter

Ask students quick-fire questions to recap equivalent fractions, decimals and percentages.
▶ What decimal is equivalent to 3 tenths?
▶ What is 1 tenth of 50?
▶ What percentage is equivalent to 0.5?

Introductory activity

Refer to the mental starter and emphasise that fractions, decimals and percentages are equivalent.

Recap how to find a fraction of an amount (unitary fractions only). Practise with simple questions: for example half of 42, a seventh of 42. Emphasise splitting the amount into a number of equal parts.

Discuss what fraction is equivalent to 10%. Use a 100 square (**R17**) to emphasise that 1 tenth is equivalent to 10 hundredths, is equivalent to 10%.

Discuss how to find 10% of an amount. Go over the example in the Students' book, dividing 30 counters into 10 sections. Emphasise that once you know 10%, you can find lots of other percentages.

Discuss half of 30, and highlight that one half is the same as 5 tenths or 50%.

Plenary

Ask for 10% of 120, then 20%, and progress through the multiples of 10. Discuss strategies.

Ask students for 5% of 120, and as a class find as many percentages as possible using this new benchmark, such as 15% = 10% + 5%.

Homework

▶ Find 10% of £80. Use this to find other percentages of £80 (as in the plenary).
▶ Springboard 7: Page 427.

Exercise Commentary

Coverage

The questions assess objectives on Framework (Y456) Page 33.

Useful resources

R17 – 100 square
R21 – multiplication table
N4.4WS – provides support for weaker students.
Counters

Differentiation

▶ Questions 1–3 focus on finding simple percentages from diagrams.
▶ Question 4 involves finding 10%.
▶ Question 5 involves finding 30%.

Support tier: focuses on writing proportions as fractions, decimals or percentages.

Misconceptions

Some students will have difficulty linking 10% of an amount with a multiple of 10%. Encourage students to gain confidence using counters. Emphasise that each 10% of the amount is the same. Weaker students will find a multiplication table (**R21**) helpful throughout these questions.

Links

Multiplying and dividing by 100: Framework (Y456) Page 7.

Worksheet Answers

1 a 30% b 30% c 30% d 10% e 5%
2 a 10 b 2 c 6 d 16
3 a 5 b 15 c 25 d 40

Exercise Answers

1 a 8 b 12 c 20 d 28 e 32 f 40
2 40
3 a 70 b 35 c 49
4 a £4 b 3 m c 6 kg d 8 km e 10 m
  f 1 hour g £20 h 32p or £0.32
5 a £12 b 9 m c 18 kg d 24 km e 30 m
  f 3 hours g £60 h 96p or £0.96

1 A pizza is cut into 10 equal slices. Each slice is 10% of the whole pizza.

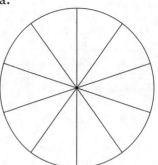

   a Colour 3 slices blue. What percentage is this? _____%

   b Colour 3 slices green. What percentage is this? _____%

   c Colour 3 slices red. What percentage is this? _____%

   d What percentage of the pizza is left? _____%

   e What percentage is **half** a slice of pizza? _____%

2 Here are 20 counters:

Share them equally into the percentage strip.

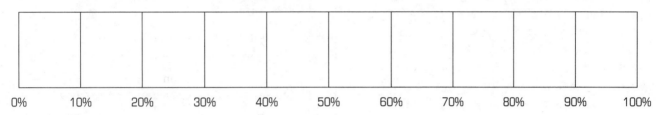

Use the strip to work out:

a 50% of 20 counters = _____

b 10% of 20 counters = _____

c 30% of 20 counters = _____

d 80% of 20 counters = _____

3 Here are 50 counters:

Share them equally into the percentage strip.

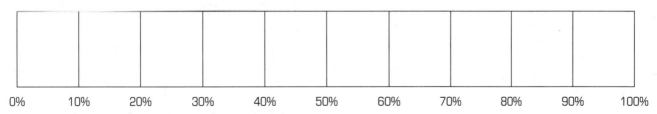

Use the strip to work out:

a 10% of 50 counters = _____

b 30% of 50 counters = _____

c 50% of 50 counters = _____

d 80% of 50 counters = _____

N4.5 Ratio

Access

This spread provides access to the Year 7 objective:
▸ Use ratio notation (78)

Lesson Plan

Mental starter

Give students mental calculations based on body parts. For example every person has 10 fingers – how many fingers for 10 people? Repeat for ears, hands, molars (8), left toes (5).

Introductory activity

Show students a repeating pattern made of multilink cubes, for example 3 red, 1 blue. Emphasise that to continue for every 3 red cubes we need 1 blue. Introduce **ratio** to compare the parts of the pattern. Write on the board 3 : 1 and highlight that this means 3 parts for every 1. Repeat for other patterns.

Discuss the paint example in the Students' book. Highlight that order is important: 3 : 1 ≠ 1 : 3.

Discuss what happens if the ration of red to yellow is changed, and highlight that ratio enables an exact recipe of quantities.

Building from 5 : 1 yellow to red, ask students questions such as how much yellow for 2 red?

Discuss strategies, highlighting key points such as:

▸ If you double the red, you need to double the yellow.

▸ What happens if you have 5 times as much red? How much yellow will you need?

Demonstrate multiplication of both quantities and highlight equivalent ratios.

Plenary

Explain that red and white are mixed 2 : 1 to produce a pink paint. You need 6 tins in total. How much of each will you need? Discuss strategies.
Discuss how much of each quantity you need for 15 or 30 tins.

Homework

▸ Students draw bead patterns for given ratios red : blue. Provide a table of numbers of red and blue for students to complete.

▸ Springboard 7: Pages 436–437.

Exercise Commentary

Coverage

The questions assess objectives on Framework (Y456) Page 27.

Useful resources

Multilink cubes, at least two colours

N4.5WS – provides support for weaker students.

Differentiation

▸ Questions 1 and 2 focus on using ratio notation.

▸ Questions 3 and 4 focus on solving problems using ratios.

▸ Question 5 extends to a non-unitary ratio.

Support tier: focuses on using ratio and proportion in context.

Misconceptions

Students may multiply by the wrong number (in question 4, multiplying by 12 rather than by 4). Using cubes will help. Students should be encouraged to think about building up the pattern of the quantities, and the key words **for every**. Weaker students will benefit from working in pairs to discuss the problems.

Links

Multiplication facts: Framework (Y456) Page 59.

Exercise Answers

1 a 3 : 1 b 3 : 2 c 2 : 2 d 3 : 1
2 a 4 : 1 b 2 : 1 c 3 : 1 d 3 : 2
3 a 10 b 3
4 a 4 b 15
5 a 4 b 15

Worksheet Answers

1 b 4 : 3
2 b 3 : 6
3 a 2 : 1 b 1 : 3 c 2 : 3 d 6 : 3
6 5

1 a Colour 4 of these tins red and 3 tins blue.

b What is the ratio of red to blue? ___ : ___

2 a Colour 3 of these tins red and 6 tins blue.

b What is the ratio of red to blue? ___ : ___

3 What is the ratio of black beads to white beads on these strings?

a    _____ : _____

b   _____ : _____

c   _____ : _____

d   _____ : _____

4 This string of beads is made up from black and white beads in the ratio of 1 : 4.
Colour in the string of beads.

5 In this string the ratio of black beads to white beads is 3 : 2.
Colour in this string of beads.

6 The ratio of black beads to white beads on a string is 2 : 1.
There are 10 black beads.

How many white beads are needed? _____

Framework MATHS — Scheme of work — Year 7

N4 Percentages, ratio and proportion (5 hours)	Teaching objectives	Framework Maths resources	Other resources
Fractions, decimals and percentages, ratio and proportion (22–3)	Use fraction notation. Recognise when two simple fractions are equivalent.	7A Student Book: N4.1 7A Teacher's Book: N4.1WS, R21	
Fractions, decimals and percentages, ratio and proportion (24–5)	Relate fractions to division	7A Student Book: N4.1 7A Teacher's Book: N4.1WS, R21	
Fractions, decimals and percentages, ratio and proportion (28–9)	Use decimal notation for tenths and hundredths. Order a set of numbers or measurements with the same number of decimal places.	7A Student Book: N4.2 7A Teacher's Book: N4.2WS, R6	
Fractions, decimals and percentages, ratio and proportion (30–1)	Relate fractions to their decimal representations	7A Student Book: N4.2 7A Teacher's Book: N4.2WS, R6	
Fractions, decimals and percentages, ratio and proportion (32–3)	Begin to understand percentage as the number of parts in every 100. Express one half, one quarter, three quarters, and tenths and hundredths, as percentages.	7A Student Book: N4.3 7A Teacher's Book: N4.3OHP, R6, R17	
Fractions, decimals and percentages, ratio and proportion (32–3)	Find simple percentages of small whole-number quantities.	7A Student Book: N4.4 7A Teacher's Book: N4.4WS, R17, R21	
Fractions, decimals and percentages, ratio and proportion (26–7)	Solve simple problems using ideas of ratio.	7A Student Book: N4.5 7A Teacher's Book: N4.5WS	
Making decisions (74–5)	Choose and use appropriate number operations to solve problems, and appropriate ways of calculating: mental, mental with jottings, written methods, calculator.	7A Student Book: N4.4–N4.5	

Overview

The aim of this unit is to develop students' understanding of equalities and inequalities, and to progress from informal methods of solving linear equations to more formal methods involving algebraic notation. Weaker students may need to focus on the concrete examples.

Spreads A4.2 and A4.3 form the focus of the unit.

Framework references

The unit covers objectives on Framework (Y456) Pages 43, 63, 81,

Useful resources

Worksheets
A4.2WS – equalities
A4.4WS – equations

OHPs
A4.1OHP – writing expressions
A4.3OHP – weighing scales

General resources
Box of counters
R6 – number lines
R7 – function machines
R21 – multiplication table

Springboard 7 pages
85, 239, 302

Introduction

Discuss how a set of balance scales works – the pans are level when the weights on either side are equal. What happens when one side is heavier?

Discuss how to balance scales using different combinations of weights, for example 5 × 1 kg weights and a 5 kg weight. Use a real balance if possible, or sketches.

Check in activity

Give each student two pieces of card. Ask them to write an addition or subtraction calculation (with an answer less than 50), say 38 + 11 on one card, and its answer on the other. The teacher must also complete two cards.

Collect the cards, shuffle questions and answers separately, and distribute one question and one answer to each student.

Read out the calculation on your card. The student who has the corresponding answer must stand up. They then read out the calculation on their card, and the student with that answer stands up, and so on.

Differentiation – spanning the bridge

Spread	Bridge to the Support tier
A4.1	Extend Support tier students to consider multiplicative expressions, and also examples where the unknown is added to or subtracted from a known value.
A4.2	Emphasise the four addition and subtraction facts that link three numbers, and extend Support tier students to the four multiplication and division facts which link three numbers.
A4.3	The two tiers cover different material in this lesson. Support tier students will need to be reminded of the order of operations – highlighting that a different order can lead to a different answer. Discuss the use of brackets to change the natural order a calculation is evaluated in.
A4.4	Extend to discuss the difference between equations (where the unknown has one value) and expressions (with variable value). Progress Support tier students to substitution into one-step expressions, considering all values.

A4.1 Using letters

Access

This spread provides access to the Year 7 objective:
▸ Use letter symbols to write expressions (112)

Lesson Plan

Mental starter

Give each student a number.

Write an operation in a function machine (**R7**). Ask students to input their number and write the output. Choose students to write their calculations under the function machine.

Repeat, with different operations.

Introductory activity

Refer to the mental starter. Ask students for the pattern or general rule in each set of calculations. Generalise them in writing: for example, **any number add 4**. Emphasise that you use algebra and letters to generalise about patterns and when a number is **unknown**.

Show a box of counters. How many counters are in here? Take suggestions, but highlight that this number is unknown. Use a letter to stand for the number of counters (s). Remove 6 counters. Encourage students to explain how many counters there are now. Highlight that there are 6 less, so you write $s - 6$.

Show **A4.1OHP** and write expressions for the numbers of sweets.

Plenary

Discuss question 4. Highlight collecting like terms in parts **c** and **d**. Extend to calculating the value of s given the total length of pipes: $32 + s$ metres gives a total of 45 metres. What must the length of s be?

Homework

▸ For five operation machines, with various inputs, including n, students find output given numerical input and write an expression for the general rule.

Exercise Commentary

Coverage

The questions assess objectives on Framework (Y456) Page 81.

Useful resources

R7 – function machines
Box of counters
A4.1OHP – writing expressions

Differentiation

▸ Question 1 focuses on writing expressions.
▸ Questions 2 and 3 involve writing expressions with less support.
▸ Question 4 extends to simplifying expressions.

Support tier: focuses on writing algebraic expressions.

Misconceptions

Students tend to use a letter to stand for the object itself, rather than the number of objects, and should be discouraged from using 'code' letters, such as s to stand for sweets.

Students sometimes find deciding which operation to use difficult. Encourage them to first decide whether there will be more or less than their start number, and link more to add, and less to subtract.

Weaker students will find this work challenging and may benefit from using counters.

Links

Generalising and predicting: Framework (Y456) Page 79.

Exercise Answers

1 a $n - 10$ b $m + 6$
2 a $x + 2$ b $y - 5$
3 $a - 50$
4 a $n + 15$ b $y + 5$ c $32 + s$ d $2n$ metres

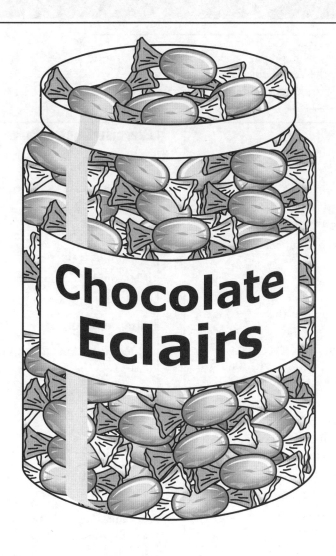

Add 3 more sweets: _____

Take out 6 sweets: _____

Add 15 more sweets: _____

Take out 10 sweets: _____

A4.2 Equalities

Access

This spread provides access to the Year 7 objective:
▸ Know how to use the laws of arithmetic and inverse operations (84)

Lesson Plan

Mental starter

Write '20' in a bubble on the board. Encourage students to give two numbers that add together to make 20. Keep going until you have all the number pairs.

Repeat with another bubble and numbers that **multiply** to make 20.

Introductory activity

Refer to the mental starter. Highlight that $17 + 3$ is the same as $3 + 17$, and also that 4×5 is the same as 5×4. Write $17 + 3 = 3 + 17$ and emphasise that this is an **equality**. Ask for other equalities, from either bubble. Emphasise that you can add or multiply two numbers in any order.

Discuss whether you can subtract two numbers in any order to produce a set of equalities. Is $20 - 17$ the same as $17 - 20$? Use a number line (**R6**) to demonstrate the difference between the calculations.

Emphasise that subtraction is the opposite of addition. Introduce the key word **inverse**. Discuss the ways three numbers can be linked: $3 + 5 = 8$, $8 - 5 = 3$, $8 - 3 = 5$.

Discuss division. Is $10 \div 2$ the same as $2 \div 10$?

Emphasise that division is the inverse of multiplication. Use multiplying to 20 as an example.

Plenary

Encourage students to calculate a missing number given an equality: $13 + 7 = 12 + ?$

Discuss strategies: find the total using one side then use the inverse to help calculate the missing value on the other.

Homework

▸ Write six calculations that give the answer 15 on a diagram similar to question 1.
▸ Springboard 7: Page 85.

Worksheet Answers

1 $30 - 10 = 20$, $5 \times 4 = 20$, $35 - 15 = 20$, $40 \div 2 = 20$, $2 \times 10 = 20$, $14 + 6 = 20$
2 a 5 cm   b 4 cm   c $6\frac{1}{2}$ cm
3 a A = 13 cm, B = 12 cm, C = 8 cm, D = 7 cm
   b A and D, B and C

Exercise Commentary

Coverage

The questions assess objectives on Framework (Y456) Pages 43 and 63.

Useful resources

R6 – number lines
R21 – multiplication table
A4.2WS – provides support for weaker students.

Differentiation

▸ Questions 1 and 2 focus on simple equalities.
▸ Questions 3–5 focus on equalities in the context of measures.
▸ Questions 6 and 7 involve multiplicative equalities.

Support tier: focuses on extending the laws of arithmetic to algebra.

Misconceptions

Encourage students to check the value of each side of the equals sign in an equality. Weaker students will benefit from a multiplication table to enable them to 'see' the equality of multiplicative relationships.

Links

Multiplication and division: Framework (Y456) Page 59.

Exercise Answers

1 a 4×3; $5 + 7$; 4×3; $12 \div 4 = 3$, $12 - 0$
   b $9 + 11$; $17 = 20 - 3$; 10×2; $11 + 9$; 2×10; $20 - 10 = 10$
2 a $3 + 4 = 4 + 3$ b $4 + 5 = 5 + 4$
   c $9 + 3 = 3 + 9$ d $9 \times 6 = 6 \times 9$
   e $10 \times 3 = 3 \times 10$ f $21 \times 4 = 4 \times 21$
3 a $10 + 5 = 5 + 10$
   b $10 = 15 - 5$ and $5 = 15 - 10$
4 a 13 m   b $3 + 10 = 10 + 3$
5 a 5 kg   b $8 + 5 = 5 + 8$
6 a Yes   b It is an equality.
7 a Yes   b No   c Yes   d No

1 Write numbers in the boxes to make the answer 20.

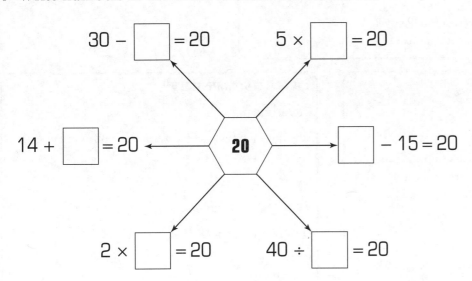

$30 - \boxed{} = 20$ $5 \times \boxed{} = 20$

$14 + \boxed{} = 20$ **20** $\boxed{} - 15 = 20$

$2 \times \boxed{} = 20$ $40 \div \boxed{} = 20$

2 Continue these strips to the given length.

a 9 cm [4 cm]

How long is the new piece? _____ cm

b 10 cm [_____]

How long is the new piece? _____ cm

c 13 cm [_____]

How long is the new piece? _____ cm

3 a Measure these lines.   A = _____   B = _____   C = _____   D = _____

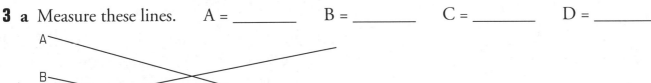

b There are two pairs of lines. Each pair add up to 20 cm.
Find the two pairs.

Pair 1 (_____ and _____)

Pair 2 (_____ and _____)

Access

This spread provides access to the Year 7 objective:
▸ Construct and solve simple linear equations (122)

Lesson Plan

Mental starter

Write a simple calculation on the board, say 27 − 13.

Invite students to give another calculation with the same total. Write the two calculations as an equality.

Repeat for calculations using all four operations.

Introductory activity

Use the examples for the Students' book (on **A4.3OHP**) to illustrate that see-saws and scales balance when the weights on each side are equal. Link to the equals sign in the equalities from the mental starter.

Give students two expressions: 6 + 3 and 8 + 2.

Discuss whether these are equal. Highlight the need to evaluate each expression first to find out.

Discuss 3 + 2 and 4 + 5. Highlight the words **smaller/less than**. Introduce the notation <. Repeat for 3 + 6 and 2 + 4 and the notation >.

Discuss strategies for remembering which to use, < or >, for different cases.

Give three 'wrong' questions for students to discuss, such as: 3 + 4 > 2 + 5. Choose students to write the correct sign between the two expressions.

Plenary

Discuss question 5. Discuss ways of making each diagram correct, either by adding to the picture, or changing the sign.

Discuss what happens to each correct expression if you add the same weights to each side.

Homework

▸ Create 20 equality calculations (e.g. $4 \times 2 = 6 + 2$) and 20 inequality calculations (e.g. $5 - 3 < 2 + 3$).
▸ Springboard 7: Page 302.

Exercise Commentary

Coverage

The questions assess objectives on Framework (Y456) Page 81.

Useful resources

A4.3OHP – weighing scales

Differentiation

▸ Question 1 focuses on simple inequalities and equalities.
▸ Questions 2–4 focus on equalities and inequalities in calculations, developing to finding unknowns.
▸ Question 5 focuses on using the correct sign.

Support tier: focuses on using brackets.

Misconceptions

Students may confuse the greater than/less than notation. Encourage students to share strategies for remembering. One way is to identify the 'small part' of each sign (the point) and highlight that this always points to the smallest calculation value.

Links

Ordering: Framework (Y456) Page 15.

Exercise Answers

1 a $5 < 9$ b $12 > 7$ c $51 > 39$ d $72 < 102$
  e $45 = 45$ f $61 > 29$ g $78 > 77$ h $89 = 89$
2 a $4 + 2 < 5 + 3$ b $5 - 1 = 2 + 2$ c $10 + 2 > 7 + 1$
  d $12 + 3 > 6 + 7$ e $5 \times 2 = 9 + 1$ f $4 \times 5 < 24 - 2$
  g $18 + 6 = 4 \times 6$ h $10 - 2 > 2 \times 3$
  i $5 + 5 = 30 \div 3$
3 a $15 = 5 + 10$ b $10 + 3 > 6 + 6$ c $10 < 2 + 2 + 7$
  d $20 + 10 = 26 + 4$
4 a 5 b 5 c 10 d 17 or greater e 4 or greater
  f 9 or less g 3 or less h 41 or greater
5 a Doesn't balance – not an equality.
  b Should balance – is an equality.

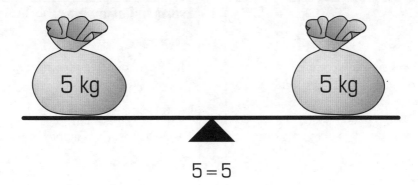

$$5 = 5$$

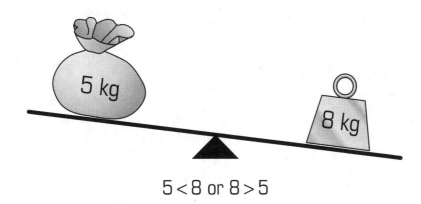

$$5 < 8 \text{ or } 8 > 5$$

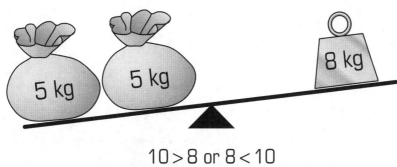

$$10 > 8 \text{ or } 8 < 10$$

Access

This spread provides access to the Year 7 objective:
▸ Construct and solve simple linear equations (122)

Lesson Plan

Mental starter

Give three numbers linked by addition, say 12, 13 and 25. Encourage students to give a calculation linking these numbers. Wait for all four. Repeat with different numbers, increasing to larger values, say 234, 38, 272

Introductory activity

Refer to the mental starter. Highlight the link between addition and subtraction. Emphasise subtraction as the **inverse** of addition, and explain that it **undoes** what addition **does**.

Give students an oral problem:

I have a number, I add 3, the answer is 14.

What is my number?

Repeat for a subtraction problem.

Discuss how to write the problem as an equation, and what to use to represent the unknown number. Emphasise that any symbol can be used. Encourage use of letters, or '?'.

Discuss the example: $20 = ? + 15$

Discuss two strategies for finding the unknown:

▸ Counting on from 15
▸ Using the subtraction fact: $20 - 15 = ?$

Discuss the example in the Students' book.

Plenary

Discuss one-step equations with multiplication, such as:

I have a number. Twice my number is 14.

Progress to writing equations using correct notation: $2d = 2 \times d$. Invite students to write an equation for a problem, and discuss strategies for solving. Highlight division as the inverse of multiplication.

Homework

▸ Create ten equations using an unknown and addition and subtraction, and provide the answers.
▸ Springboard 7: Page 239.

Exercise Commentary

Coverage

The questions assess objectives on Framework (Y456) Page 43.

Useful resources

A4.4WS – provides support for weaker students.

Differentiation

▸ Questions 1 and 2 involve informal problem solving.
▸ Questions 3 and 4 focus on solving equations more formally.
▸ Question 5 involves finding the values of letters in equations.

Support tier: focuses on substitution and solving equations using all four operations.

Misconceptions

Students solve problems informally with ease, but the formal equations may confuse them. Encourage students to say each equation out loud, substituting 'something' or 'a number' whenever they see a symbol or letter. This helps them build a natural link between formal and informal representations.

Links

Generalising: Framework (Y456) Page 81.

Exercise Answers

1 a $30 = ? + ? + 10$ b $8 + ? = 22$
2 a 2 b 6 c 4 d 7 e 9
3 a 6 b 2 c 9 d 7 e 5 f 6 g 20 h 4 i 0
  j 20 k 7 l 20
4 a 5 b 2 c 12 d 5 e 12 f 3 g 4 h 17
5 a 4 b 4 c 5 d 4 e 11 f 16 g 2 h 20
  i 16 j 20 k 4 l 6

Worksheet Answers

1 a 10 kg b 22 kg c 10 kg d 15 kg e 25 kg
  f 23 kg

1 Calculate the weights of the parcels needed to make the scales balance.
Write the weights onto the parcels.

a
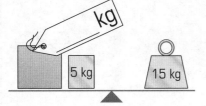

b
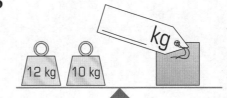

c
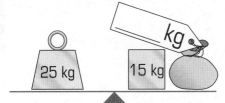

d
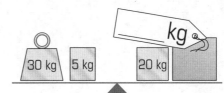

e
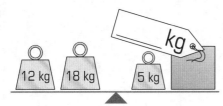

f
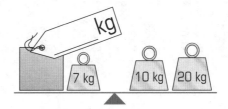

2 Write weights onto this drawing to make these scales balance.

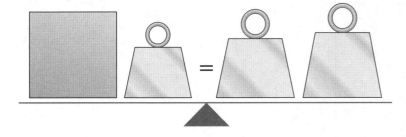

3 Write weights onto these parcels to make the scales **unbalanced**.

a
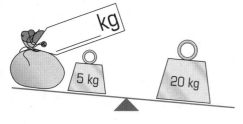

b

Framework MATHS   Scheme of work   Year 7

A4 Linear Equations (6 hours)	Teaching objectives	Framework Maths resources	Other resources
Reasoning and generalising about numbers or shapes (80–1)	Develop from explaining a generalised relationship in words to expressing it in a formula using letters as symbols.	7A Student Book: A4.1 7A Teacher's Book: A4.1OHP, R7	
Understanding multiplication and division (52–5)	Understand the effect of and relationships between the four operations.	7A Student Book: A4.2, A4.4 7A Teacher's Book: A4.2WS, A4.4WS, R6, R21	
Place value, ordering and rounding (8–9)	Use the vocabulary of comparing and ordering numbers, including symbols such as $<$, $>$, $\leqslant$, $\geqslant$, $=$.	7A Student Book: A4.3 7A Teacher's Book: A4.3OHP	
Reasoning and generalising about numbers or shapes (80–1)	Make a general statement about familiar numbers.	7A Student Book: A4.3 7A Teacher's Book: A4.3OHP	
Checking results of calculations (72–3)	Check with the inverse operation when using a calculator.	7A Student Book: A4.4 7A Teacher's Book: A4.4WS	

Access

Overview

This unit aims to develop students' understanding of symmetry and the transformations reflection, translation and rotation. The emphasis is on practical work, using mirrors and tracing paper to check results.

Spreads S4.1, S4.2 and S4.4 form the focus of the unit.

Framework references

The unit covers objectives on Framework (Y456) Pages 107, 111

Introduction

Discuss examples of symmetry in everyday objects, such as plates, glasses, desks, chairs. Discuss why a cup or saucepan may not be symmetrical.

Check in activity

Show the students 'half' of symmetrical pictures and ask them to predict or sketch what the other half looks like. For example, use pictures of faces, symmetrical buildings, reflections in water (either simple drawings, or taken from magazines etc.) Discuss how they could predict the other half – because the picture is symmetrical.

Useful resources

Worksheets
S4.1WS – symmetry
S4.2WS – reflection symmetry
S4.4WS – translating shapes
S4.5WS – rotation

OHPS
S4.3OHP – reflections on a grid
S4.6OHP – letters of the alphabet

General resources
R8 – coordinate grid
R15 – quadrilaterals
R17 – 100 square
R20 – analogue clock
R24 – squared grid
Mirrors
Paper
Scissors
Rulers
Cut-out triangle
Pencils
Tracing paper

Springboard 7 pages
274, 275, 451, 452, 461

Differentiation – spanning the bridge

Spread	Bridge to the Support tier
S4.1	Access and Support students can work alongside one another in this lesson. Support tier students should progress to identifying lines of reflective symmetry in more complex shapes.
S4.2	Access and Support students can work alongside one another in this lesson. Support tier students should focus on properties of shapes created by reflection (as in the starter activity).
S4.3	Extend Support tier students to consider coordinates in all four quadrants and using the x and y axes as mirror lines. Take time, in particular, to introduce coordinates on an axis $(0, n)$, $(n, 0)$.
S4.4	Reinforce coordinates with Support tier students and extend them to consider translation within the context of coordinates.
S4.5	Consider turns of 45° with Support tier students. Emphasise that this is half of 90°.
S4.6	Progress Support tier students to cover compass directions, and consider transformations on coordinate grids in all four quadrants.

S4.1 Symmetry

Access

This spread provides access to the Year 7 objective:
▸ Recognise and visualise symmetries of shapes (202)

Lesson Plan

Mental starter

Show a quadrilateral (**R15**). Encourage students to name the shape and describe its properties.

Repeat for other quadrilaterals, using different orientations.

Introductory activity

Discuss what students understand by the word symmetry. Fold a piece of paper in half, cut a shape along the folded edge, and unfold the paper.

Discuss special features of the resulting shape, informally highlighting that corresponding points are equidistant from line of symmetry.

Use the shape to define symmetry in a shape as being able to fold onto itself exactly. Introduce the name of the fold line: **line of symmetry**.

Refer to the mental starter. Choose students to draw lines of symmetry on the shapes. Highlight that some shapes have more than one. Emphasise that a parallelogram has no lines of symmetry. Demonstrate how to use a mirror to see if the reflection completes the whole shape, as a checking procedure.

Show one half of parallelogram, and choose a student to complete the shape, using a mirror to create an isosceles trapezium.

Plenary

Choose students to draw a shape with: no lines of symmetry; 1 line of symmetry; 2 lines, etc.

Homework

▸ Group capital letters of the alphabet according to how many lines of symmetry they have.
▸ Springboard 7: Page 451.

Exercise Commentary

Coverage

The questions assess objectives on Framework (Y456) Page 107.

Useful resources

R15 – quadrilaterals

Mirrors
Paper
Scissors

S4.1WS – provides further practice of the key ideas.

Differentiation

▸ Question 1 involves completing shapes on a grid.
▸ Questions 2 and 3 focus on identifying lines of symmetry.
▸ Question 4 focuses on symmetries of regular shapes.

Support tier: involves more complex shapes.

Misconceptions

Students find horizontal and vertical lines of symmetry easier to spot than diagonals. Encourage students to turn the page to see they can spot more lines in a different orientation. Weaker students can cut out each shape and fold it to reveal lines of symmetry.

Encourage students to use mirrors to check their work.

Links

Properties of shapes: Framework (Y456) Page 103.

Exercise Answers

1 **a** Rectangle **b** Triangle **c** Trapezium **d** Kite
4 Number of lines of symmetry: 3, 4, 5, 6.

Draw all the lines of symmetry onto these shapes.
Remember to use a ruler.

The lines of symmetry are
dashed lines. ⟶

1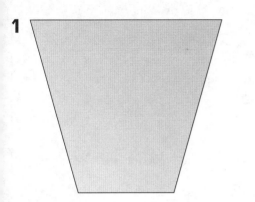

2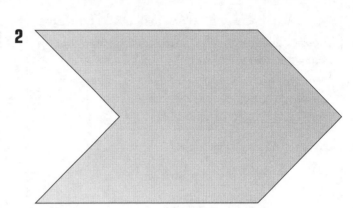

3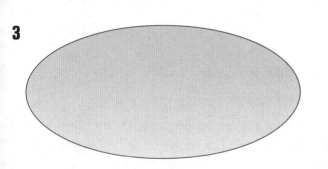

4

5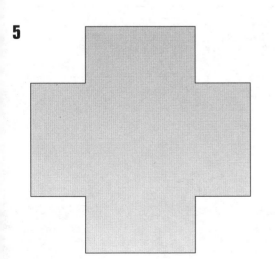

6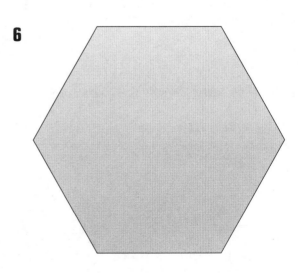

S4.2 Reflection symmetry

Access

This spread provides access to the Year 7 objective:
▸ Recognise and visualise reflections (202)

Lesson Plan

Mental starter

Show a coordinate grid (**R8**) from 0 to 8 on both axes.

Choose students to plot a series of coordinates, joining them with straight lines: (1, 1), (5, 1), (1, 4), (5, 4).

Encourage students to name the shape, and draw its lines of symmetry.

Repeat for isosceles triangle: (1, 1) (2, 5), (3, 1).

Introductory activity

Draw a vertical dashed line on a squared grid (**R24**).

Introduce the keyword **mirror line**.

Mark a point on one side of the grid and discuss where the reflection of that point in the mirror line will be.

Repeat with more points and develop to drawing the reflection of a line in the mirror line. Introduce the keywords **object** and **image**.

Draw a shape on the grid. Discuss how to reflect it in a vertical mirror line. Emphasise that you consider each vertex of the shape separately. Highlight that corresponding points on the object and image are equidistant from the mirror line.

Repeat for reflection in horizontal mirror line.

Plenary

Discuss question 3. Repeat for another simple shape on a squared grid, reflecting first in a vertical line, then a horizontal one. Choose students to draw the reflections.

Homework

▸ Complete a simple symmetrical picture, given half on a squared grid.
▸ Springboard 7: Page 452.

Exercise Commentary

Coverage

The questions assess objectives on Framework (Y456) Page 107.

Useful resources

R8 – coordinate grid

R24 – squared grid

Mirrors

Rulers

S4.2WS – provides further practice of the key ideas.

Differentiation

▸ Question 1 involves recognising a reflection.
▸ Question 2 focuses on reflecting shapes in vertical mirror lines.
▸ Question 3 extends to include a horizontal mirror line.

Support tier: extends to series of reflections.

Misconceptions

Encourage students to use mirrors to check their work.

Students may find the shapes difficult to copy. **S4.2WS** provides alternative 'write on' reflections.

Links

Coordinates: Framework (Y456) Page 107.

Exercise Answers

1 C

1 Draw the reflection of each shape in the mirror line.

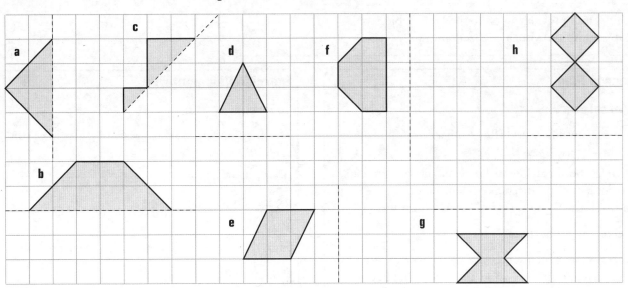

2 Reflect this drawing in the mirror line to complete the 'happy' face.

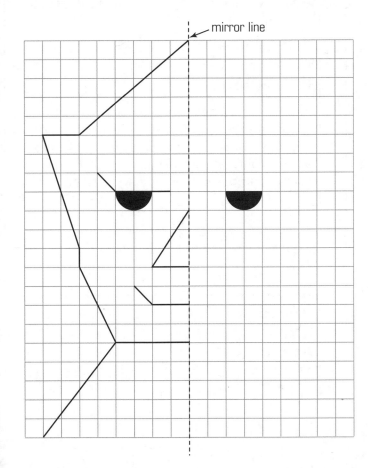

mirror line

S4.3 Symmetry on a grid

Access

This spread provides access to the Year 7 objective:
▸ Recognise and visualise reflections (202)

Lesson Plan

Mental starter

Show a coordinate grid (**R8**), with a mirror line drawn at $x = 4$ or use **S4.3OHP**.

Write a coordinate on the board and choose students to plot it and its reflection. Include points **on** the mirror line. Progress to a horizontal mirror line.

Introductory activity

Refer to the mental starter. Recap the correct order for plotting coordinates – across first, then up. Highlight that a point is the same distance from the mirror line as its reflection.

Show the rectangle on a coordinate grid on **S4.3OHP**. Ask students to give the coordinates of its corners.

Discuss how to reflect the rectangle in the mirror line.

Emphasise that it is easiest to consider one point at a time. Choose students to reflect each point, and write the coordinates of the new shape.

Show the diagram from the Students' book example on **S4.3OHP**. Encourage students to predict what the complete drawing will show after reflection in the mirror line. Complete the reflection.
Emphasise that the horizontal coordinate does not change when reflecting in a horizontal mirror line.

Plenary

Discuss question 4.

Show a squared grid with a vertical mirror line. Challenge students to draw a shape which, when reflected, will give the letter T.

Homework

▸ Reflect given shapes on a coordinate grid in a vertical mirror line.
▸ Springboard 7: Page 275.

Exercise Commentary

Coverage

The questions assess objectives on Framework (Y456) Page 107.

Useful resources

R8 – grid in all four quadrants

Mirrors

S4.3OHP – diagrams from the Students' book.

Differentiation

▸ Question 1 involves reading coordinates.
▸ Questions 2 and 3 focus on reflecting shapes in vertical mirror lines.
▸ Question 4 involves plotting points, then reflecting them in a vertical mirror line.

Support tier: focuses on reflecting in all four quadrants.

Misconceptions

Students may continue to plot (y, x). Encourage them to share strategies (into lift before up in lift). Encourage students to use mirrors to check their work. Students have difficulties copying coordinate grids. Provide weaker students with copies for each question.

Links

Coordinates: Framework (Y456) Page 109.

Exercise Answers

1 D (7, 7), E (4, 7), F (2, 4), G (4, 1), H (7, 1)
2 d A′ = (8, 7), B′ = (11, 7), C′ = (9, 1)
3 d S′ = (9, 7), T′ = (11, 7), U′ = (11, 1), R′ = (9, 1)
4 f Face

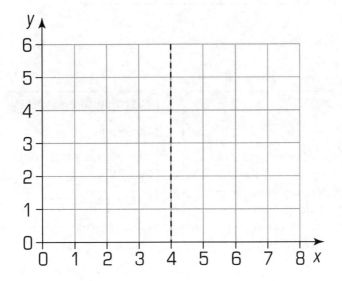

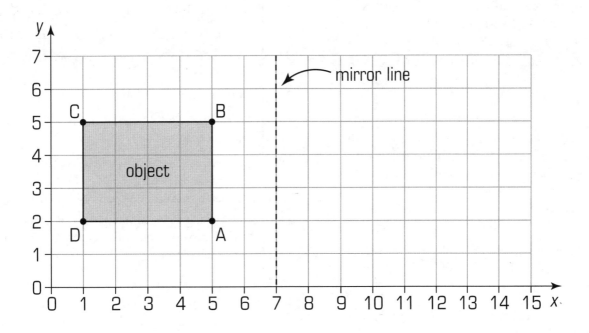

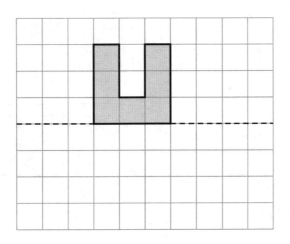

S4.4 Translating shapes

Lesson Plan

Mental starter

Ask one student to stand. Define directions relating to the person who is currently standing. Give a position: forward 3. The student 3 forward of the one standing should now stand up (the other sits). Continue with other positions (left, right, forward, backward) progressing to combinations of instructions.

Introductory activity

Refer to a chess board. Emphasise that chess pieces **move** by sliding forward or back/left or right. Introduce the key word **translation**, as a sliding movement.

Place a triangular cut-out on a squared grid (**R24**). Demonstrate it sliding forward 3 and right 2. Emphasise that the shape does not change.

Draw a triangle on the grid.

Choose students to draw the triangle after various translations (starting with single directions and progressing to combinations of horizontal and vertical movements). Highlight the need to translate each point separately.

Choose students to describe the translations in the Students' book example. Emphasise that as for coordinates we go across first, then up or down.

Plenary

Show a squared grid with several isosceles triangles and a couple of scalene triangles. Encourage students to identify the translations that take one triangle to another. Can an isosceles triangle translate to a scalene triangle?

Homework

▸ Give students a grid with 10 identical shapes, labelled A–J, at various positions. Ask students to describe the translation from A to each of the others.
▸ Springboard 7: Page 274.

Exercise Commentary

Coverage

The questions assess objectives on Framework (Y456) Page 107.

Useful resources

R24 – squared grid

Cut-out triangle

S4.4WS – provides support for weaker students.

Differentiation

▸ Question 1 involves describing simple translations.
▸ Question 2 focuses on carrying out translations.
▸ Question 3 involves translating shapes and drawing the image.

Support tier: focuses on translating shapes on a coordinate grid.

Misconceptions

Students may translate by the wrong amount, focusing on empty squares between the two shapes. Encourage students to translate one point of the shape at a time.

Students may have difficulty copying shapes on a grid. **S4.4WS** provides translation questions with no copying involved.

Links

Coordinates: Framework (Y456) Page 107.

Exercise Answers

1 a 3 to the right, 1 up **b** 2 to the left, 3 down
2 a 3 **b** 4 **c** 5 **d** 1 **e** 6 **f** 2

Worksheet Answers

2 a 6 right and 3 up **b** 4 right and 9 down
 c 6 left and 6 up **d** 8 left

1 Use these instructions to translate each shape and draw its new position.
The first one is done for you

Shape **a** 8 right and
3 up

Shape **b** 10 right and
2 down

Shape **c** 7 left and
2 down

Shape **d** 5 left and
3 up

Shape **e** 2 left and
4 up

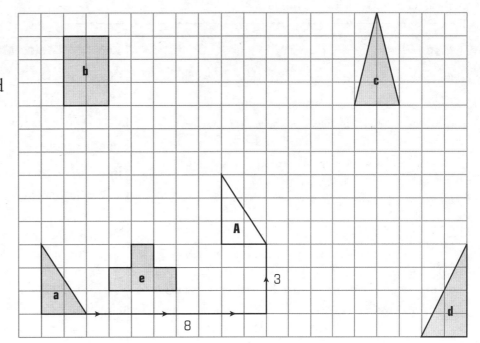

2 Describe the translation of each shape.

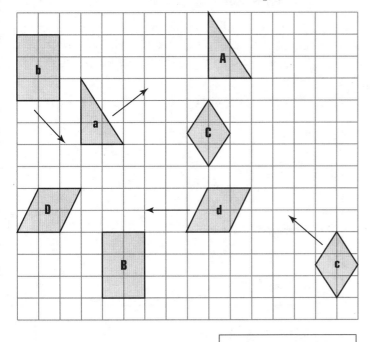

Count across first
then up or down

a to **A** 6 right and
_____ up

b to **B** ____ right and
_____ down

c to **C** _____
_____

d to **D** _____
_____

173

S4.5 Rotation

Access

This spread provides access to the Year 7 objective:
▸ Recognise and visualise rotations (208)

Lesson Plan

Mental starter

Show a clock face with one hand pointing to 12.

Ask students where the hand will be after a quarter turn. Highlight that it could be 3 **or** 9.

Recap clockwise – moving in the direction a clock hand would move – and anticlockwise.

Repeat for other turns.

Introductory activity

Refer to the mental starter. Encourage students to link **turn** with degrees:
▸ How many degrees to move the hand from 12 to 3?
▸ What direction?

Recap previous work on angle from S3: quarter turn = 90°, half turn = 180°, full turn = 360°

Emphasise that the clock hand turns about a fixed point (the clock centre) in two directions.

Highlight that a shape can also be turned about a fixed point. Introduce the key word **rotation**, meaning turn.

Show a right-angled triangle on a squared grid (**R24**). Demonstrate a rotation, clockwise 90° about one of its points:
▸ Trace the original shape.
▸ Use a pencil on the point of rotation to hold the shape in place.
▸ Copy the shape's new position on the grid.

Plenary

Using the clock face, ask for start numbers and end numbers (with direction) to create an angle of 90°. For example from 1 to 4 clockwise is 90°.

Homework

▸ List 10 times where the angle between the two hands on a clock is 90° (for example, 3.30).
▸ Springboard 7: Page 461.

Exercise Commentary

Coverage

The questions assess objectives on Framework (Y456) Page 107 and 111.

Useful resources

R20 – clock face
R24 – squared grid
Pencils
Tracing paper
S4.5WS – provides further practice of the key ideas.

Differentiation

▸ Question 1 involves describing simple turns.
▸ Questions 2 and 3 focus on rotating through 90° and 180°.
▸ Question 4 involves repeated rotation through 90°.

Support tier: extends to rotating through 45°.

Misconceptions

Rotations are difficult for students to visualise. Tracing paper is essential to support this, but must be held firmly in place on the point of rotation with a pencil point.

Students will tend to rotate clockwise. Emphasise that for 90° rotations the resulting shape may be in the wrong place (as in the starter).

Links

Angles: Framework (Y456) Page 111.

Exercise Answers

1 a anticlockwise 90°   b clockwise 180°
  c anticlockwise 360°   d anticlockwise 180°
  e clockwise 90°

Worksheet Answers

1 a 90°   b 360°   c 90°   d 180°
2 anticlockwise; clockwise

1 How many degrees are shown in these angles?

a

b

c

d

_____ °   _____ °   _____ °   _____ °

2 One wheel is turning clockwise and the other is turning anticlockwise.
Label each wheel correctly.

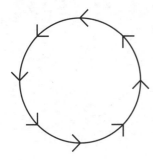   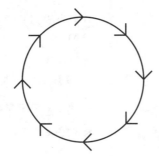

_____   _____

3 Rotate this shape through 180°.
Draw the new shape.

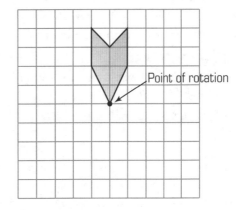

Point of rotation

4 a Rotate this shape **A** through 90° clockwise.
Label the new shape **B**.

b Now, rotate the original shape **A** through
90° anticlockwise.
Label the new shape **C**.

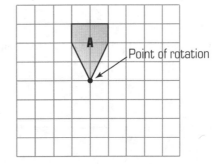

A

Point of rotation

S4.6 Movement on a grid

Access

This spread provides access to the Year 7 objective:
▸ Recognise and visualise transformations (202–212)

Lesson Plan

Mental starter

Show the letters of the alphabet on **S4.6OHP**.

Choose students to draw in lines of symmetry.

Rotate **S4.6OHP** through 180°, and discuss which letters remain the same. Define these letters as having rotational symmetry.

Introductory activity

Review the transformations students have used so far: Reflection as a 'flip'; translation as a slide; rotation as a turn.

Emphasise that although the translation moves the shape or flips it, the shape remains exactly the same. Introduce the key word **congruent** – if the shapes were cut out they would fit exactly on top of one another.

Show a 100 square (**R17**), with a vertical mirror line drawn through the middle. Ask students questions about transformations of a shaded square, say 23. What number will the shaded square land on after:

▸ Translation 3 up/2 across/a combination of both

▸ Reflection in the mirror line

▸ Rotation clockwise about the bottom right corner of the square, through 90°/180°?

Repeat with other squares and transformations.

Plenary

Repeat the introductory activity with the 100 square, extending to giving students a start square and an end square and asking them to describe the single transformation.

Homework

▸ Design a pattern on a squared grid, using rotations or translations of a simple shape.

Exercise Commentary

Coverage

The questions assess objectives on the Primary Framework (Y456) Page 107.

Useful resources

R17 – 100 square

Tracing paper

Mirrors

Pencils

S4.6OHP – letters of the alphabet

Differentiation

▸ Questions 1 and 2 focus on reflections.

▸ Question 3 focuses on translations.

▸ Question 4 involves rotations.

Support tier: extends to transformations on a coordinate grid.

Misconceptions

The problems identified throughout this topic will apply to this lesson too. A supply of tracing paper and mirrors should be readily available to enable students to check their work.

Links

Properties of shapes: Framework (Y456) Page 103.

Exercise Answers

3 a 3   **b** 3 left and 1 down
4 A anticlockwise
   B clockwise
   C anticlockwise
   D clockwise
   E clockwise
   F anticlockwise
   G anticlockwise

A B C D E

F G H I J

K L M N O

P Q R S T

U V W X Y

Z

Framework MATHS Scheme of work Year 7

S4 Transformations (6 hours)	Teaching objectives	Framework Maths resources		Other resources
Shape and space (106–7)	Recognise reflection symmetry in regular polygons.Complete symmetrical patterns with two lines of symmetry at right angles.	7A Student Book: S4.1 7A Teacher's Book: S4.1WS, R15		
Shape and space (102–3)	**Recognise properties of rectangles.**	7A Student Book: S4.1 7A Teacher's Book: S4.1WS, R15		
Shape and space (106–7)	Recognise where a shape will be after reflection in a mirror line parallel to one side.	7A Student Book: S4.2, S4.3, S4.6 7A Teacher's Book: S4.2WS, S4.3OHP, S4.6OHP, R8, R17, R24		
Shape and space (108–9)	Read and plot coordinates in the first quadrant.	7A Student Book: S4.3 7A Teacher's Book: S4.3OHP, R8		
Shape and space (106–7)	Recognise where a shape will be after a translation.	7A Student Book: S4.4, S4.6 7A Teacher's Book: S4.4WS, S4.6OHP, R17, R24		
Shape and space (110–11)	Make and measure clockwise and anticlockwise turns. Begin to know that angles are measured in degrees.	7A Student Book: S4.5 7A Teacher's Book: S4.5WS, R20, R24		
Reasoning and generalising about numbers or shapes (78–9)	Solve mathematical problems or puzzles and recognise patterns and relationships.	7A Student Book: S4.6		

Access

Overview

This unit starts with rounding, developing to using approximations to check calculations. Informal written methods are developed for multiplication and division calculations. Equivalent fractions are revisited, and the link between percentages and fractions is reinforced.

Spreads N5.1, N5.2, N5.4, N5.5 and N5.6 form the focus of the unit.

Framework references

The unit covers objectives on Framework (Y456) Pages 11, 13, 19, 23, 25, 33, 61, 67, 69, 91

Introduction

Discuss metric units used in measurement (mm, cm, m, km). Choose items around the room and ask students to suggest which unit they should be measured in. Choose different students to measure them, and compare their measurements, emphasising the difficulty of measuring accurately.

Check in activity

Show students a multiplication table (**R21**). Ask spot questions. Progress to division.

Show a square. Demonstrate splitting up into quarters (with 3 vertical lines). Shade $\frac{1}{4}$ and discuss fraction notation and equal parts. Show a square. Without lines, shade approximately a third.

Repeat for a sixth. Encourage students to imagine how many parts the square has been divided into.

Useful resources

Worksheets

N5.1WS – estimating
N5.3WS – using factors
N5.4WS – written calculations
N5.5WS – written division
N5.6WS – equivalent fractions
N5.7WS – finding fractions of amounts

OHPS

N5.2OHP – approximation calculations
N5.8OHP – equivalent fractions and percentages

General resources

R4 – place value table
R6 – number lines
R17 – 100 square
R21 – multiplication table
Rules

Springboard 7 pages

188, 198, 232, 315, 339, 344, 355, 377, 428

Differentiation – spanning the bridge

Spread	Bridge to the Support tier
N5.1	Link estimation to rounding with Support tier students. Progress, using a number line, to rounding a number (say 7.8) to nearest integer, ten, and hundred, focusing on the decider digit in each case.
N5.2	The Support tier moves directly to factors, multiples and primes (to be covered in N5.3 for Access tier), recapping work in A3.1. Discuss how to differentiate between the three number types.
N5.3	Extend Support tier students to consider using factors to help with division ($96 \div 16 = 96 \div 2 \div 8$). Progress to multiplication by partitioning, and division by repeated subtraction (this is covered in the next two Access lessons, and extended in the next two Support lessons).
N5.4	Progress Support tier students to consider HTU × TU, and to consider decimal multiplication. The starter activity can be adapted to include dividing by 10 and 100, and then discuss how to adapt the grid method to decimals.
N5.5	Extend to division of HTU by TU and consider calculations with a remainder. Essentially the method is the same for both tiers.
N5.6	Progress Support tier students to comparing fractions by finding equivalent fractions with a common denominator. Discuss in particular how to find a common denominator (a multiple of both denominators).
N5.7	Give Support tier students a 10 × 10 square and ask them to shade a half, a quarter, a fifth, etc. Once the Access students are working on exercises, use the square as a point of reference to recap equivalences between fractions, decimals and percentages. Discuss how to convert fractions to decimals using a calculator, and appropriate rounding.
N5.8	Support tier students should be given some practice at converting more complex percentages such as 35% to fractions in their simplest form, and looking at strategies such as 35% = 10% + 10% + 10% + 5%.

N5.1 Estimating

Access

This spread provides access to the Year 7 objective:
▸ Make and justify estimates and approximations of calculations (102)

Lesson Plan

Mental starter

Ask students how long it takes them to get to school. Encourage students to order themselves in a line to represent these times from shortest to longest.

Introductory activity

Refer to the mental starter, and ask the students exactly how long it takes to get to school.

Introduce keyword **estimating**. Explain that an estimate is not an exact measurement – it is **approximate**. Highlight the keyword **about**.

Emphasise that estimation is not just a random guess, it is based upon known knowledge.

Ask students for units used to measure length, and discuss where you would use them:
▸ Centimetres for short lengths – an exercise book, the length of a pencil, etc.
▸ Metres for longer lengths – half the height of a door.
▸ Kilometres for longer lengths – 1 km takes about 20 minutes to walk.

Discuss the approximate distance from school to students' homes using approximate time taken to walk. Discuss what units they would use to measure the length of: a leaf, a house, the playground, the distance from school to Birmingham, etc.

Ask a student to stand against the classroom door. Discuss how to estimate the student's height from the door.

Discuss how to write the height in metres and in centimetres.

Plenary

Ask students to close their eyes.

Tell them when to start. They are to put their hands up when they think 1 minute has passed.

Highlight how difficult it can be to estimate units of time.

Homework

▸ Estimate the length of several objects at home, and then measure them accurately.
▸ Springboard 7: Page 377.

Exercise Commentary

Coverage

The questions assess objectives on Framework (Y456) Pages 11, 13 and 91.

Useful resources

Rulers

N5.1WS – provides further practice of the key ideas.

Differentiation

▸ Questions 1 and 2 focus on identifying units.
▸ Question 3 involves estimating a length.
▸ Question 4 requires more accurate estimations.

Support tier: focuses on rounding numbers.

Misconceptions

Students may have difficulty in question 3, where the required length is approximately one sixth of the reference length. Encourage them to split the reference length into halves to ease breaking it into parts.

In question 4, students may need to be prompted to convert metres to centimetres, or to consider tenths of a metre. Encourage students to have a feel for the approximate size they are dealing with in each question, using reference points – a ruler for cm, the desk length for metres, etc.

Links

Measures: Framework (Y456) Pages 93 and 95.

Exercise Answers

1 b 20 metres
2 b 100 km
3 a 13 m   **b** It is about $\frac{1}{5}$.
4 a 4 m   **b** 3 m   **c** 2 m   **d** 1 m   **e** 10 cm

Worksheet Answers

2 a 80 km
  b 100 km
  c 300 km
  d 700 km

1 Estimate each of these measures.
Write the units that you are using to estimate each measure.

Item	Estimate	Units
Length of your classroom		(m) metres
Height of the classroom door		
Height of your friend		
Weight of your Framework book		
How many students in your school		students
Cost of a portion of fish and chips		
Weight of a cricket ball		
Flight time from London to New York		
The length of a marathon race	42	
The cost to run your school for one year		

2 The distance from London to Edinburgh is about 600 km.
Estimate the distance in km between these towns.

a London to Cambridge

km

b Brighton to London

km

c Cardiff to Cambridge

km

d Edinburgh to Weymouth

km

N5.2 Approximations

Access

This spread provides access to the Year 7 objective:
▸ Make and justify estimates and approximations of calculations (102)

Lesson Plan

Mental starter

Give each student a number, say 10, 20, 30, 40, etc.
Call out a number, say 38.
Students stand up if their number is the 'nearest 10'.

Introductory activity

The tallest man ever to live, Robert Wadlow was 2.8 metres tall (see N5.1).

Discuss whether this is nearer 2 metres or 3 metres. A number line (**R6**) may be useful.
Emphasise that you can round a decimal number to a whole number. Link to N3.1 on estimating and keyword **about**.

Using a number line (**R6**) from 3 to 4 with ten equal intervals, invite a student to place 3.7 on the line.
Discuss which whole number it is closest to.
Highlight that 3.7 rounds to 4.

Emphasise that the tenths digit helps you **decide** which whole number it is nearest to.
Discuss the idea of halfway (.5) values being rounded up.
Refer to a number line as necessary, and ask students some spot questions.

Ask students how many times they have dialled the wrong telephone number, or answered the phone to a wrong number? Discuss how easy it is to type in numbers wrongly – linking with calculator work.
Explain that approximation can be used to check work.

Work through the examples in the Students' book (shown on **N5.2OHP**) highlighting that approximations can help you to check calculations.

Plenary

Draw a rectangle 2.9 m × 1.2 m. Explain that Tasneem has used a calculator to work out the perimeter. She says it is 18.3 m. Is she right? Introduce approximation as a checking procedure.

Homework

▸ Design a poster about how to round, and how this helps with approximation.
▸ Springboard 7: Pages 344 and 355.

Exercise Commentary

Coverage

The questions assess objectives on Framework (Y456) Pages 11 and 13.

Useful resources

R6 – number lines
N5.2OHP – Students' book examples

Differentiation

▸ Question 1 focuses on rounding 1 dp to the nearest integer.
▸ Questions 2–4 focus on rounding in context.
▸ Question 5 develops to approximating area.

Support tier: focuses on factors, multiples and primes.

Misconceptions

Some students may look at the wrong digit to help them decide whether to round up or down, for example rounding 8.3 to 9 because 8 > 5. Encourage students to use number line jottings. Identifying the right numbers to be placed on the number line is critical here and supportive questioning can be used – which two whole numbers is this between?

Links

Decimals: Framework (Y456) Page 31.

Exercise Answers

1 a 6 kg   b 10 kg   c 81   d 13 m   e 51 cm
   f 1 m   g 1 km   h £13   i 32 mm   j 6 cm
   k 0 litres   l 20 tonnes
2 £20
3 42 cm
4 12.3 tonnes
5 a 28 cm   b 48 cm^2

3 large cars at 1.8 tonnes
2 small cars at 0.7 tonnes

1.8 m

1.4 m

Access

This spread provides access to the Year 7 objective:
▸ Recognise and use factors (52)

Lesson Plan

Mental starter

Sketch a rectangle on the board, with width and length labelled. Ask students to calculate area.
Repeat using different dimensions.
Show a rectangle with area of 24 cm². Ask students for suggestions for the dimensions.

Introductory activity

Choose students to circle the number 24 on an OHP of a multiplication table (**R21**).
Encourage them to give the multiplication.
Repeat until all 24's in the square are circled, and all multiplications identified.
Emphasise that each of the numbers that multiply together to make 24 are **factors**.
Encourage use of the multiplication table to find factors of 18, of 60, etc.
Highlight that 1 and 18 are also factors of 18.
Emphasise that factors can be used to help break down a complicated multiplication.
Discuss how to break down the calculation 14×6 into a more manageable calculation:
$14 \times 2 \times 3$ or $7 \times 2 \times 2 \times 6$
Emphasise setting jottings out line by line, to encourage systematic working.
Encourage students to do easier calculations last.

Plenary

Refer to the mental starter, and discuss the link between area and dimensions of a rectangle.
Sketch a rectangle with 36 cm² area. Ask students for all possible dimensions (integer values only).

Homework

▸ Find all the rectangles with an area of 48 cm² and calculate the perimeter of each.
▸ Springboard 7: Page 315.

Worksheet Answers

1 a $1 \times 10, 2 \times 5$ b $1 \times 15, 3 \times 5$
2 68, 120, 72, 189, 90, 168, 250

Exercise Commentary

Coverage

The questions assess objectives on Framework (Y456) Pages 19 and 61.

Useful resources

R21 – multiplication table
N5.3WS – provides support for weaker students.

Differentiation

▸ Questions 1 and 2 focus on identifying factor pairs.
▸ Question 3 focuses on breaking a number into its factors.
▸ Question 4 involves calculating using factors.

Support tier: focuses on using factors in mental calculations.

Misconceptions

Students find it difficult to keep track of where they are in a long calculation. Encourage them to use jottings to help them set their work out in a logical way.

Some students will still find multiplication difficult and may need a multiplication table (**R21**). Also, encourage them to keep breaking the numbers down into factors until they are more manageable.

Links

Area: Framework (Y456) Page 97.

Exercise Answers

1 a 10: 2×5; 1×10 b 15: 3×5; 1×15
  c 20: 10×2; 5×4; 1×20 d 25: 5×5; 1×25
  e 14: 7×2; 1×14 f 16: 8×2; 4×4; 1×16
  g 24: 12×2; 8×3; 6×4; 1×24
  h 30: 15×2; 10×3; 6×5; 1×30
  i 40: 20×2; 10×4; 8×5; 1×40
2 a 8×1; 4×2 b 5×4; 10×2; 20×1
  c 10×3; 15×2; 6×5; 30×1
3 a $40 = 4 \times 5 \times 2$ b $70 = 7 \times 5 \times 2$
  c $80 = 8 \times 5 \times 2$ d $90 = 9 \times 5 \times 2$
  e $30 = 3 \times 5 \times 2$ f $50 = 5 \times 5 \times 2$
4 a 52   b 120   c 144   d 126   e 180   f 224
  g 216   h 378

1 Rearrange these squares to make as many different rectangles as you can.
Draw on the grids to help you.

a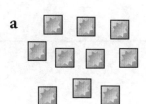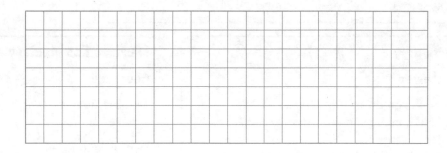

What are the **factor pairs** of 10? _____

b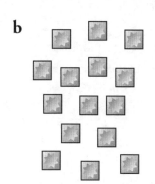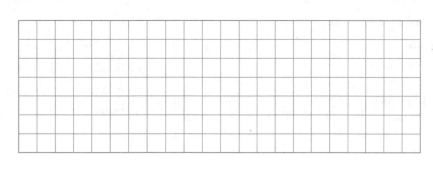

What are the **factor pairs** of 15? _____

2 Fill in this table to complete these calculations.

Multiplication	Factors	First multiplication	Second multiplication	Third multiplication
(17) × 4	4 = 2 × 2	(17) × 2 = (34)	34 × 2 = ☐	
15 × 8	8 = 2 × 2 × 2	15 × 2 = ☐	30 × 2 = ☐	60 × 2 = ☐
12 × 6	6 = 2 × 3	12 × 2 = ☐	24 × 3 = ☐	
21 × 9	9 = ☐ × ☐	21 × 3 = ☐	63 × 3 = ☐	
15 × 6	6 = ☐ × ☐	15 × 2 = ☐	30 × 3 = ☐	
14 × 12	12 = 2 × 2 × 3	14 × 2 = ☐	☐ × 2 = ☐	56 × 3 = ☐
25 × 10	10 = 2 × 5	25 × 2 = ☐	☐ × 5 = ☐	

N5.4 Written calculations

Access

This spread provides access to the Year 7 objective:
▸ Multiply three-digit by two-digit numbers (104)

Lesson Plan

Mental starter

Write two rules on the board: ×10 and ×100
Give students a number, point to a rule, and ask students for the answer.
Use a place value table (**R4**) to reinforce that multiplying by 10 (100) means moving each digit to the next highest column on the place value table.

Introductory activity

Give students a number, say 438. Discuss how many hundreds, tens and units.
Introduce the keyword **partition** and emphasise it means split into **parts**.
Introduce the calculation: 23 × 7. Discuss how 23 **lots of** 7 can be split into 20 **lots of** 7 and 3 **lots of** 7.
Discuss partitioning 23, placing it within a grid, and dealing with the parts separately.
Refer to the mental starter, and link to N5.3 to emphasise that ×20 is the same as × 10 × 2.

Work through the example in the Students' book, emphasising the steps:
▸ Approximate first to help check final answer
▸ Partition larger number and place into grid
▸ Multiply each part separately
▸ Add the totals of each part together.

Plenary

Write a calculation and three possible answers,
say 313 × 5 and **a** 155 **b** 1575 **c** 1265
Discuss how to check which is correct without doing the calculation. Encourage discussion about estimation and approximation. In particular discuss which of **b** and **c** it will be (313 is **more than** 300).

Homework

▸ Five calculations including TU × U extending to HTU × U, to approximate first, then calculate.
▸ Springboard 7: Page 232.

Exercise Commentary

Coverage

The questions assess objectives on Framework (Y456) Pages 67 and 69.

Useful resources

R4 – place value table
N5.4WS – provides support for weaker students.

Differentiation

▸ Question 1 focuses on partitioning numbers.
▸ Questions 2–4 focus on using the grid method.
▸ Question 5 involves a real-life application.
Support tier develops to include decimals.

Misconceptions

Some students may place the numbers incorrectly in the grid. Encourage them to think about which number is more complex and needs to be broken down. Encourage a system where the partitioned numbers are placed along the length of the grid, and the easier number placed along the height.

Supportive questioning can help students as they progress to HTU × U: How many digits does that number have? How many parts will it be split into?

Students may fail to add the totals together at the end. Encourage them to check their answers with a partner, and discuss where mistakes have occurred.

Links

Place value: Framework (Y456) Page 3.

Worksheet Answers

1 a 100 + 70 + 5 b 90 + 8 c 200 + 9 d 500 + 30
2 a 96 b 172 c 390 d 198 e 368 f 378
  g 372 h 408

Exercise Answers

1 a 100 + 50 + 2 b 20 + 9 c 50 + 7 d 90 + 8
  e 60 + 6 f 70 g 100 + 90 + 7 h 100 + 50
  i 100 + 40 + 9 j 200 + 30 + 8 k 200 + 3
  l 500 + 80 m 400 n 300 + 9

2 a

×	20	9
3	60	27

b Yes 3 a 360 b

×	50	8
6	300	48

4 a 180 b 392 c 420 d 396 e 216 f 412
  g 844 h 624   5 a 480 b 456

1 Split up these numbers into hundreds, tens and units.
For example: 163 = 100 + 60 + 3

a 175 = _____ + _____ + _____

b 98 = _____ + _____

c 209 = _____ + _____

d 530 = _____ + _____

2 Use these grids to complete these multiplications.

a 32 × 3 = _____

×	30	2
3		

b 43 × 4 = _____

×	40	3
4		

c 65 × 6 = _____

×	60	5
6		

d 28 × 7 = _____

×	20	8
7		

e 92 × 4 = _____

×		

f 54 × 7 = _____

×		

g 124 × 3 = _____

×	100	20	4
3			

h 136 × 3 = _____

×			

N5.5 Written division

Access

This spread provides access to the Year 7 objective:
▸ Divide three-digit by two-digit numbers (106)

Lesson Plan

Mental starter

Ask students division questions (TU by U) in different contexts:
▸ What is 24 ÷ 8?
▸ How many 7s in 56?
Students may need to use a multiplication table (**R21**).

Introductory activity

Refer to the mental starter and emphasise that division is the opposite of multiplication.

Emphasise that multiplication is a form of repeated addition: 3 + 3 + 3 + 3 = 4 × 3 (4 **lots of** 3 added together).
Discuss how this links to division: division is a form of repeated subtraction.
Discuss how to work out 27 ÷ 3.
Emphasise that you can take 3 away 9 times – use the idea of dealing 27 cards to 3 people.

Discuss the example in the Students' book.
Discuss the operation to use, emphasising **splitting** 153 beads into groups of 3.
Emphasise that you could repeatedly subtract 3 from 153, but this will take too long.
Emphasise that you can subtract groups of 10 × 3 from 153.
Discuss repeated subtraction of 30 from 153, asking students at each subtraction – have we got enough for another group of ten 3s?

Emphasise the importance of working methodically and using jottings to record the work.

Plenary

Introduce a problem with a remainder:
Eggs are packed in boxes of 8. I have 121 eggs in total. How many boxes will I need?
Discuss what to do with the remainder. Emphasise that you round up in this case.

Homework

▸ Practise questions similar to question 2 (no remainders).
▸ Springboard 7: Page 339.

Exercise Commentary

Coverage

The questions assess objectives on Framework (Y456) Pages 67 and 69.

Useful resources

R21 – multiplication table
N5.5WS – provides support for weaker students.

Differentiation

▸ Question 1 focuses on multiplying by 10.
▸ Question 2 focuses on repeated subtraction.
▸ Questions 3–6 involve real-life applications.

Support tier: develops to HTU ÷ TU and includes remainders.

Misconceptions

Students find it difficult to keep track of where they are in a long calculation. Encourage them to use jottings to help them set their work out in a logical way.

In questions 3–6, students may order the values incorrectly, for example, 4 divided by 132. Encourage them to think about what needs **splitting/dividing**.

Links

Multiplication facts: Framework (Y456) Page 59.

Exercise Answers

1 a 60 b 30 c 80 d 50 e 70 f 90 g 20
  h 10
2 a 53 b 44 c 31 d 39 e 51 f 22 g 33
  h 26 i 62 j 31 k 32 l 41
3 33   4 47   5 33   6 52

Worksheet Answers

1 31   2 32   3 12   4 23

Fill in the spaces to help you complete the divisions.

1 $93 \div 3$

```
    9   3
-   3   0        ...... 10 × 3
_____
    6   3
-  [    ]
                 ...... 10 × 3
  [        ]

-  [      ]
                 ...... 10 × 3
  [      ]
      [   ]
- [   ]
                 ...... 1 × 3
_____
```

$93 \div 3 = $ [   ]

2 $192 \div 6$

```
    1   9   2
-       6   0      ..... 10 × 6
_____
    1   3   2
-   [       ]
                   ...... 10 × 6
  [         ]

- [         ]
                   ......   [   ×   ]
  [         ]

- [         ]
                   ......   [   ×   ]
```

$192 \div 6 = $ [   ]

3 $108 \div 9$

```
    1   0   8
-       9   0      .....  [    ] × 9
      [       ]

-   [       ]      ......  [    ] × 9
_____
```

$108 \div 9 = $ [   ]

4 $92 \div 4$

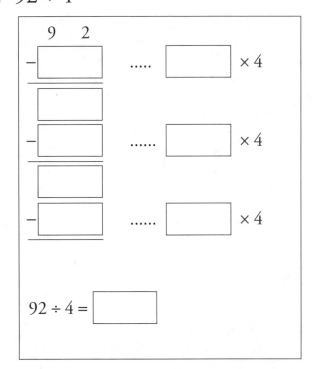

$92 \div 4 = $ [   ]

Access

This spread provides access to the Year 7 objective:
▶ Simplify fractions by cancelling and identify equivalent fractions (62)

Lesson Plan

Mental starter

Ask for a number that is:
▶ a multiple of 4
▶ a factor 12
▶ a multiple of 2 and a multiple of 3
▶ a prime number.

Introductory activity

Draw a circle on the board, and ask students to imagine it is a pizza. Explain that regardless how many slices it is cut into, you want exactly half of it.

Split the circle into 2 equal pieces. Discuss how many pieces you should take.

Highlight 1 piece out of 2 equal shares, and link to fractions.

Split the circle into 4 equal pieces, and repeat.

Split the circle into 6, then 8 pieces and repeat questioning.

Highlight $\frac{2}{4}$, $\frac{3}{6}$, $\frac{4}{8}$ are all the same as half, and introduce keyword **equivalent**.

Demonstrate multiplication of numerator and denominator by the **same number** to create each equivalent fraction.

Link with the pizza – multiplication shows how many new pieces each piece is being split into.

Demonstrate division of numerator and denominator of equivalent fractions to **simplify** each fraction.

Emphasise that the **same number** must be used to multiply both parts of the fraction.

Plenary

Show students a selection of fractions (all equivalent to a third, or a half). Invite them to sort them into two sets.

Homework

▶ Give 10 fractions that are each equivalent to one third.
▶ Springboard 7: Page 198.

Exercise Commentary

Coverage

The questions assess objectives on Framework (Y456) Page 23.

Useful resources

N5.6WS – provides support for weaker students.

Differentiation

▶ Question 1 focuses on identifying equivalent fractions from diagrams.
▶ Question 2 focuses on finding numerators or denominators.
▶ Question 3 gives no pictorial support.

Support tier: focuses on using equivalent fractions to compare fractions.

Misconceptions

In question 3, students may add rather than multiply to find equivalent fractions. Encourage them to draw rectangles to illustrate their answers until confident. In question 3f, students should be encouraged to continue dividing until they can go no further.

Links

Multiplication facts: Framework (Y456) Page 59.

Exercise Answers

1 a Yes b No c Yes d Yes e No f Yes
2 a $\frac{1}{3} = \frac{3}{9}$ b $\frac{1}{2} = \frac{6}{12}$ c $\frac{1}{3} = \frac{5}{15}$
3 a $\frac{3}{4} = \frac{6}{8}$ b $\frac{1}{3} = \frac{5}{15}$ c $\frac{6}{10} = \frac{3}{5}$ d $\frac{2}{7} = \frac{4}{14}$ e $\frac{4}{10} = \frac{2}{5}$
  f $\frac{10}{20} = \frac{1}{2}$

Worksheet Answers

1 a $\frac{2}{4}$ b $\frac{3}{6}$ c $\frac{4}{8}$ d $\frac{2}{4}$ 2 $\frac{2}{10}$ 3 $\frac{3}{12}$
4 $\frac{3}{18}$ 5 $\frac{4}{20}$

1 ▶ Shade $\frac{1}{2}$ of each shape.

▶ Write the fraction that is equivalent to $\frac{1}{2}$ in each drawing.

a
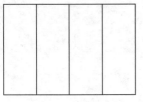

$\frac{1}{2}$ is the same as

b

$\frac{1}{2}$ is the same as ☐

c

$\frac{1}{2}$ is the same as ☐

d
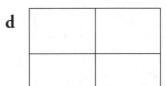

$\frac{1}{2}$ is the same as ☐

2 Shade $\frac{1}{5}$ of this shape.

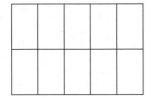

$\frac{1}{5}$ is the same as ☐

3 Shade $\frac{1}{4}$ of this shape.

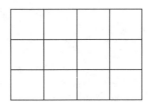

$\frac{1}{4}$ is the same as ☐

4 Shade $\frac{1}{6}$ of this shape.

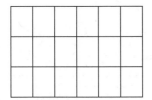

$\frac{1}{6}$ is the same as ☐

5 Shade $\frac{1}{5}$ of this shape.

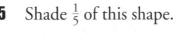
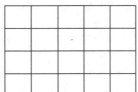

$\frac{1}{5}$ is the same as ☐

N5.7 Finding fractions of amounts

Access

This spread provides access to the Year 7 objective:
▸ Calculate fractions of quantities and measurements (66)

Lesson Plan

Mental starter

Write these four rules:

$\times 10$ $\quad \times 100$ $\quad \div 10$ $\quad \div 100$

Give students a number (integer), point to a rule, students give the answer (no more than 1 dp).
Use a place value table (**R4**) to support and reinforce movement of digits.

Introductory activity

Ask students for half of £50, of 40 m, and so on.
Discuss how to find half, and extend to a third, a quarter, and to the general case.
Highlight that to find a unit fraction (where the numerator is 1), you divide by the denominator.

Draw a circle on the board, and split it into quarters. Demonstrate that $\frac{3}{4}$ is 3 **lots of** $\frac{1}{4}$.
Discuss the example in the Students' book.
Ask how many sheep in each quarter.
Link to the circle diagram, and emphasise that you multiply the number of sheep in one quarter by 3.
Formalise working out:
▸ $\frac{1}{4}$ of 12 = 3
▸ $\frac{3}{4}$ of 12 is $3 \times 3 = 9$

Discuss how to find $\frac{2}{5}$ of £20.
Emphasise finding $\frac{1}{5}$, and then multiplying by 2.
Generalise: to find a fraction of an amount, you divide by the denominator, and then multiply by the numerator.

Plenary

Draw a bubble in the centre of the board and write £200 in the bubble.
Invite students to calculate a fraction of the amount and write it spidering off from the bubble.
Encourage students to build upon unit fractions, explaining their reasoning.

Homework

▸ Calculate 20 or more fractions of £400, writing them in a spider diagram as in the plenary.
▸ Springboard 7: Page 188.

Exercise Commentary

Coverage

The questions assess objectives on Framework (Y456) Page 25.

Useful resources

R4 – place value table
N5.7WS – provides support for weaker students.

Differentiation

▸ Question 1 focuses on finding unitary fractions of amounts.
▸ Question 2 focuses on using doubling to find fractions of larger amounts.
▸ Questions 3 and 4 involve non-unitary fractions.

Support tier: focuses on converting between fractions, decimals and percentages.

Misconceptions

A common error is for students to find just one part of the amount – finding $\frac{1}{4}$, not $\frac{3}{4}$. Encourage students to consider how many quarters make up $\frac{3}{4}$, and work logically. Encourage students to use $\frac{1}{2}$ as a benchmark – is it more or less than $\frac{1}{2}$?

Links

Multiplication facts: Framework (Y456) Page 59.

Exercise Answers

1 a 4   b 5   c 10   d 9   e 10   f 5   g 8   h 10
  i 9   j 10   k 6   l 3   m 5   n 6   o 8
2 a 20   b 18   c 16   d 14   e 18   f 12   g 16
  h 14   i 16
3 a 12   b 15   c 30   d 27   e 20   f 16   g 20
  h 12   i 30   j 16
4 10

Worksheet Answers

1 $\frac{1}{3}$ of, ÷3; $\frac{1}{8}$ of, ÷8; $\frac{1}{6}$ of, ÷6; $\frac{1}{2}$ of, ÷2; $\frac{1}{10}$ of, ÷10;
  $\frac{1}{5}$ of, ÷5
2 a 9   b 15   c 10   d 20   e 20

1 Which division goes with each calculation?
Draw arrows to connect them.

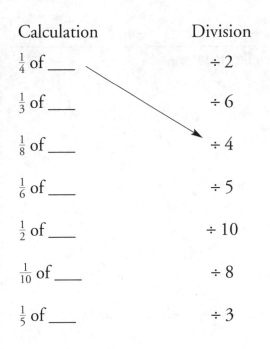

Calculation   Division

$\frac{1}{4}$ of ____   ÷ 2

$\frac{1}{3}$ of ____   ÷ 6

$\frac{1}{8}$ of ____   ÷ 4

$\frac{1}{6}$ of ____   ÷ 5

$\frac{1}{2}$ of ____   ÷ 10

$\frac{1}{10}$ of ____   ÷ 8

$\frac{1}{5}$ of ____   ÷ 3

> For example:
> $\frac{1}{4}$ of 12 means 12 ÷ 4 = 3

2 Use the machines to find these fractions of amounts.

a $\frac{3}{4}$ of 12 :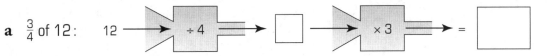

b $\frac{3}{4}$ of 20 :   20 → ÷ 4 → ☐ → × 3 → = ☐

c $\frac{2}{3}$ of 15 :

d $\frac{2}{3}$ of 30 :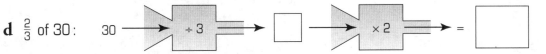

e $\frac{4}{5}$ of 25 :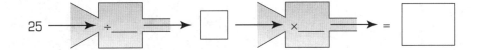

N5.8 Finding percentages

Access

This spread provides access to the Year 7 objective:
▸ Calculate simple percentages (72)

Lesson Plan

Mental starter

Ask students quick-fire questions based around their existing knowledge:
What is $\frac{1}{4}$ of 20; What is $\frac{3}{4}$ of 20; What is $\frac{1}{5}$ of 30?

Introductory activity

Refer to the mental starter and emphasise that to find a fraction of an amount you divide by the denominator and multiply by the numerator. Using a 100 square (**R17**), discuss the equivalence between percentages and fractions.

Emphasise that a percentage is a fraction out of 100. Demonstrate some equivalences by shading the square:
▸ $\frac{50}{100}$ or 50% is the same as $\frac{1}{2}$
▸ $\frac{25}{100}$ or 15% is the same as $\frac{3}{4}$

Emphasise that if you can find fractions of amounts, you can also find percentages of amounts.

Highlight that to find 50% of something, you find $\frac{1}{2}$, and further examples (as in the Students' book).
Discuss how to find 30% of £90. Highlight that 30% is equivalent to $\frac{3}{10}$. So, you work out 90 ÷ 10, then ×3. Extend to finding 60% of £90.

Discuss strategies – encourage shortcuts (60% is double 30% so double the answer). **N5.8OHP** shows fractions and percentage equivalents.

Discuss the sale signs in the Students' book as real-life examples of percentages.
Work through the examples in the book, emphasising the language used in percentage questions.

Plenary

Write the calculation 60% of 120 on the board and tell students that:
▸ Jas says divide by 10, then ×6.
▸ Kyesha says divide by 5, then ×3.
▸ David says divide by 100 and then ×60.

Discuss: Who is right? Which calculation is easiest?

Homework

▸ Find examples of percentages used in magazines/advertisements.
▸ Springboard 7: Page 428.

Exercise Commentary

Coverage

The questions assess objectives on Framework (Y456) Page 33.

Useful resources

R17 – 100 square

N5.8OHP – equivalent fractions and percentages

Differentiation

▸ Question 1 focuses on estimating percentages.
▸ Questions 2–8 focus on calculating fractions of an amount.
▸ Question 9 involves percentage increase.

Support tier: focuses on calculating harder percentages and fractions.

Misconceptions

Some students will confuse finding percentages with finding fractions of amounts – dividing by 20 to find 20%. Encourage them to convert the percentage to a fraction first, before dealing with the amount. Refer to the number line showing equivalent percentages and fractions on **N5.8OHP**.

In question 9, students may find 20%, but forget to **increase** the original amount by this amount. Encourage them to think carefully about whether an answer is sensible, and write answers in full sentences to add context to their work.

Links

Multiplication facts: Framework (Y456) Page 59.

Exercise Answers

1 a $\frac{1}{2}$ b $\frac{1}{4}$ c $\frac{1}{6}$ d $\frac{1}{5}$
2 a £4 b £6 c £10 d £15 e £42
3 a £4 b £9 c £5 d £12 e £24
4 a £11 b £2 c £11 d £16
5 a £6 b £8 c £9 d £8 e £15 f £12
6 £10
7 £34
8 £6.25
9 £12

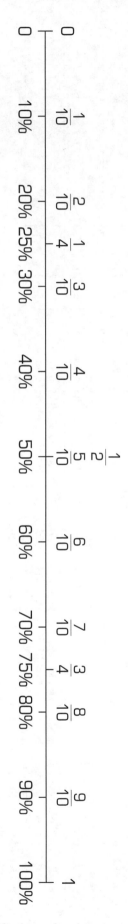

0		0
10%		$\frac{1}{10}$
20%		$\frac{2}{10}$
25%		$\frac{1}{4}$
30%		$\frac{3}{10}$
40%		$\frac{4}{10}$
50%	$\frac{1}{2}$	$\frac{5}{10}$
60%		$\frac{6}{10}$
70%		$\frac{7}{10}$
75%		$\frac{3}{4}$
80%		$\frac{8}{10}$
90%		$\frac{9}{10}$
100%		1

N5 More number calculations (8 hours)	Teaching objectives	Framework Maths resources	Other resources
Place value, ordering and rounding (10–13)	Use the vocabulary of estimation and approximation. Make and justify estimates of large numbers.	7A Student Book: N5.1, N5.2 7A Teacher's Book: N5.1WS, N5.2OHP, R6	
Measures (90–1)	Use, read and write standard metric units.	7A Student Book: N5.1, N5.2 7A Teacher's Book: N5.1WS, N5.2OHP, R6	
Fractions, decimals and percentages, ratio and proportion (30–1)	**Round a number with one decimal place to the nearest integer.**	7A Student Book: N5.2 7A Teacher's Book: N5.2OHP, R6	
Properties of numbers and number sequences (20–21)	Find all the pairs of factors of any number up to 100.	7A Student Book: N5.3 7A Teacher's Book: N5.3WS, R21	
Mental calculation strategies (× and ÷) (60–1)	Use factors (e.g. 8 × 12 = 8 × 4 × 3).	7A Student Book: N5.3 7A Teacher's Book: N5.3WS, R21	
Pencil and paper procedures (× and ÷) (66–9)	Approximate first. **Extend written methods to short multiplication of HTU or U**	7A Student Book: N5.4 7A Teacher's Book: N5.4WS, R4	
Pencil and paper procedures (× and ÷) (66–9)	Approximate first. **Extend written methods to short division of HTU or U**	7A Student Book: N5.5 7A Teacher's Book: N5.5WS, R21	
Fractions, decimals and percentages, ratio and proportion (22–3)	Recognise when two simple fractions are equivalent.	7A Student Book: N5.6 7A Teacher's Book: N5.6WS	
Fractions, decimals and percentages, ratio and proportion (24–5)	**Relate fractions to division,** and use division to find simple fractions.	7A Student Book: N5.7, N5.8 7A Teacher's Book: N5.7WS, N5.8OHP, R4, R17	
Fractions, decimals and percentages, ratio and proportion (32–3)	Find simple percentages of small whole-number quantities.	7A Student Book: N5.8 7A Teacher's Book: N5.8OHP, R17	
Problems involving 'real life', money and measures (82–9)	Use all four operations to solve simple word problems.	7A Student Book: N5.4–N5.8	

Access

Overview

This unit aims to develop students' understanding of the key stages in the handling data cycle: collecting data, representing it in charts or diagrams, and interpreting those diagrams. Students draw and interpret pictograms, bar charts, bar line graphs and line graphs, and find the mode from raw data, bar charts and frequency tables.

Spreads D3.3, D3.4 and D3.5 form the focus of the unit.

Framework references

The unit covers objectives on Framework (Y456) Pages 114, 115, 117

Useful resources

Worksheets
D3.3WS – drawing charts and graphs
D3.4WS – using statistics

OHPS
D3.1OHP – tally charts
D3.2OHP – pictograms
D3.5OHP – bar charts

General resources
R11 – tally chart
R24 – squared grid

Springboard 7 pages
154, 393, 394, 401

Introduction

Give the scenario of a mobile phone company wanting to know whether different ages of people text or phone each other. What questions could they ask in a survey? (Age, number of texts per week, number of phone calls per week) How could they use this information? (Advertise cheap text rates to the group that text most, for example in magazines for 12–14 year olds.)

Check in activity

Discuss the steps involved in handling data:
▸ Deciding how/where to find the data
▸ Collecting the data
▸ Organising the data: tally charts and frequency charts
▸ Displaying the data: for example in pictograms.

Differentiation – spanning the bridge

Spread	Bridge to the Support tier
D3.1	Extend Support tier students to consider the differences between, and examples of, **secondary** and **primary data**. Discuss suggestions on how to efficiently record the data from the introductory activity and discuss the features of the data collection sheet.
D3.2	Consider the use of pie charts, line charts and bar charts with Support tier students, linking bar charts with pictograms. Discuss the key features: pie charts represent few categories, line graphs can be used for measured data and the points can be joined to indicate trends. Discuss examples in the Support student book before progressing to the exercises.
D3.3	Support tier students need to think about which chart is best for representing different data. Extend these students to consider how the same information looks in different charts, using the final example from the student book (dual bar chart and line graph).
D3.4	Extend Support tier students to consider calculating the mean and the median from tabled data. Introduce the range of data.
D3.5	Extend Support tier students to give a more detailed articulation of each chart during the Access introductory activity, discussing which chart they might use in different circumstances. Encourage an open conversation with opinions on each other's interpretations.

D3.1 Collecting data

Access

This spread provides access to the Year 7 objective:
▸ Construct frequency tables for discrete data (252)

Lesson Plan

Mental starter

Practise counting in 5s, going round the class, from different starting numbers. Recap how to draw 'tallies' in groups of 5. How do we show 22? What number is this: ⅏ Ⅲ?

Introductory activity

Discuss what students understand by the word **data**. Introduce the problem from the Students' book. Emphasise that the data to be collected is on students' favourite vegetable. Discuss the best way to get this information – a survey.

Survey students' favourite fruit, writing the responses in long hand on the board.

Discuss a more effective way of recording this information. Emphasise limiting the responses – giving a choice, but not allowing for hundreds of different answers. Highlight the use of a tally chart. Tally students' responses into a tally chart (**R11**). Emphasise grouping tallies into 5s to help with counting. Calculate the frequencies and fill these in. Highlight that this is a **frequency table**.

Ask questions based upon the data:
▸ What is the favourite fruit?
▸ How many people prefer x to y?
▸ How many people were asked in total?

Plenary

Refer to question 4. Explain to students that the information they have collected is **primary data**. Define **secondary data**. Give different examples of data sets for students to classify as primary or secondary data. Encourage students to give their own examples of each.

Homework

▸ Collect some examples of secondary data from newspapers and magazines.
▸ Springboard 7: Page 401.

Exercise Commentary

Coverage

The questions assess objectives on Framework (Y456) Page 114.

Useful resources

R11 – tally chart

D3.1OHP – tally charts for exercise

Differentiation

▸ Questions 1 and 2 focus on completing tally charts.
▸ Question 3 focuses on making a tally chart.
▸ Question 4 involves carrying out a survey.

Support tier: focuses on identifying sources of data and designing data collection sheets.

Misconceptions

Tallying results will prove problematic for some students. Encourage them to work from left to right when tallying, and to cross off each result once it has been recorded in the tally.

Highlight checking their work, by totalling the frequencies, and checking this matches the total number of people asked. Question 2 can be used for this. **D3.1OHP** provides tally charts, to save time copying.

Links

Multiples: Framework (Y456) Page 19.

Exercise Answers

1 Frequencies: 15, 5, 30, 10, 15, 10, 20
2 Frequencies: 5, 2, 12, 6, 5
3 Chocolate

	Tally	Frequency

	Tally	Frequency

	Tally	Frequency

	Tally	Frequency

D3.2 Drawing pictograms

Access

This spread provides access to the Year 7 objective:
▸ Construct graphs and diagrams to represent data (262)

Lesson Plan

Mental starter

Practise interpreting pictogram keys.
For example: ☺ stands for 2 people.
What does ☺☺ stand for? Extend to half symbols.

Introductory activity

Refer to the mental starter. Emphasise that diagrams
are easier to interpret than tables.

Recap that in the last lesson, Marvin collected data on
the vegetables students liked. Discuss how to show the
data in a pictogram.

Emphasise that:

▸ The **key** indicates the number of values each picture
  represents.
▸ You use the same picture each time, to allow easy
  comparison.
▸ You line the pictures up to allow easy comparison of
  values.
▸ You put each category in its own row.

Ask questions based upon the pictogram in the
Students' book example (shown on **D3.2OHP**):

▸ How many people like cauliflower best?

Emphasise:

Number of pictures × 5 = number of people.

Plenary

Discuss an appropriate key for question 3. Emphasise
that all the frequencies are **multiples** of 5, and that a
picture representing 5 people might be sensible.
Discuss how it would look if each picture represented
10, and what picture to choose to enable 'half' values.

Homework

▸ Draw a pictogram of students' favourite vegetables
  (collected in D3.1 question 4).

Exercise Commentary

Coverage

The questions assess objectives on Framework (Y456)
Page 114.

Useful resources

D3.2OHP – pictogram from Students' book and a
blank chart

Differentiation

▸ Question 1 involves a simple pictogram with unit
  scale.
▸ Question 2 involves use of a key.
▸ Question 3 involves choosing an appropriate key.

Support tier: focuses on constructing pie charts and
line graphs.

Misconceptions

Students may understand one picture to represent one
unit. Encourage them to refer back to the key.

Students may not draw the pictures uniformly, or with
equal intervals. Encourage students to compare their
pictograms with a partner to invite discussion around
this point. **D3.2OHP** provides a grid to use for
pictograms, to save copying.

Links

Reading scales: Framework (Y456) Page 95.

Exercise Answers

1 Ice skating: 2 symbols, Cinema: 11 symbols,
  Bowling: 8 symbols, Stayed in: 6 symbols,
  Other: 3 symbols
2 Measles: 2 symbols, Mumps: 3 symbols,
  Chickenpox: 7 symbols, Whooping cough: 4 symbols,
  German measles: 1 symbol
3 Use one symbol for 5 students.

Favourite vegetable

Broccoli	
Cabbage	
Carrots	
Cauliflower	
Peas	
Spinach	
Sweetcorn	

Number of people

Key: = 5 people

Key:

D3.3 Drawing charts and graphs

Access

This spread provides access to the Year 7 objective:
▸ Construct diagrams and graphs (262)

Lesson Plan

Mental starter

Show a squared grid (**R24**) on the OHP, with axes drawn for Number of students (1 square represents 1 student) and Favourite fruit.

Encourage students to shade 1 square each to show their fruit choice, making a bar chart.

Introductory activity

Refer to the mental starter, and highlight that students have drawn a bar chart. Ask questions based on it.

Look at the bar charts in the Students' book and discuss the scale. Ask questions based on them.

Look at the bar line graph, highlighting that it is like a bar chart with very thin bars.

Discuss how to find the total number of people asked.

Discuss the line graph. Emphasise that this graph shows how the temperature changed over time.

Discuss how the data was plotted and the y-axis scale. Emphasise that the values are temperatures recorded.

Ask students questions based upon the line graph.

What was the temperature in March?

Emphasise that we join the points with a line, to give an idea of the temperature between the data recorded. This is only an **estimate** of the temperature.

Plenary

Draw an x-axis, representing hours of the day and a y-axis showing levels of happiness (increasing).

Talk the class through your day: I wake up, feeling okay, miss the bus, feeling grumpy etc. Discuss the patterns in the graph.

Homework

▸ Sketch a happiness graph for a day, as in the plenary.
▸ Springboard 7: Page 393.

Exercise Commentary

Coverage

The questions assess objectives on Framework (Y456) Page 115.

Useful resources

R24 – squared grid

D3.3WS – provides support for weaker students.

Differentiation

▸ Questions 1 and 2 focus on a simple bar chart and bar line graph.
▸ Question 3 involves choosing a scale for the y-axis.
▸ Question 4 focuses on drawing a line graph.

Support tier: focuses on comparing data in diagrams.

Misconceptions

The use of scales can cause difficulties. Encourage students to consider the scale before even beginning to approach the questions. Some students will have difficulties constructing the axes. **D3.3WS** provides questions with pre-drawn axes.

Links

Reading scales: Framework (Y456) Page 95.

Exercise Answers

1 Heights: 12, 4, 8, 6
2 Heights: 4, 16, 14, 4, 1
3 Heights: 10, 20, 25, 15, 15
4 Points at 35, 40, 45, 25, 10

Worksheet Answers

1 Heights: 4, 8, 2, 6
2 Heights: 14, 10, 4, 6, 2
3 Heights: 5, 5, 10, 20, 15

1 Use the data to fill in this bar chart.

Fruit	Apple	Banana	Pear	Orange
Frequency	4	8	2	6

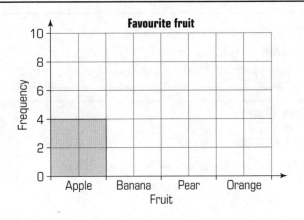

2 Use the data to complete this bar line graph.

Number of pets	0	1	2	3	4
Frequency	14	10	4	6	2

3 Use the data to draw a bar chart.

Bird	Number in garden
Jay	5
Robin	5
Bluetit	10
Crow	20
Sparrow	15

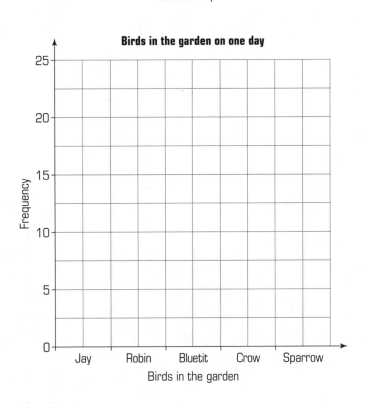

D3.4 Using statistics

Access

This spread provides access to the Year 7 objective:
▸ Find the mode for a small set of discrete data (256)

Lesson Plan

Mental starter

Record students' favourite colours in a tally chart (**R11**). Calculate the frequencies and complete the frequency table.

Introductory activity

Refer to the frequency table from the mental starter.

Which colour did **most** students choose? Introduce the key word: **mode**. Highlight that the highest frequency indicates the mode. Discuss how the mode will appear on a bar chart.

Discuss how to construct a bar chart for the data. Decide on a scale and draw the axes (on **R24**).

Choose students to help complete the bar chart. Highlight that the mode is represented by the longest bar.

Refer to the raw data set in the Students' book example. Discuss the mode here. Use the second example to highlight that there can be two modes.

Plenary

Show a bar chart with no labelling or title. Ask students for an interpretation. Highlight that without a title, there is no context to the data; without labelling, the data is meaningless; and without scale, the height of the bar is meaningless.

Homework

▸ Students design five questions (with answers) based upon the information displayed in a pre-drawn bar chart.
▸ Springboard 7: Page 154.

Worksheet Answers

1 **a** Silver **b** Yellow **c** Blue **d** 27
2 Red: 4 symbols, Blue: $2\frac{1}{2}$ symbols, Silver: $5\frac{1}{2}$ symbols
   Black: 3 symbols, Yellow: $1\frac{1}{2}$ symbols

Exercise Commentary

Coverage

The questions assess objectives on Framework (Y456) Pages 115 and 117.

Useful resources

R11 – tally chart
R24 – squared grid
D3.4WS – provides support for weaker students.

Differentiation

▸ Questions 1 and 2 focus on identifying the mode from diagrams.
▸ Questions 3–5 focus on finding the mode from raw data and a frequency table.
▸ Question 6 requires students to suggest data given the mode.

Support tier: focuses on calculating statistics from frequency tables.

Misconceptions

A typical mistake students make is writing the frequency rather than the category as the mode. Questions 4 and 5 will highlight this problem. Remind students that the mode will be a value from the original data set. Answering each question in full sentences can help to put their findings in context.

Links

Reading scales: Framework Page 95.

Exercise Answers

1 Eastie Boys
2 April
3 Walk
4 6
5 Cooking

1 This bar chart shows the sale of cars during one week.
The cars are sorted by colour.

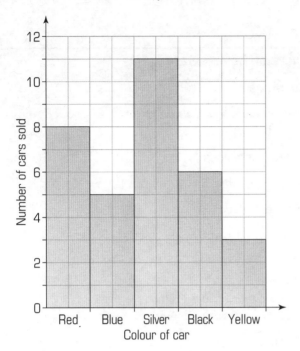

a Which colour was the biggest seller? _____

| This is the mode. |

b Which colour was the least popular? _____

c 5 cars of one colour were sold. What colour were they? _____

d How many cars were sold in total? _____

2 Draw the data from the bar chart onto this pictogram.
Use the key to help you.

	Number of cars sold
Red	
Blue	
Silver	
Black	
Yellow	

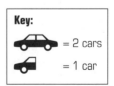

Key:
= 2 cars
= 1 car

D3.5 Discussing findings

Lesson Plan

Mental starter

▸ Write a set of six numbers, say 14, 12, 10, 14, 15, 11. What is the mode?
▸ The mode of a set of five numbers is 4. What could the numbers be?

Introductory activity

Recap the names of the types of diagrams used to display data: bar charts, bar line graphs, pictograms, line graphs. Emphasise that each diagram helps to show a picture of data.

Discuss the bar chart of favourite vegetables from D3.4 (shown on **D3.5OHP**).

▸ Which vegetable is the mode/most popular?
▸ Which is the least popular?
▸ What are the top three?

Refer to the scenario in the Students' book. Discuss why the top four vegetables were chosen.

Discuss the example in the Students' book. The bar chart is shown on **D3.5OHP**. Ask for feedback on the information shown on the chart.

Plenary

Discuss the scales for each graph in exercise D3.5. Ask questions based on the graphs, to check students' understanding of the scale.

Discuss graph 3C, noting the different times fruit gums were eaten, and encourage students to suggest reasons for this.

Homework

▸ Collect examples of charts and graphs used in newspapers and magazines for a class display.
▸ Springboard 7: Page 394.

Exercise Commentary

Coverage

The questions assess objectives on Framework (Y456) Pages 115 and 117.

Useful resources

D3.5OHP – bar charts from the Students' book

Differentiation

▸ Question 1 involves a simple bar chart.
▸ Question 2 focuses on a bar line graph.
▸ Question 3 involves comparing different graphs.

Support tier: focuses on interpreting statistical diagrams and writing reports.

Misconceptions

Students sometimes treat the different diagrams as alternative ways of displaying the same information. Emphasise the purpose of each diagram. Students should be encouraged to answer questions in full sentences to put their answers in context.

Links

Reading scales: Framework (Y456) Page 95.

Exercise Answers

1 Strawberry. Mango/raspberry
2 a December. Christmas.
  b About 980
  c December
  d Band only just formed.
3 a Graph B. 40 fruit gums.
  b Graph A. 2 fruit gums.
  c Graph B. 80 fruit gums.
  d Graph C. 10 fruit gums.
  e Graph A. 6 fruit gums.

Favourite vegetable

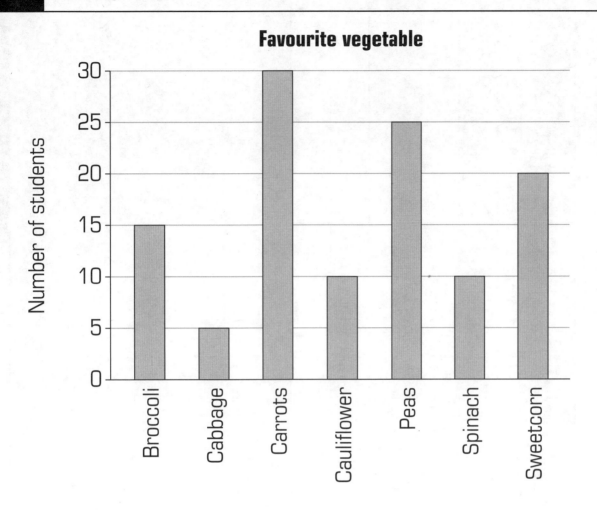

Different after school activities

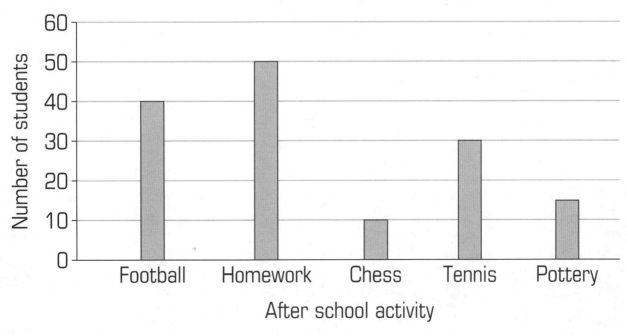

Framework MATHS   Scheme of work   Year 7

D3 The handling data cycle (5 hours)	Teaching objectives	Framework Maths resources	Other resources
Organising and interpreting data (114–17)	Solve a problem by collecting quickly and organising data in tables and charts.	7A Student Book: D3.1 7A Teacher's Book: D3.1OHP, R11	
Organising and interpreting data (114–17)	Solve a problem by representing data in pictograms.	7A Student Book: D3.2 7A Teacher's Book: D3.2OHP	
Organising and interpreting data (114–17)	Solve a problem by representing data in bar charts, bar line charts and line graphs.	7A Student Book: D3.3 7A Teacher's Book: D3.3WS, R24	
Organising and interpreting data (114–17)	Solve a problem by interpreting data in tables, charts, graphs and diagrams.	7A Student Book: D3.4, D3.5 7A Teacher's Book: D3.4WS, D3.5OHP, R11, R24	
Organising and interpreting data (116–17)	Find the mode of a set of data.	7A Student Book: D3.4 7A Teacher's Book: D3.4WS, R11, R24	
Reasoning and generalising about numbers or shapes (76–7)	Explain methods and reasoning, orally and in writing.	7A Student Book: D3.1–D3.5	

Access

Overview

The aim of this unit is to develop students' understanding of probability through carrying out simple probability experiments. Students practise the skills they learned in D3, recording outcomes in a tally chart and frequency table, and interpreting their results. They calculate experimental frequency as number of successful outcomes ÷ number of trials.

Spread D4.1 forms the focus of the unit.

Framework references

The unit covers objectives on Framework (Y456) Page 113

Introduction

Discuss use of probability in real life. For example: if the sky is grey, you think it is likely to rain, so you take an umbrella.
If you toss a coin to see who bats first at rounders, you know it is a fair way to decide because head and tail are equally likely.

Check in activity

Discuss the probability of these events:
▸ You will see a pig flying on your way home tonight
▸ You will see a celebrity on the way home
▸ You will eat dinner tonight
▸ You will throw an even number on a dice
▸ You will throw a five on a dice.
Encourage students to use the language of probability and calculate probabilities where appropriate.

Useful resources

Worksheets
D4.1WS – describing probabilities
D4.2WS – a probability experiment
D4.3WS – more experiments

General resources
R6 – number lines
R11 – tally chart
Coloured cubes and a bag
Dice
Coins

Springboard 7 page
260

Differentiation – spanning the bridge

Spread	Bridge to the Support tier
D4.1	Progress Support tier students to consider whether outcomes are equally likely or not. Use questions 1 and 2 in the Support student book for discussion, then students can continue with the exercise.
D4.2	Extend Support tier students to consider formula for experimental probability. Focus on experimental probability to indicate fairness of outcomes in the Access introductory activity.
D4.3	Support tier students will benefit from more discussion around the comparison of theoretical and experimental probabilities, in particular, at which point they may assume 'loaded' or 'biased' equipment and non-equally-likely outcomes.

D4.1 Describing probabilities

Access

This spread provides access to the Year 7 objective:
▸ Understand and use the probability scale from 0 to 1 (278)

Lesson Plan

Mental starter

Write on the board a selection of fractions, all but one equivalent to a half. Ask students for the odd one out. Recap simplifying by dividing both numerator and denominator by the same number.

Introductory activity

Discuss students' understanding of chance and probability. Ask for examples of events to describe key words: **certain, impossible, likely, unlikely**. Place events on a probability scale (**R6**), and highlight the values of 0 for impossible and 1 for certain.

Discuss what numbers you can use to describe the values between 0 and 1, and link to fractions in the mental starter.

Discuss how many different numbers could come up on a dice. Highlight the key word **outcome**. Ask students what the probability of rolling a 2 is: there is a 1 in 6 chance. Write $\frac{1}{6}$ as a fraction, reminding students that the denominator is the **total number of outcomes**. Place $\frac{1}{6}$ on the probability scale. Highlight the outcome as **unlikely**.

Show a bag in which there are 5 cubes – 1 red, 4 blue. Ask students for the probability of pulling out a red. Highlight there are **5 outcomes** even though there are only **2** colours. Only 1 outcome is red so the probability is $\frac{1}{5}$.

Plenary

Give students a scenario: 5 balls, 4 red and 1 blue.

Jane says the probability of picking a red is $\frac{4}{10}$.

John says the probability of picking a red is $\frac{4}{2}$.

Discuss who is right and why. Emphasise that John's probability is greater than 1, which it cannot be.

Homework

▸ Find the probability of each letter from the name of a TV programme being picked from a bag.
▸ Springboard 7: Page 260.

Exercise Commentary

Coverage

The questions assess objectives on Framework (Y456) Page 113.

Useful resources

R6 – number lines

Coloured cubes

Bag

D4.1WS – provides practice of the key ideas.

Differentiation

▸ Questions 1 and 2 focus on the language of probability.
▸ Question 3 focuses on equally likely outcomes.
▸ Question 4 focuses on identifying outcomes.

Support tier: focuses on theoretical probability.

Misconceptions

Students may consider the denominator to describe the chance of an event not happening. Emphasise that the denominator is the total number of outcomes.

Links

Fractions: Framework (Y456) Page 23.

Exercise Answers

1 a Likely   b Unlikely   c Likely
   d Certain   e Likely
3 a $\frac{1}{6}$ b $\frac{1}{6}$ c $\frac{1}{2}$
4 a Heads, tails
   b 1, 2, 3, 4, 5, 6, 7, 8, 9, 10
   c C, E, R, T, A, I, N

Worksheet Answers

1 a Unlikely
2 a $\frac{1}{8}$
3 a $\frac{1}{2}$ b $\frac{1}{8}$ c $\frac{2}{8}$ d $\frac{3}{8}$ e $\frac{2}{5}$ f a   g b

1 When this arrow is spun round it can land on white or grey.

   a Circle the word that best describes the chance of the spinner landing on grey:

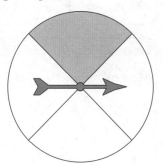

     Impossible   Unlikely   Likely   Certain

   b Describe the chance by putting an X on this probability scale.

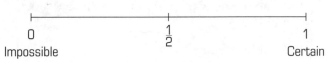

2 Here is another spinner.

   a Complete these statements:

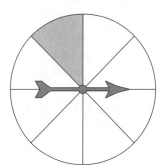

     There are _____ possible outcomes.

     _____ of the outcomes is grey.

     There is a _____ in _____ chance of landing on grey.

     The probability of landing on grey is _____.

   b Describe the probability by putting an X on this probability scale.

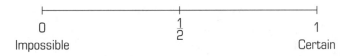

3 As a fraction, write the probability of the arrow landing on grey for each spinner.

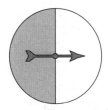 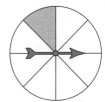 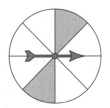 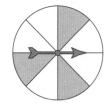 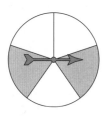

  a _____   **b** _____   **c** _____   **d** _____   **e** _____

  f Which spinner has the best chance of landing on grey? _____

  g Which spinner has the worst chance of landing on grey? _____

D4.2 A probability experiment

Access

This spread provides access to the Year 7 objective:
▸ Collect data from a simple experiment and record in a frequency table (282)

Lesson Plan

Mental starter

Ask students questions based on throwing a dice:
▸ What is the probability of throwing an even number prime number/multiple of 3/multiple of 1?
Simplify fractions where possible.

Introductory activity

Discuss the scenario in the Students' book. Who do the students think is correct?

Discuss how you can test who is correct – by experiment. Throw the dice lots of times and see which scores comes up.

Show a tally chart for the results (**R11**). Throw the dice a couple of times, and demonstrate recording the results.

Choose students to throw the dice. Record results for 50 throws.

Ask students for the probability of scoring each number based upon the results. Highlight:
▸ The numerator tells you how many times the outcome came up.
▸ The denominator tells you how many **trials** were done.

Discuss whether these results imply that the dice is not fair and each outcome is not equally likely.

Plenary

Discuss the outcomes of students' experiments. Did students find similar results? How could we compare the results? Why flip the coin 50 times? Why not 10?

Homework

▸ Flip a coin 50 more times, and record the results in the frequency table from question 4. Do more trials/flips change the probability?

Exercise Commentary

Coverage

The questions assess objectives on Framework (Y456) Page 113.

Useful resources

R11 – tally chart

Dice and coins

D4.2WS – provides extended practice of the key ideas.

Differentiation

▸ Questions 1 and 2 focus on writing experimental probabilities as fractions.
▸ Question 3 focuses on carrying out a dice experiment.
▸ Question 4 focuses on carrying out a coin experiment.

Support tier: focuses on experimental probability.

Misconceptions

Students may find writing probabilities as fractions confusing. Encourage them to think about the total number of trials, and what fraction of this is represented by each outcome.

Links

Fractions: Framework (Y456) Page 23.

Exercise Answers

1 $\frac{9}{50}$
2 a $\frac{12}{50}$ b $\frac{4}{50}$ c $\frac{6}{50}$ d $\frac{11}{50}$

Worksheet Answers

1 1 in 4
2 HHT, HTH, THH, TTH, THT, HTT, TTT

1 If you spin two coins, there are four possible outcomes.

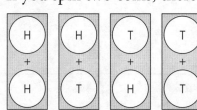

H means heads
T means tails

What are your chances of correctly guessing the outcome?

Answer: _____ chance in _____.

2 Fill in as many possible outcomes as you can think of, when you spin three coins. One possible outcome is done for you.

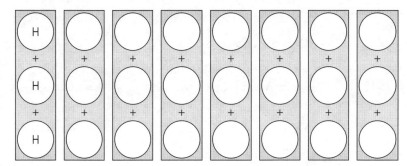

3 Which outcome do you think is the most likely when you spin three coins?

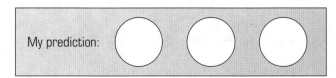

My prediction:

4 Spin three coins 25 times. Record the outcomes on the table as a tally.

Three heads	Two heads and one tail	Two tails and one head	Three tails

5 Which outcome was the most common?

6 Which outcome was the least common?

Access

This spread provides access to the Year 7 objective:
▸ Compare experimental and theoretical probabilities (284)

Lesson Plan

Mental starter

Assign fractions to five students, say $\frac{1}{2}$, $\frac{1}{4}$, $\frac{3}{4}$, $\frac{1}{10}$, $\frac{3}{10}$.

Encourage students to order these five from smallest to largest. Repeat for different fractions and students.

Introductory activity

Ask students for the outcomes of throwing a coin. Discuss the probability of throwing a head. Emphasise that calculated probability is based upon assumptions – no coins are actually thrown. Experimental probability is based upon actual results of trials or tests.

Flip a coin 20 times and record the results in a tally chart (**R11**). Highlight that the frequencies total 20 – the number of trials. Discuss how to describe the experimental probability of a head as a fraction.

Discuss the results:
▸ Which result is more likely?
▸ Is the coin fair?
▸ Should heads have come up exactly the same amount of times as tails?

Discuss how to improve results: more trials give greater accuracy.

Plenary

Place 12 cubes (say red, blue and green) in a bag. (Do not let the students see how many of each.) Choose students to pick a cube from the bag and replace it. Record the outcome. After several trials, ask the students to predict how many of each colour are in the bag.

Homework

▸ Throw two coins 100 times, record how many times they get 2 heads, and calculate the experimental probability of getting 2 heads.

Exercise Commentary

Coverage

The questions assess objectives on Framework (Y456) Page 113.

Useful resources

R11 – tally chart

Dice, coins

Coloured cubes and bag

D4.3WS – provides further practice of the key ideas.

Differentiation

▸ Question 1 involves interpreting results of a simple experiment.
▸ Question 2 involves a larger number of trials.
▸ Question 3 involves testing predictions through an experiment.

Support tier: focuses on comparing experimental and theoretical probabilities.

Misconceptions

Students may not intuitively recognise that increasing trial size increases accuracy of results. Discuss whether 2 tosses of a coin would be adequate to predict the likelihood of each outcome. Would they assume that 2 heads means a head is certain next time?

Links

Fractions: Framework (Y456) Page 23.

Exercise Answers

1 a 20   b 12
  c $\frac{12}{20}$ d Heads
2 a 100   b Tails

If you roll two dice,

the smallest score you can get is 2

... and the biggest score you can get is 12.

1 Roll two dice, 50 times.
Record the scores on this tally chart.

Score	Total	Tally	Frequency
⚀ ⚀	2		
⚀ ⚁	3		
⚁ ⚁ or ⚀ ⚂	4		
⚁ ⚂ or ⚃ ⚀	5		
⚂ ⚂ or ⚃ ⚁	6		
⚂ ⚃ or ⚃ ⚂ or ⚄ ⚀	7		
⚃ ⚃ or ⚄ ⚂ or ⚅ ⚁	8		
⚃ ⚄ or ⚄ ⚃	9		
⚄ ⚄ or ⚅ ⚃	10		
⚅ ⚄	11		
⚅ ⚅	12		

2 Draw your results onto the bar chart.

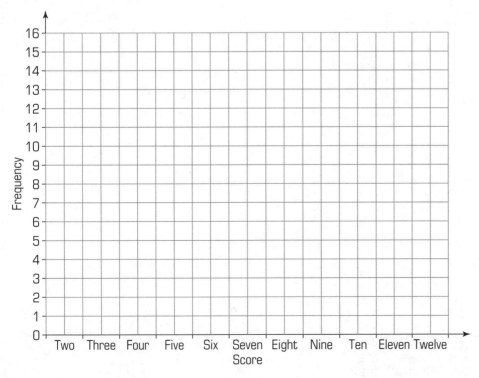

3 What is the modal score? _____

The modal score is the one that occurs most often.

Framework MATHS

Scheme of work

Year 7

D4 Probability experiments (3 hours)	Teaching objectives	Framework Maths resources	Other resources
Organising and interpreting data (112–13)	Discuss the chance or likelihood of particular events.	7A Student Book: D4.1, D4.2, D4.3 7A Teacher's Book: D4.1WS, D4.2WS, D4.3WS, R6, R11	
Organising and interpreting data (114–17)	Solve a problem by collecting quickly, organising and interpreting data in tables and charts.	7A Student Book: D4.2 7A Teacher's Book: D4.2WS, R11	
Reasoning and generalising about numbers or shapes (76–7)	Explain methods and reasoning, orally and in writing.	7A Student Book: D4.1–D4.3	
Reasoning and generalising about numbers or shapes (78–9)	Solve mathematical problems or puzzles, recognise and explain patterns and relationships, generalise and predict. Suggest extensions by asking 'What if...?'	7A Student Book: D4.1–D4.3	

Access

Overview

The aim of this unit is to develop students' understanding of sequences and formulae, including drawing graphs to represent the relationship between variables. The unit begins with solving linear equations, and then focuses on constructing and using simple formulae for sequences, relating these to mappings. Students plot graphs of formulae in the first quadrant, before looking at coordinates in all four quadrants.

Spreads A5.1, A5.2, A5.4 and A5.5 form the focus of the unit.

Framework references

The unit covers objectives on Framework (Y456) Pages 17, 53, 55, 65, 81, 109

Introduction

Discuss graphs and charts that students have used in everyday life.

Practise reading values and converting pounds to euros and vice versa, using the conversion graph on page 217 in the Students' book.

Check in activity

Show students a video of a weather forecast or an OHP of temperatures on a map (with positive and negatives (Springboard, pages 77 and 78)).

Discuss which places are hotter and colder.

Write the temperatures in order from smallest to largest.

Useful resources

Worksheets
A5.2WS – using formulas
A5.4WS – making sequences
A5.5WS – rules
A5.6WS – rules and graphs
A5.7WS – graphs of formulas

OHPs
A5.1OHP – function machines
A5.3OHP – matchstick triangles
A5.8OHP – coordinate grid in four quadrants

General resources
R4 – place value grid
R6 – number lines
R8 – coordinate grid
R24 – squared grid
Blue and red cubes

Springboard 7 pages
50, 51, 77, 78, 126, 395

Differentiation – spanning the bridge

Spread	Bridge to the Support tier
A5.1	Focus Support tier students on writing equations from word problems (addressed briefly in the Access introductory activity), and on using the inverse operation to solve using the balance method. Discuss the convention: $3n = 3 \times n$.
A5.2	Progress Support tier students to look at formulae containing multiple operations, e.g. the cost of a phone bill including a line rental charge as well as a cost based upon the number of minutes used.
A5.3	Extend Support tier students to consider a formula with multiplication (reminding of convention: $5 \times d = 5d$), and a formula containing multiple operations: $5d + 20$.
A5.4	Progress Support tier students to write the rule for the sequence as a formula: next pattern = current pattern + 3.
A5.5	Both tiers cover the same material, although Support tier students should be given some practice at two-step function machines.
A5.6	Progress from mapping diagrams to tables of values with Support tier students, emphasising the input value as x and the output as y. Support tier students will need to construct axes for their graphs, so may need to discuss this also.
A5.7	Support tier students focus on scale, and will benefit from discussion based around larger output values, and what a suitable scale to use would be. Use the introductory discussion to consider the appropriateness of joining plotted points (can Angela iron 3.5 shirts?).
A5.8	Both tiers cover coordinates in all four quadrants, and the Access introductory activity should provide ample opportunity to elicit everything required for both groups.

A5.1 Solving equations

Access

This spread provides access to the Year 7 objective:
▸ Solve simple linear equations (122)

Lesson Plan

Mental starter

Give 'I think of a number' problems: I think of a number. I add 3 and I get 14. Repeat, including all four operations.

Introductory activity

Refer to the mental starter. Emphasise that students have been solving equations to find the value of the unknown.

Link a problem to its equation: $x + 3 = 14$. Emphasise the use of a letter to represent the unknown value.

Discuss students' strategies for **solving** this equation in the starter: either counting on from 3, or using subtraction.

Emphasise that subtraction undoes addition, and vice versa.

Discuss what undoes multiplication. Use examples: $3 \times 2 = 6$. How do you get back from 6 to 3? ($\div 2$) Introduce the key word **inverse**.

Demonstrate using function machines and inverse operations to solve equations. Use the function machines on **A5.1OHP**.

Highlight:
▸ Start with the unknown.
▸ Draw a function machine of the equation.
▸ Reverse the function machine using the inverse operation.

Plenary

Consider two-step equations – first informally (I have a number, I double it, then I add 5, the answer is 11), then link to function machine method for $n \times 2 + 5 = 11$.

Homework

▸ Solve 20 equations using function machines.
▸ Springboard 7: Page 239.

Exercise Commentary

Coverage

The questions assess objectives on Framework (Y456) Pages 53 and 55.

Useful resources

A5.1OHP – function machines and inverse machines.

Differentiation

▸ Question 1 focuses on informal problems.
▸ Questions 2 and 3 focus on the inverse method.
▸ Question 4 extends to all four operations.

Support tier: focuses on constructing and solving equations using the balance method.

Misconceptions

Students informally solve problems with ease, but the formal equations may confuse them. Encourage students to say each equation out loud substituting 'something' or 'a number' for each letter, to help them build a natural link between formal and informal representations.

Some students will forget to use the inverse operation to solve each equation. They should be encouraged to substitute their values back into the equations as a checking procedure.

Links

Problem solving: Framework (Y456) Page 79.

Exercise Answers

1 a 7   b 10   c 11   d 2
  e 30   f 100   g 3
2 9
3 b 33, 21   c 33
4 a 9   b 12   c 13   d 15
  e 11   f 10   g 5
  h 10   i 4   j 20
  k 3   l 10

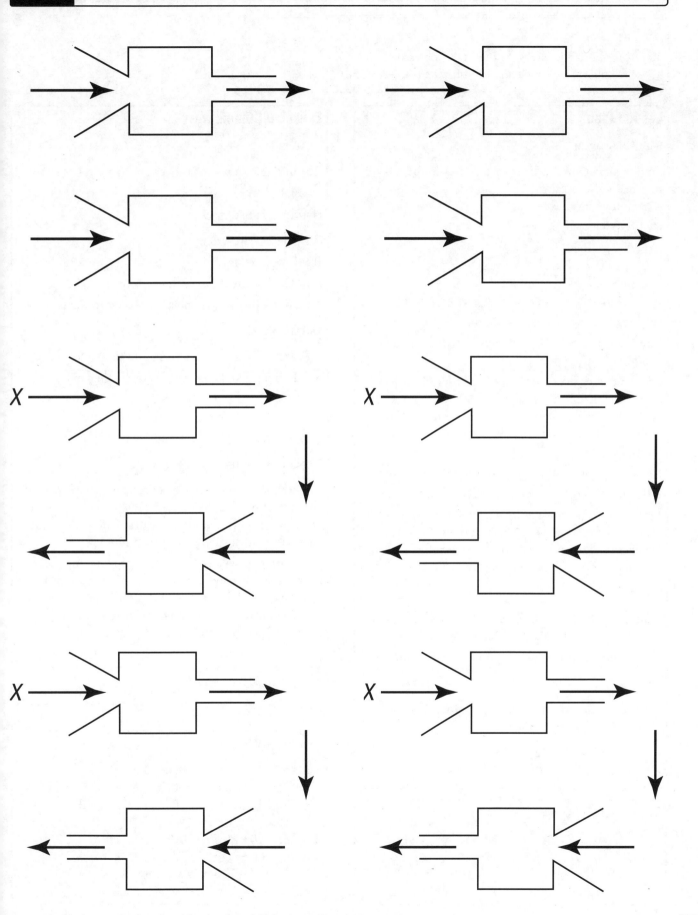

A5.2 Using formulas

Access

This spread provides access to the Year 7 objective:
▸ Use formulae from mathematics and other subjects (138)

Lesson Plan

Mental starter

Draw a rectangle on a cm square grid. Ask students for the area of the rectangle, discussing strategies:
▸ Counting cm squares
▸ Multiplying length by width.
Repeat for different rectangles.

Introductory activity

Refer to the mental starter. Highlight the formula:

area of a rectangle = length × width.

Emphasise that this formula links area with length and width.

Discuss the formula for Mike's wage from the Students' book. Emphasise that this formula links Mike's wage with the number of cars he makes. Highlight the key words **for every**, and link to multiplication.

Ask students spot questions based upon the formula:
▸ If Mike makes 5 cars, how much will he earn?

Discuss strategies for multiplying by 30, or 40 or 50. Link to multiplying by 3, 4 or 5, and then by 10. Emphasise that multiplying by 10 moves the digits to the next highest column on the place value table (**R4**).

Plenary

Extend the Students' book example to problems such as: Mike gets paid £90. How many cars did he make?

Discuss how to solve this using function machines.

Homework

▸ Calculate cost of mobile phone bill for different lengths of calls, given the formula:

cost = number of minutes × 20p.

▸ Springboard 7: Page 126.

Worksheet Answers

1 a £60   b £180   c £210   d £120   e £600
  f £450
2 a £100   b £200   c £250   d £400   e £500
  f £750   g £600   h £1000   i £1500   j £1250

Exercise Commentary

Coverage

The questions assess objectives on Framework (Y456) Pages 65 and 81.

Useful resources

R4 – place value table
R24 – squared grid
A5.1OHP – function machines
A5.2WS – provides support for weaker students.

Differentiation

▸ Questions 1 and 2 focus on using simple formulae.
▸ Questions 3 and 4 extend to completing and using a formula.
▸ Question 5 extends to constructing a formula.

Support tier: includes formulae with two operations.

Misconceptions

In question 4, students need to be encouraged to think about the units for their answer. Direct them to think about the original question posed, to link with pounds and pence rather than just abstract numbers.

Some students will have difficulty constructing the formula for question 5. Encourage them to think about the two quantities that have a relationship, and what that relationship is. Working in pairs can help to generate discussion around constructing formulae.

Links

Area: Framework (Y456) Page 97.

Exercise Answers

1 a £30   b £100   c £290   d £270   e £300
  f £360   g £420   h £0
2 a £80   b £120   c £200   d £320   e £160
  f £280   g £40   h £400
3 Wage = 50p × parcels delivered
4 a 50p   b £1   c £2   d £1.50   e £5
  f £6   g £10   h £3.50   i £5.50
5 Pay = £50 × number of games made

1 Mike is paid £30 for every car that he makes.
You can show the formula like this:

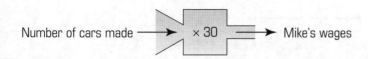

Number of cars made ⟶ × 30 ⟶ Mike's wages

Use the machines to work out Mike's wages for these
number of cars made.

> To multiply by 30 you multiply
> by 3 and then multiply by 10

a   2 cars ⟶ × 30 ⟶ [ ]

b   6 cars ⟶ × 30 ⟶ [ ]

c   7 cars ⟶ × 30 ⟶ [ ]

d   4 cars ⟶ × 30 ⟶ [ ]

e   20 cars ⟶ × 30 ⟶ [ ]

f   15 cars ⟶ × 30 ⟶ [ ]

2 Fill in these machines to show Mike's wages when he is
paid £50 per car.

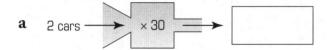

a   2 cars ⟶ × 50 ⟶ [ ]

b   4 cars ⟶ × 50 ⟶ [ ]

c   5 cars ⟶ × 50 ⟶ [ ]

d   8 cars ⟶ × 50 ⟶ [ ]

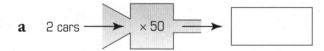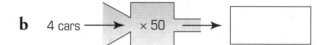

e   10 cars ⟶ × 50 ⟶ [ ]

f   15 cars ⟶ × 50 ⟶ [ ]

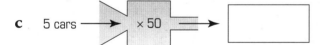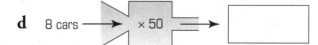

g   12 cars ⟶ × 50 ⟶ [ ]

h   20 cars ⟶ × 50 ⟶ [ ]

i   30 cars ⟶ × 50 ⟶ [ ]

j   25 cars ⟶ × 50 ⟶ [ ]

A5.3 Using symbols in formulas

Lesson Plan

Mental starter

Write the formula for area of a rectangle on the board. Give students length and width dimensions and encourage them to calculate the area of the rectangle using the formula.

Introductory activity

Refer to the mental starter and A5.2. Emphasise that a formula links two or more quantities. Discuss the example in the Students' book.

Ask students how many pegs are required for 1 shirt/2 shirts. Write the answers as a **mapping** between number of shirts and number of pegs needed. Ask students how many pegs for 50 shirts/100 shirts, etc. and extend to the general case (in words).

Number of pegs = number of shirts + 1

Ask spot questions based upon this formula.

Emphasise that you can use algebra as shorthand:

$p = s + 1$

Emphasise that p stands for **number of** pegs, s stands for **number of** shirts. Practise substituting s values into the formula.

Extend to find s when p is given, using function machines (**A5.1OHP**) and inverses.

Link to solving equations using inverses and a flowchart.

Plenary

Discuss question 4 (shown on **A5.3OHP**). Extend to number of triangles for a given number of matches finding (using the inverse method).

Highlight what happens if the value is substituted into the incorrect place in the formula, e.g. if the number of matches is substituted into formula as the number of triangles.

Homework

▶ Use the information from questions 1 and 2 to create a mapping diagram from s to p.

Exercise Commentary

Coverage

The questions assess objectives on Framework (Y456) Page 81.

Useful resources

A5.1OHP – function machines
A5.3OHP – Students' book question 4.

Differentiation

▶ Questions 1 and 3 involve simple substitution.
▶ Question 2 extends to include solving equations.
▶ Question 4 involves developing a formula from a pattern.

Support tier: focuses on writing formulae with two operations.

Misconceptions

Emphasise that a letter represents the number of objects not the object itself, so p stands for the **number of pegs** (not peg).

Students may substitute incorrectly in question 2. Remind students to read questions carefully and think about the information they have been given before attempting the substitution and calculation. Encourage estimation of answers first to direct this train of thought within the context of the question.

Links

Area: Framework (Y456) Page 97.

Exercise Answers

1 a 13 b 26 c 20 d 35 e 100
2 a 7 b 10 c 3 d 14 e 19 f 30 g 50
  h 24 i 31
3 a 7 b 9 c 12 d 15 e 20
4 a 1 and 3, 2 and 5, 3 and 7, 4 and 9
  c Number of matches = number of triangles + 2
  d $m = t + 2$

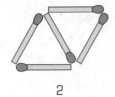 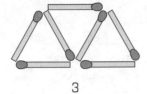 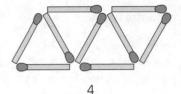

Pattern number: 1   2   3   4

Number of
matchsticks:

 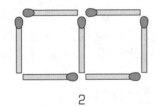 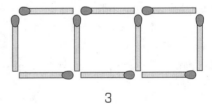

Pattern number: 1   2   3

Number of
matchsticks:

A5.4 Making sequences

Access

This spread provides access to the Year 7 objective:
▸ Generate and describe simple integer sequences (144)

Lesson Plan

Mental starter

Give students a start number and a rule (add 5). Go around the class, each student giving the next number in the sequence. Repeat with different start numbers and rules (including subtraction)

Introductory activity

Refer to the mental starter and recap on keywords: **sequence**, **term**, **pattern**, from A1.

Write a number sequence on the board, say 4, 7, 10, 13.

Encourage students to give the rule to get to the next term [add 3].

Discuss the example in the Students' book. Emphasise that the pattern can be written using numbers, as a sequence. Write in a table with headings number of days, number of leaves. Emphasise that the number of leaves **increases** each day. Point out that as the number of days goes up by 1, the number of leaves increases by 2. Emphasise that the rule indicates how to get from numbers of leaves on one day to the number of leaves the next.

Practise calculations based upon the rule, as in the Students' book example.

Plenary

Discuss question 4 from A5.3 (shown on **A5.3OHP**) and the rule to move from one pattern to the next. Discuss which rule you would use to find the 5th pattern, or the 100th pattern.

Homework

▸ Design and draw the first five terms of a matchstick pattern where the rule is add 4 each time.
▸ Springboard 7: Page 51.

Worksheet Answers

1 b 5   c ×5   2 b 4   c ×4

Exercise Commentary

Coverage

The questions assess objectives on Framework (Y456) Page 17.

Useful resources

A5.4WS – provides further practice of the key ideas.
A5.3OHP – matchstick diagrams from A5.3.

Differentiation

▸ Question 1 involves finding a rule.
▸ Questions 2 and 3 focus on using a rule to find terms.
▸ Question 4 extends to predicting terms.

Support tier: focuses on finding term-to-term rules for sequences.

Misconceptions

In question 1 students may confuse the pattern number with the sequence, focusing on a rule for number of tables. Encourage students to consider the pattern that does not start at 1 and increase by 1 each time.

Encourage students to check their rules with the information they have been given, and to verify their ideas by drawing more patterns.

Links

Solving problems: Framework (Y456) Page 79.

Exercise Answers

1 a 1, 3; 2, 6; 3, 9
  b +3
2 21
3 18
4 a 4, 7, 10   b Add 3 matches.
  c 10   d 12
  e 6th
5 3, 5, 7, 9, 11

1 This drawing shows 1 table and 5 chairs:

a Complete the third drawing in this sequence:

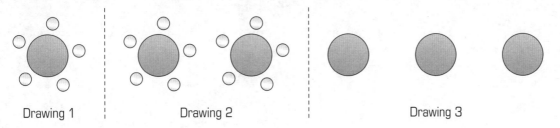

| Drawing 1 | Drawing 2 | Drawing 3 |

b Complete this sentence: 'Each table has _____ chairs'.

c Write the rule that connects the number of tables and the number of chairs.

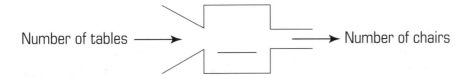

Number of tables ⟶ [_____] ⟶ Number of chairs

2 a Add the next drawing in this sequence

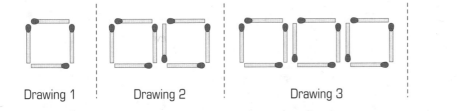

| Drawing 1 | Drawing 2 | Drawing 3 | Drawing 4 |

b Complete this sentence: 'Each square uses _____ matches'.

c Write the rule that connects the number of squares and the number of matches.

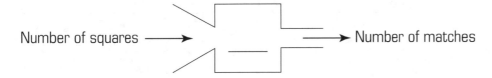

Number of squares ⟶ [_____] ⟶ Number of matches

Access

This spread provides access to the Year 7 objective:
▸ Generate terms of a sequence given a rule (148)

Lesson Plan

Mental starter

Give students a start number and a rule. Go around the class, each student giving the next number in the sequence. Repeat with different start numbers and rules (focusing on addition and subtraction).

Introductory activity

Refer to the mental starter. Write the last number sequence and rule on the board. Emphasise that the rule tells you how to get from one term to the next.

Emphasise the key words **term** and **value**. Ask students spot questions to gain familiarity with these words:
▸ What is the value of the 4th term?
▸ What term has value ___?

Discuss how to find the 10th term/the 50th term/etc.

Emphasise that using this rule would mean having to generate all terms up to term 49, to work out the value of term 50.

Discuss the example in the Students' book. Ask students how many chairs for 10 tables/50 tables.

Discuss the rule that connects number of tables with number of chairs.

Encourage the use of function machines to generate numbers of chairs for a given number of tables.

Plenary

Discuss question 3d.

Ask for suggestions for the rule. Highlight that using the first values, two rules would be possible (×2 and +8), and the need to check with the other values to determine which rule fits all.

Homework

▸ Complete mappings given some input and output values, and find the rule.
▸ Springboard 7: Page 50.

Exercise Commentary

Coverage

The questions assess objectives on Framework (Y456) Page 17.

Useful resources

A5.1OHP – function machines

A5.5WS – provides further practice of the key ideas.

Differentiation

▸ Question 1 involves using function machines.
▸ Question 2 focuses on finding a rule from a pattern.
▸ Question 3 involves finding patterns from mappings.

Support tier: extends to writing formulae for function machines.

Misconceptions

In question 3 students may be confused with non-consecutive inputs. Emphasise the link between input and output (term and value), and encourage students to consider them in pairs.

Students may use the first rule they see that connects a pair of values. They must be encouraged to check that this rule works for all values given.

Links

Multiplication facts: Framework (Y456) Page 59.

Exercise Answers

1 a 21, 27, 45, 60   b 20, 8, 12, 40
2 a 2, 4, 6   b ×2   c 20, 60, 100, 90
3 a +4   b –3   c –6   d ×2

Worksheet Answers

1 a 7, 20, 36   b 6, 30, 90   c 3, 5, 12
2 a ×4, 20   b ⁻4, 11   c ÷2, 25

1 Use the rule in the machine to complete each number mapping.

a 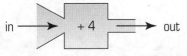   **b** 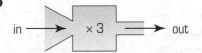   **c**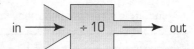

in	→	out		in	→	out		in	→	out
3	→	7		2	→	6		30	→	☐
16	→	☐		10	→	☐		50	→	☐
32	→	☐		30	→	☐		120	→	☐

2 For each mapping:

▸ Use pairs of values in the mappings to decide on the rule.
▸ Write the rule into the machine.
▸ Use the rule to complete the mapping.

a    **b**    **c**

in	→	out		in	→	out		in	→	out
3	→	12		15	→	☐		30	→	15
5	→	☐		10	→	6		50	→	☐
10	→	40		28	→	24		12	→	6

3 This is the rule that connects the number of white and grey beads in a necklace.

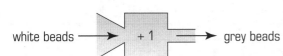

Shade the grey beads on the drawing using the rule.

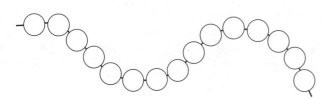

A5.6 Rules and graphs

Access

This spread provides access to the Year 7 objective:
▸ Generate coordinate pairs that satisfy a simple linear rule (164)

Lesson Plan

Mental starter

Show students a coordinate grid (**R8**, first quadrant). Encourage them to write down four coordinates pairs from the grid. Plot a coordinate.

Students cross this off if it is one of theirs.

The first to cross off all four coordinates wins.

Introductory activity

Show a pattern of blue and red cubes – 1 blue cube for every 2 red cubes. Choose students to complete the mapping for blue to red on the board.

Highlight that there is a relationship between red and blue. Emphasise that you can see this relationship on a graph. Emphasise that the mapping pairs can be written as coordinates. Write the coordinate pair next to each mapping. Choose students to plot the coordinates on an OHP (**R8**). Join the points. Emphasise that the relationship makes a straight line.

Discuss extending the line to find other pairs of values for blue and red. Encourage students to give coordinates on the extended line. Write these values in the mapping diagram, and highlight that these values fit the same rule.

Plenary

Explain that the rule connecting blue and red beads is × 4. Encourage students to give coordinates to fit this rule. Plot the coordinates and draw the line.

Homework

▸ Complete a mapping diagram for a function machine (+2), using input values 1–5. Write the values as coordinates and plot them on axes.

Worksheet Answers

1 White: 1, 2, 3, 4
2 (2, 1), (4, 2), (6, 3), (8, 4)
5 (10, 5), (12, 6)

Exercise Commentary

Coverage

The questions assess objectives on Framework (Y456) Page 109.

Useful resources

R8 – coordinate grid
R24 – squared grid
Blue and red cubes
A5.6WS – provides support for weaker students.

Differentiation

▸ Question 1 involves completing a mapping and drawing its graph.
▸ Question 2 focuses on finding a rule from a graph.
▸ Question 3 involves extending a graph to find more values that obey the rule.

Support tier: focuses on drawing straight-line graphs from a table of values.

Misconceptions

The jump from mappings to coordinates may confuse some students, who may write them in the wrong order. Students should work in pairs for question 1 to help overcome difficulties. Encourage students to share strategies for remembering the order (x, y).

Weaker students will have difficulties constructing the axes for their graphs. Providing pre-drawn axes may help.

Links

Sequences: Framework (Y456) Page 17.

Exercise Answers

1 a Yellow: 1, 2, 3, 4, 5
  b (1, 1), (2, 2), (3, 3), (4, 4), (5, 5)
  g green = yellow   **h** 8
2 a (1, 3), (2, 6), (3, 9)   **b** Black: 3, 6, 9   **c** ×3
3 16

228

1 In this bead pattern there are two black beads for every white bead.

Use the bead pattern to complete this mapping.

black ⟶ white

2 ⟶ ▢

4 ⟶ ▢

6 ⟶ ▢

8 ⟶ ▢

2 Write the mapping pairs as graph coordinates.

(2, 1)   (4, ___)   (6, ___)   (8, ___)

3 Plot these coordinates onto this grid.

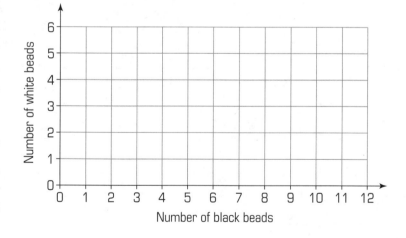

4 Draw a line through the coordinates and extend it as far as you can.

5 Complete these coordinates from the graph.

(10, ___)   (___, 6)

A5.7 Graphs of formulas

Access

This spread provides access to the Year 7 objective:
▸ Generate coordinate pairs that satisfy a simple linear relationship (164)

Lesson Plan

Mental starter

Write on the board the formula to calculate number of pegs required to hang a number of shirts: $p = s + 1$ (refer to A5.3)

Ask students spot questions based upon the formula: How many pegs for 20 shirts? How many shirts can be hung with 52 pegs?

Introductory activity

Refer to the mental starter. Emphasise that the relationship gives pairs of values that you can plot to make a graph.

Discuss each of the stages:
▸ Generating a mapping diagram.
▸ Listing coordinate pairs
▸ Plotting the pairs and drawing a line.

Introduce the example from Students' book. Discuss the two quantities linked in this example. Derive a formula in words and then symbols:

Wage = £1 **for every** shirt ironed + £4

$w = 1 \times n + 4 = n + 4$

Emphasise that $1 \times n = n$ using numerical examples.

Encourage students to complete each stage to plot the graph (on **R8**). Emphasise that there is a clear pattern, and the line can be extended to find Angela's wage without having to calculate.

Ask questions based on the graph. Discuss which axes to use each time and why.

Plenary

Discuss question 3. Draw the graph on the same axes as for Angela's wage in the introductory activity. Discuss who gets the best pay. Does it depend on how many shirts are ironed?

Homework

▸ Construct a graph showing John's wages: $w = 3 \times n$.
▸ Springboard 7: Page 395.

Exercise Commentary

Coverage

The questions assess objectives on Framework (Y456) Page 109.

Useful resources

R8 – coordinate grid
A5.7WS – provides support for weaker students.

Differentiation

▸ Question 1 involves reading values from a graph.
▸ Question 2 focuses on drawing a graph on given axes.
▸ Question 3 involves a multiplicative relationship.

Support tier: extends to choosing the scales for axes.

Misconceptions

Some students will continue to plot (y, x). Encourage them to share strategies for remembering the order.

Weaker students may have difficulties constructing the axes. Pre-drawn axes may help, or use **R8** or **A5.7WS**.

Links

Sequences: Framework (Y456) Page 17.

Exercise Answers

1 £11
2 a w: 3, 4, 5, 6, 7
  c Arrow to (7, 9)
  d £10
3 a w: 2, 4, 6, 8, 10
  f i (7, 14)
    ii (9, 18)
    iii (10, 20)

Worksheet Answers

1 (1, 4), (2, 5), (3, 6), (4, 7), (5, 8)
3 £7

The formula for Gareth's wage is: $w = n + 3$

w stands for Gareth's wage.

n stands for the number of shirts that Gareth irons.

1 Use the formula to complete this mapping and the coordinate pairs.

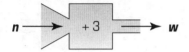

n		w	
1	⟶	4	(1, 4)
2	⟶	_____	(2, _____)
3	⟶	_____	(3, _____)
4	⟶	_____	(_____ , _____)
5	⟶	_____	(_____ , _____)

2 Plot the coordinates onto this grid.
Join the coordinates with a straight line.

3 How much is Gareth paid when he irons 4 shirts?

_____

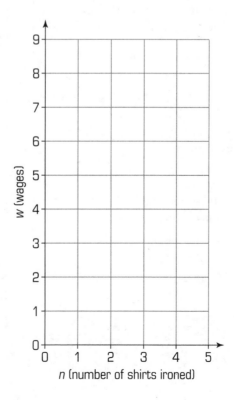

A5.8 Coordinates in all quadrants

Access

This spread provides access to the Year 7 objective:
▶ Generate coordinate pairs that satisfy a simple linear relationship (164)

Lesson Plan

Mental starter

Give students a start number, and a rule, say subtract 2. Go around the class, each student giving the next number. Carry on into negative numbers. (Using a number line until students are confident.) Repeat with different start numbers and rules.

Introductory activity

Using the number line from the mental starter, highlight that negative numbers are to the left of 0 and positive numbers are to the right.

Show a grid with all four quadrants marked and no numbering on the axes (**A5.8OHP**). Emphasise that coordinates help to communicate an exact position. Place zero at the centre and discuss how to number the axes. Link to negative numbers in the mental starter.

Place a cross in each quadrant, one at a time. Introduce the key word **quadrant**.

Discuss how to communicate each position.

Practise reading and plotting coordinates.

Emphasise that the first value in a coordinate pair indicates horizontal movement, and the second value vertical movement.

Plenary

Show a grid with four quadrants (**R8**). Ask students for any coordinate in the 1st quadrant. List the coordinates. Repeat for coordinates in the 2nd, 3rd and 4th quadrants. Discuss patterns.

Homework

▶ Use the coordinate grid from question 1 to write the name of the school using coordinate pairs.

Exercise Commentary

Coverage

The questions assess objectives on Framework (Y456) Page 109.

Useful resources

R6 – number lines
R8 – coordinate grid
A5.8OHP – unlabelled coordinate grid in four quadrants

Differentiation

▶ Question 1 involves reading coordinates.
▶ Question 2 focuses on plotting coordinates.
▶ Question 3 involves identifying the quadrant from the coordinate pair.

Support tier: extends to constructing grids and plotting points in all four quadrants.

Misconceptions

Negative coordinates may disconcert some students and make them more likely to confuse the order of the values (y, x). Encourage them to share strategies for remembering the order.

Encourage students to take their time and work with each coordinate pair individually, as sometimes the collection of coordinates, and multitude of abstract numbers can be overwhelming.

Weaker students may have difficulties constructing axes. Encourage them to copy the examples in the book exactly, or provide pre-drawn axes.

Links

Negative numbers: Framework (456) Page 15.

Exercise Answers

1 THE BIG BALD BLOKES BACK BRAKE BLOCK BROKE
2 d Triangle, rectangle, kite
3 a Second **b** Third **c** First **d** Fourth

Second quadrant

First quadrant

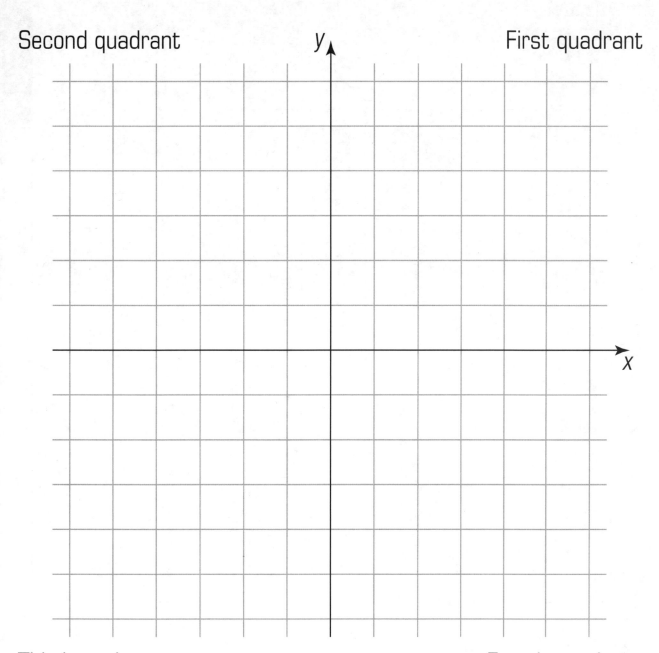

Third quadrant

Fourth quadrant

Framework MATHS   Scheme of work   Year 7

A5 Equations and graphs (8 hours)	Teaching objectives	Framework Maths resources	Other resources
Mental calculation strategies (+ and −) (42–3)	Develop further the relationship between addition and subtraction.	7A Student Book: A5.1 7A Teacher's Book: A5.1OHP	
Mental calculation strategies (× and ÷) (62–3)	Use the relationship between multiplication and division.	7A Student Book: A5.1 7A Teacher's Book: A5.1OHP	
Mental calculation strategies (× and ÷) (64–5)	Use known facts and place value to multiply and divide mentally.	7A Student Book: A5.2 7A Teacher's Book: A5.1OHP, A5.2WS, R4, R24	
Reasoning and generalising about numbers or shapes (80–1)	Develop from explaining a generalised relationship in words to expressing it in a formula using letters as symbols.	7A Student Book: A5.2, A5.3, A5.7 7A Teacher's Book: A5.1OHP, A5.2WS, A5.3OHP, A5.7WS, R4, R8, R24	
Properties of numbers and number sequences (16–17)	Recognise and extend number sequences.	7A Student Book: A5.4, A5.5, A5.6 7A Teacher's Book: A5.1OHP, A5.3OHP, A5.4WS, A5.5WS, A5.6WS, R8, R24	
Shape and space (108–9)	Read and plot coordinates in the first quadrant.	7A Student Book: A5.6, A5.7 7A Teacher's Book: A5.6WS, A5.7WS, R8, R24	
Shape and space (108–9)	Read and plot coordinates in all four quadrants.	7A Student Book: A5.8 7A Teacher's Book: A5.8OHP, R6, R8	
Reasoning and generalising about numbers or shapes (78–9)	Recognise and explain patterns and relationships, generalise and predict.	7A Student Book: A5.1–A5.8	

Overview

This unit starts by recapping types of angle and finding missing angles in right angles and on straight lines, extending to full turns. Students revisit the properties of 2-D shapes and extend to 3-D shapes and drawing nets.

The last three spreads recap and extend knowledge of line symmetry, and build on their understanding of transformations to consider rotational symmetry and tessellations.

Spreads S5.2, S5.3 and S5.6 form the focus of the unit.

Framework references

The unit covers objectives on Framework (Y456) Pages 103, 105, 107, 111

Introduction

Show students 2-D shapes – a square, isosceles triangle, rectangle and parallelogram (use **S5.2OHP**). Discuss their lines of symmetry.

Check in activity

With students standing, play 'Simon Says':
▶ Simon says, turn a quarter turn clockwise
▶ Simon says turn a half turn
▶ Simon says turn 90 degrees anticlockwise, etc.

Students sit down when they get it wrong. The winner is the last one standing.

Useful resources

Worksheets
S5.4WS – line symmetry
S5.5WS – rotational symmetry
S5.6WS – tessellations

OHPs
S5.1OHP – calculating angles
S5.2OHP – properties of shapes
S5.3OHP – nets for open boxes
S4.6OHP – the alphabet

General resources
R12 – protractor
R14 – triangles
R15 – quadrilaterals
R16 – common 3-D shapes
R24 – squared grid
Multilink cubes
Set of solids
Mirrors
A4 size cut-outs of square and equilateral triangle
Cut-out shapes
Tracing paper
Cut-out L-shape

Springboard 7 pages
132, 270, 451, 464

Differentiation – spanning the bridge

Spread	Bridge to the Support tier
S5.1	Progress Support tier students to calculate missing angles in a triangle, recapping work from S3.3. Also progress students to consider vertically opposite angles based upon two straight lines crossing.
S5.2	Support tier students focus on constructing triangles but would benefit from the general discussion in the Access introductory activity. Extend to discuss methods for constructing each type of triangle in turn.
S5.3	Progress Support tier students to consider the accurate construction of a square and in turn the net of a cube.
S5.4	Building on introductory activity, recap with Support tier students notation for equal sides and angles and parallel lines, as they will combine line symmetry with geometrical properties of shapes.
S5.5	Progress Support tier students to consider how many times a shape repeats itself in a full turn. Emphasise this is the order of rotational symmetry.
S5.6	Support tier extends to more complex shapes where reflection will be more predominant but essentially the Access introductory activity will be adequate for both tiers.

S5.1 Angle facts

Access

This spread provides access to the Year 7 objective:
▸ Know the sum of angles at a point and on a straight line (180)

Lesson Plan

Mental starter

Draw several angles (obtuse, acute) and ask students to name them. Progress to estimation, using reference points of 90°, 45° and 180°. Encourage students to measure the angles using a protractor (**R12**) or 360° angle measurer.

Introductory activity

Discuss students' understanding of angles. Emphasise an angle as a measure of turn, and ask students for the degrees of common turns: full, half, quarter, etc. Emphasise notation for right angles. Refer to the mental starter and emphasise that students can find missing angles using some of the angle facts.

Draw an obtuse angle, and label it 120°. Ask students to imagine they have turned 120°. How much more will you have to turn to make a half turn?

Discuss strategies:
▸ Counting on from 120 to make 180.
▸ Using equations: $120 + a = 180$ (emphasise the inverse function machine method).

Formalise with more examples. **S5.1OHP** provides a selection based on right angle, straight line and full turn.

Ask students what the full angle should measure.
▸ Discuss how much of the turn they already know
▸ Encourage students to explain their calculations.

Emphasise that the letter just stands for a missing value.

Plenary

Draw two circles on the board. Write 90 in one and 180 in the other. Write a number, spidering off one of the targets. Students give the number to add to make the target total. Write this number on the 'leg'. Repeat for different numbers.

Homework

▸ Target 90, 180, 360. Students create 20 chains of two numbers that total the target, as in the plenary.
▸ Springboard 7: Page 464.

Exercise Commentary

Coverage

The questions assess objectives on Framework (Y456) Page 111.

Useful resources

R12 – protractor
S5.1OHP – calculating angles

Differentiation

▸ Question 1 focuses on estimating angles.
▸ Question 2 focuses on naming angles.
▸ Questions 3–5 focus on finding missing angles.

Support tier: extends to finding angles in a triangle.

Misconceptions

Students may mix up the angle facts. Encourage students to first consider the full angle in the diagram. Students can discuss this in pairs.

Encourage them to check their answers by considering whether the angle should be acute or obtuse, and whether their calculated value matches this.

Links

Comparing numbers: Framework (Y456) Page 9.

Exercise Answers

1 a 80° b 40° c 100° d 150°
2 a Acute b Acute c Obtuse d Acute
  e Obtuse f Acute g Obtuse h Obtuse
3 **b + c, f + h, e + d, a + g**
4 a 70° b 35° c 29° d 130° e 35° f 40°
5 a 100° b 290° c 170°

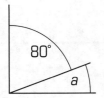

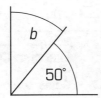

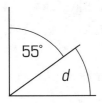

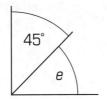

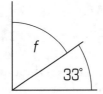

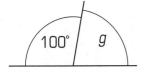

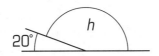

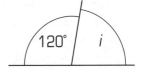

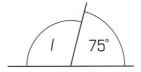

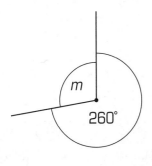

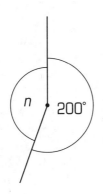

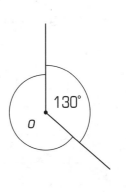

S5.2 Triangles and quadrilaterals

Access

This spread provides access to the Year 7 objective:
▸ Begin to identify properties of triangles and quadrilaterals (184)

Lesson Plan

Mental starter

Draw a bubble on the board, with 180 in the centre. Give a number, and ask students to give the complement to 180. Progress from easy numbers, say 30, to more complex numbers, say 56.

Introductory activity

Show a right-angled triangle, on **R14**. Ask students to name it, and highlight the right-angled notation. Highlight that a **triangle** has **three angles**. Show an isosceles, equilateral and scalene triangle (**R14**). Ask students to name each triangle, and discuss the side and angle properties of each triangle. Introduce equal side and equal angle notation. Encourage volunteers to label equal side and equal angles.

Progress to quadrilaterals. Emphasise that **quad** means **four** and ask students for examples of words in which they see **quad** (quad bikes – four wheels, quadruplets). Show a square, a rectangle, a parallelogram and a rhombus, on **R15**. Ask students to name them, and discuss the side and angle properties. Encourage students to label right angles, equal sides, equal angles. Discuss notation for parallel lines, and encourage students to label all parallel lines. Practise labelling diagrams on **S5.2OHP**.

Plenary

Read out a description of a shape:
▸ I have three sides. 2 sides are equal in length, and 2 of my angles are equal.
▸ I have 4 sides, and 4 right angles. I have two pairs of equal sides, and 2 pairs of parallel sides.
Students sketch the description, and hold up shape, or name shape.

Homework

▸ Label the shapes (square, rectangle, equilateral triangle, isosceles triangle, parallelogram) with proper notation.
▸ Springboard 7: Page 270.

Exercise Commentary

Coverage

The questions assess objectives on Framework (Y456) Page 103.

Useful resources

R14 and **R15** – triangles and quadrilaterals
S5.2OHP – properties of shapes

Differentiation

▸ Questions 1–3 focus on properties of triangles.
▸ Question 4 focuses on quadrilaterals.
▸ Question 5 involves visualisation.

Support tier: focuses on constructing triangles.

Misconceptions

Students may confuse notation for parallel and equal sides. Emphasise the 'direction' implied in parallel line notation and emphasise that parallel lines will never meet – they go in exactly the same direction.

Links

Angles: Framework Page 111.

Exercise Answers

1 a Right-angled b Isosceles c Isosceles
  d Equilateral e Scalene f Right-angled
  g Scalene h Isosceles
2 a Right-angled. One of the angles is 90°.
  b Isosceles. 2 sides and 2 angles are equal.
  c Isosceles. 2 sides and 2 angles are equal.
  d Equilateral. 3 sides and 3 angles are equal.
  e Scalene. No sides or angles are equal.
  f Right-angled. One of the angles is 90°.
  g Scalene. No sides or angles are equal.
  h Isosceles. 2 sides and 2 angles are equal.
3 a Right-angled. One of the angles is 90°.
  b Isosceles. 2 sides and 2 angles are equal.
  c Equilateral. 3 sides and 3 angles are equal.
  d Scalene. No sides or angles are equal.
4 a Rhombus b Rectangle c Square d Rhombus
5 a Equilateral triangle b Square or rectangle
  c Right-angled triangle d Rhombus

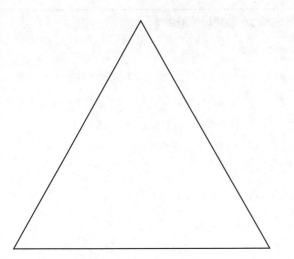

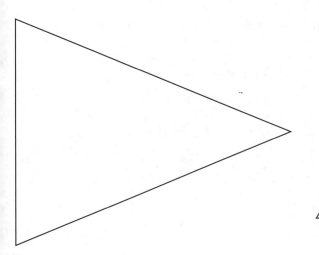

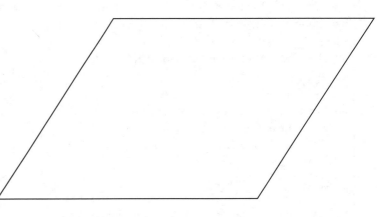

S5.3 Solid shapes

Access

This spread provides access to the Year 7 objective:
▶ Use 2-D representations to visualise 3-D shapes (198)

Lesson Plan

Mental starter

Describe 2-D shapes in steps, revealing a new property at each stage. For example: I have 3 sides and 3 angles. All my angles are different. One angle is 90° (right-angled triangle). Students sketch shape and hold it up.

Introductory activity

Refer to the mental starter and emphasise that all these shapes had 2 dimensions – length and width. They are **flat** shapes, and can easily be drawn.

Emphasise that most shapes have 3 dimensions – they are not flat. Use examples around the classroom to highlight this. Introduce keywords: **cube**, **cuboid**, **pyramid**, **prism** (**R16**). Discuss real-life examples of these shapes.

Group students into pairs, and give each group a multilink cube. Encourage pairs to describe the shape. Introduce keywords: **equal**, **edge**, **face**, **vertices**. Distinguish **side** from **edge** explaining **side** can be confused with both **edge** (as in 2-D shape) and **face** (3-D shape). Formalise number of vertices, edges, faces of a cube. Highlight that the faces of a cube are all squares, and all edges are equal.

Emphasise that a flat shape can be designed so that it folds into a 3-D shape and define the flat shape as a **net**. Look at some nets of cubes, and discuss which edges match up when folded. Distinguish between nets of cubes and nets of **open boxes** on **S5.3OHP**.

Plenary

Discuss the 3-D shapes in question 3a–d. Encourage students to work in pairs to sketch the nets. Encourage technical language and use of colour to indicate matching edges.

Homework

▶ Draw the net of a dice, placing the numbers so that opposite faces add to 7.
▶ Springboard 7: Page 132.

Exercise Commentary

Coverage

The questions assess objectives on Framework (Y456) Page 105.

Useful resources

R16 – common 3-D shapes
Multilink cubes
Set of solids
S5.3OHP – nets for open boxes

Differentiation

▶ Questions 1 and 2 involve making shapes from cubes.
▶ Question 3 involves counting faces.
▶ Question 4 focuses on interpreting nets of open boxes.

Support tier: focuses on constructing nets of cubes.

Misconceptions

Students find it difficult to visualise 2-D representations of 3-D shapes. Encourage them to refer to models of solid shapes. For question 4, encourage students to cut out nets (from **S5.3OHP**) and fold them to see the transformation from 2-D to 3-D.

Links

Properties of shapes: Framework (Y456) Page 103.

Exercise Answers

1 a 2   b 2   c 4   d 4
2 a 2   b 2   c 4   d 4
3 a 5   b 6   c 5   d 6   e 8   f 6   g 3   h 5
4 a Green   b Blue   c Red   d Grey   e Yellow
  f Red   g Black   h Blue

S5.30HP Solid shapes

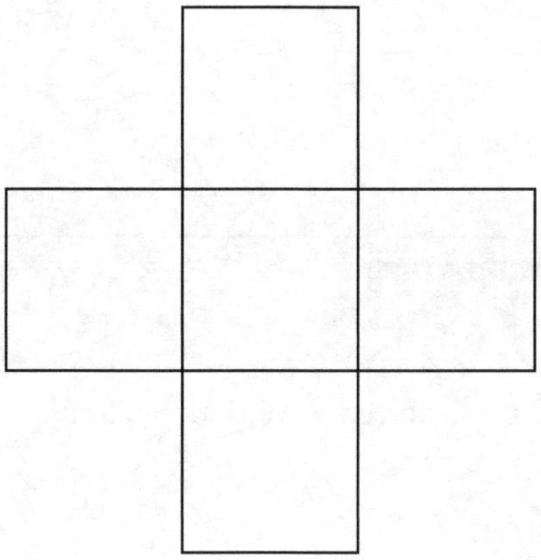

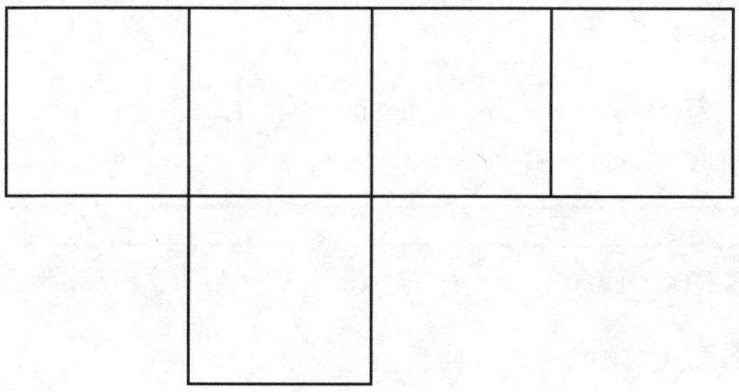

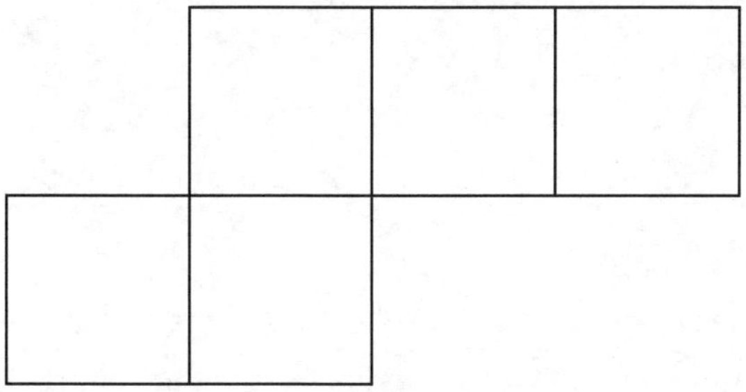

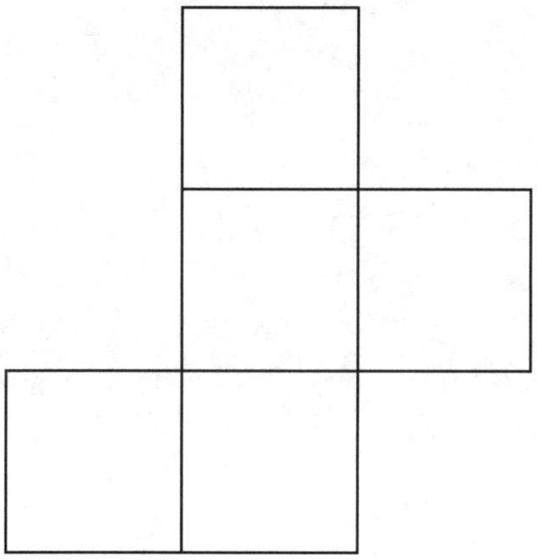

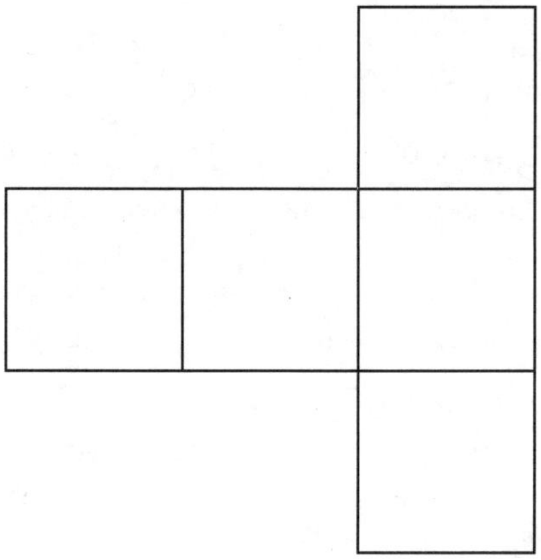

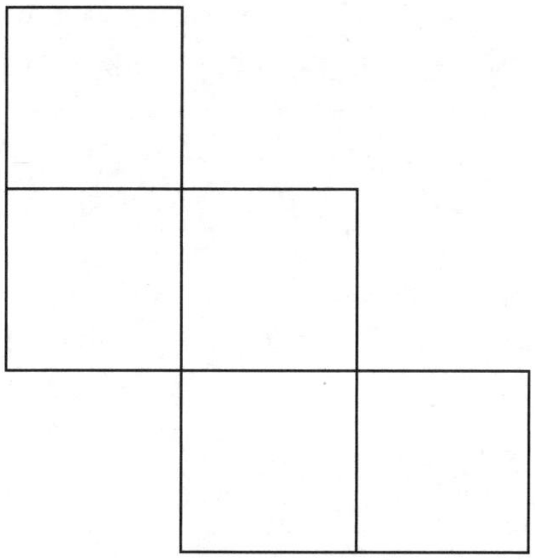

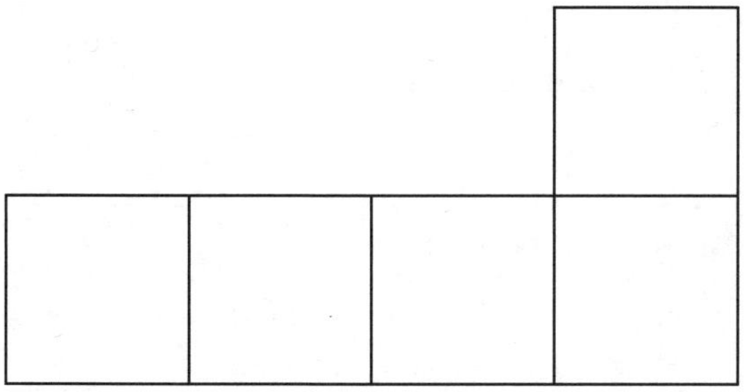

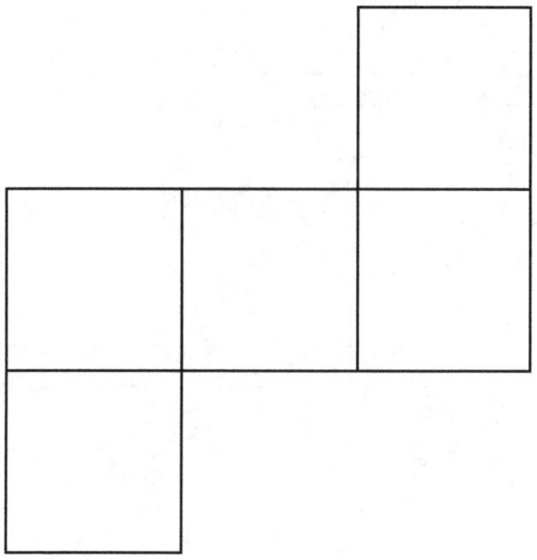

S5.4 Line symmetry

Access

This spread provides access to the Year 7 objective:
▸ Recognise and visualise line symmetry (206)

Lesson Plan

Mental starter

Cut out some shapes with line symmetry (rectangle, square, equilateral triangle, isosceles triangle, isosceles trapezium from **R14** and **R15**) and fold them along their line of symmetry.

Explain to the students what you have done.

Ask students to identify shape from the half shown, naming angle and side properties.

Introductory activity

Refer to the mental starter. Discuss the name for the **fold line (line of symmetry)**. Define shapes with a line of symmetry as having **line symmetry**. Demonstrate how to use a mirror to check a line of symmetry, and also to complete a shape with line symmetry.

Give pairs of students A4 size cut-outs of a square; equilateral triangle. Challenge the students to find all the lines of symmetry in these shapes (explain that each shape has more than one). Discuss their findings and formalise them using the diagrams in the Students' book. Emphasise that shapes with equal sides and angles are called **regular**.

Plenary

Ask students to sketch a shape with just one line of symmetry. Progress to 2 lines, 3 lines, and 0 lines of symmetry.

Homework

▸ Draw shapes seen in real life that have one line of symmetry (as in question 1).
▸ Springboard 7: Page 451.

Exercise Answers

1 a, b, c
3 a 4 b 3 c 4 d Many e 4 f 2
4 5 lines of symmetry
5 6 equal sides, 6 equal angles, 6 lines of symmetry

Exercise Commentary

Coverage

The questions assess objectives on Framework (Y456) Page 107.

Useful resources

R14 and **R15** – triangles and quadrilaterals

Mirrors

S5.4WS – provides support for weaker students.

A4 size cut-outs of square and equilateral triangle.

Differentiation

▸ Questions 1 and 2 involve identifying line symmetry.
▸ Question 3 involves finding all the lines of symmetry of a shape.
▸ Questions 4 and 5 focus on symmetry of regular polygons.

Support tier: extends to drawing shapes given symmetry properties.

Misconceptions

Students find vertical and horizontal lines of symmetry easier to spot, and will need encouragement to find others. Suggest that they turn the page and look for others. Photocopy the exercise for weaker students, to enable them to cut out and fold each picture/shape.

In question 1d, students may identify a line of symmetry where there is none, ignoring the features within the shape. As with all questions, encourage students to check their work with a mirror.

Links

Properties of shapes: Framework (Y456) Page 103.

Worksheet Answers

2 a Kite b Octagon c Triangle d Rectangle
  e Pentagon f Square g Hexagon

1 Here are the names of some shapes.
Find and highlight each name in the
word search.

OCTAGON

RECTANGLE

TRIANGLE

SQUARE

KITE

POLYGONS

RHOMBUS

PENTAGON

HEXAGON

TRAPEZIUM

G	O	N	R	H	E	C	E	Z	T
P	E	N	H	E	X	A	G	O	N
L	E	P	O	L	Y	G	O	N	S
S	Q	I	M	U	Z	T	O	N	T
X	A	H	B	I	T	E	C	E	R
I	S	Q	U	A	R	E	T	R	A
T	R	A	S	U	I	M	A	E	P
S	R	E	C	T	A	N	G	L	E
T	R	Y	A	A	N	G	O	N	Z
P	E	N	T	A	G	O	N	U	I
R	E	X	E	Z	L	E	T	H	U
F	R	K	I	T	E	L	G	O	M

2 Complete the reflection of these shapes.
Name the completed shapes using the words in question 1.

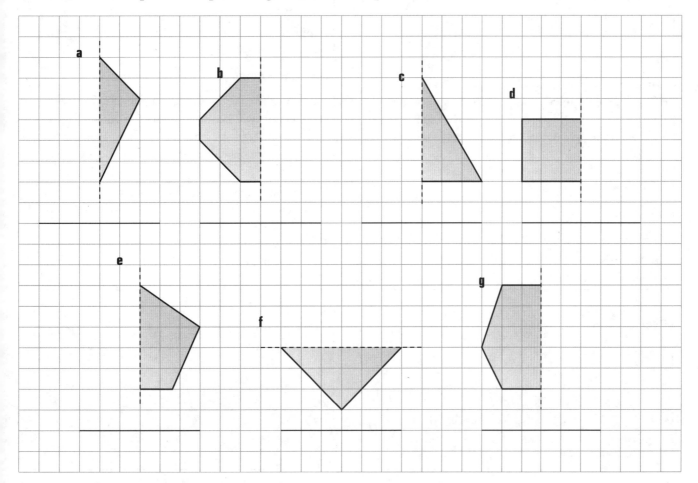

Access

This spread provides access to the Year 7 objective:
▶ Recognise and visualise rotation symmetry (210)

Lesson Plan

Mental starter

Ask students to name a shape with 0/1/2 lines of symmetry. Check using mirrors/folding.

Introductory activity

Recap work on rotating shapes in Unit S4.5, using a cut out rectangle, and rotating it 90° clockwise. Highlight rotation as **turn**.

Introduce the idea of **rotational symmetry**. Show how a rectangle repeats itself at the half turn point of a full turn. Trace around the shape – place a cross at the top to help indicate when it has made a full turn.

Define: **A shape has rotational symmetry if it repeats in a full turn**.

Demonstrate with other cut-out shapes (from **R15**). Emphasise tracing the shape initially to help. Highlight the need for a cross at the top of a shape to help determine a full turn.

Plenary

Challenge students to sketch a shape with:
▶ One line of symmetry that repeats itself once in a full turn.
▶ Two lines of symmetry that repeats itself once in a full turn.
▶ Two lines of symmetry that repeats itself **twice** in a full turn.

Homework

▶ Identify the letters of the alphabet (**S4.6OHP**) that have rotational symmetry. Make up words with rotational symmetry.

Exercise Commentary

Coverage

The questions assess objectives on Framework (Y456) Page 111.

Useful resources

R15 – quadrilaterals
Cut-out rectangle and other shapes.
Tracing paper
S4.6OHP – the alphabet
S5.5WS – provides further practice of the key ideas.

Differentiation

▶ Question 1 involves identifying rotation symmetry.
▶ Questions 2–5 involve finding rotation symmetry in more complex shapes.
▶ Question 6 focuses on visualising shapes with rotation symmetry.

Support tier: focuses on the order of rotation symmetry.

Misconceptions

It can be difficult to visualise rotational symmetries, and students will benefit from having cut-outs of the shapes to rotate with a pencil. Tracing paper can help with the more detailed shapes, and can be used to check work.

Encourage students to mark one point on the shape with a cross, so they can correctly identify a full turn.

Links

Angles: Framework (Y456) Page 111.

Exercise Answers

1 a No   b Yes   c Yes   d No   e Yes
2 a Yes   b Yes   c Yes   d No   e Yes
3 a Yes   b Yes   c Yes   d No   e Yes
4 For example: NON, SOS, pud
5 a Yes   b No   c Yes   d Yes   e Yes   f Yes
  g No   h Yes
6 a 1881, 1001, 8008, 1111, 8888   b 8008

Worksheet Answers

1 a 96MW96,
    H01810H,
    XH88HX
2 No rotational symmetry: a, c, g
  Repeats twice: b, e, j
  Repeats more than twice: d, f, h, i
3 f

1 Tick (✓) the car number plates that look the same when
you turn them up side-down.
They have rotational symmetry.

| 96MW96 | | I85I85 | | 60406 | | H0I8I0H | | XH88HX |

2 These shapes can be put into three categories:

‣ no rotational symmetry
‣ repeats twice in one rotation
‣ repeats more than twice in one rotation.

a   b   c   d   e

f   g   h   i   j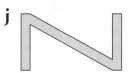

Put the letter of each shape into the correct column.

No rotational symmetry	Shape repeats twice in one rotation	Shape repeats more than twice in one rotation

3 Which shape in question 2 repeats most times? _____

4 Draw a shape of your own that has rotational
symmetry in the box.

S5.6 Tessellations

Access

This spread provides access to the Year 7 objective:
▶ Recognise and visualise translation (212)

Lesson Plan

Mental starter

Sketch me
Encourage students to sketch shapes/patterns or words which repeat themselves in a full turn. Once complete, rotate the shapes and see who was right.

Introductory activity

Show the L-shape from the Students' book on an OHP of a squared grid (**R24**). Demonstrate different transformations of the shape to recap work done in S4. Emphasise that:
▶ Reflection is a flip.
▶ Rotation is a turn.
▶ Translation is a slide.

Highlight the key word **congruent** – the shape has not changed in any of these transformations.

Repeat the translation, moving the image by exactly the same translation as before. Highlight that it creates a pattern.

Emphasise that a pattern where there are no gaps or overlaps is called a **tessellation**. Explain that the L-shape tessellates, and discuss how it can be drawn to leave no gaps.

Using a right-angled triangle, demonstrate that shapes can be reflected to tessellate.

Plenary

Discuss tessellations used in everyday life (tile patterns/floorboards/wallpaper designs/roof tiles). Discuss why shapes that tessellate are used (fewer shapes for production and less space taken up).

Homework

▶ Sketch tessellations seen in real life. What shapes have been used?

Exercise Commentary

Coverage

The questions assess objectives on Framework (Y456) Page 107.

Useful resources

R24 – squared grid
Cut-out L-shape, as in Students' book
Cut-out right-angled triangle
S5.6WS – provides further practice of the key ideas.

Differentiation

▶ Question 1 focuses on translations.
▶ Question 2 includes reflections.
▶ Question 3 involves combinations of transformations.
Support tier: extends to more complex tessellations.

Misconceptions

Students will need to use cut-outs of the shapes to see whether they tessellate. Some students may find it difficult to copy shapes, and cutting out may be time consuming. To support these students, pre-cut out copies could be provided.

Links

Problem solving: Framework Page 79.

Worksheet Answers

2 a, b and **e** tessellate.

1 Tessellate this shape 15 times on the grid.
It must fit together with no gaps or overlaps.

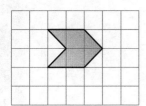 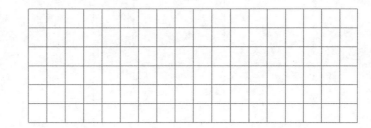

2 Which of these shapes will tessellate? Use the grid to test each shape.
If the shape tessellates, put a tick (✔) inside it.

a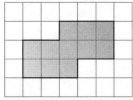

b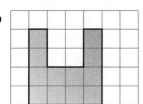

c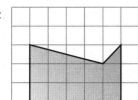

d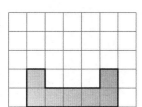

e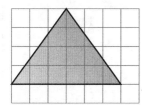

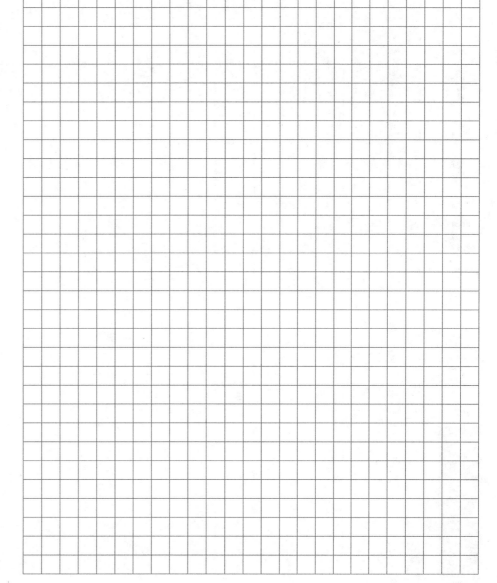

Framework MATHS   Scheme of work   Year 7

S5 Angles and symmetry (6 hours)	Teaching objectives	Framework Maths resources		Other resources
Shape and space (110–11)	Identify, estimate and order acute and obtuse angles. Calculate angles in a straight line.	7A Student Book: 7A Teacher's Book:	S5.1 S5.1OHP, R12	
Shape and space (102–3)	Classify triangles. Classify quadrilaterals.	7A Student Book: 7A Teacher's Book:	S5.2 S5.2OHP, R14, R15	
Shape and space (104–5)	Make shapes with increasing accuracy. Visualise 3-D shapes from 2-D drawings and identify different nets for an open cube.	7A Student Book: 7A Teacher's Book:	S5.3 S5.3OHP, R16	
Shape and space (106–7)	Recognise reflection symmetry in regular polygons.	7A Student Book: 7A Teacher's Book:	S5.4 S5.4WS, R14, R15	
Shape and space (109–110)	Recognise where a shape will be after a rotation.	7A Student Book: 7A Teacher's Book:	S5.5 S4.6OHP, S5.5WS, R15	
Shape and space (106–7)	Recognise where a shape will be after a translation.	7A Student Book: 7A Teacher's Book:	S5.6 S5.6WS, R24	
Reasoning and generalising about numbers or shapes (80–1)	Make a general statement about shapes by finding examples that satisfy it.	7A Student Book:	S5.1 - S5.6	

Access

© Oxford University Press 2004 for use within purchaser's institution

Assessment

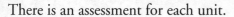

There is an assessment for each unit.

Each assessment is designed so that sudents can write on their answers.

The assessment are 10 minutes long.

The questions are based on past paper National Test questions from KS2.

The questions are mostly at Level 3 with two or three marks at Level 2.

Students should be able to score around 70% on each assessment.

Assessments		**250–287**
A1	Sequences	250–251
N1	Number calculations	252–253
S1	Perimeter and area	254–255
N2	Fractions, decimals and percentages	256–257
D1	Data and probability	258–269
A2	Using symbols	260–261
S2	Angles and shapes	262–263
D2	Handling data	264–265
N3	Multiplication and division	266–267
A3	Functions and graphs	268–269
S3	Triangles and quadrilaterals	270–271
N4	Percentages, ratio and proportion	272–273
A4	Linear equations	274–275
S4	Transformations	276–277
N5	More number calculations	278–279
D3	The handling data cycle	280–281
D4	Probability experiments	282–283
A5	Equations and graphs	284–285
S5	Angles and symmetry	286–287
Assessment Answers		288–292
General Resources		293–310

1 Continue this sequence.

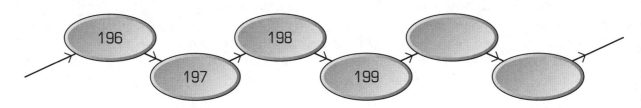

1 mark

2 Complete this sequence: 3,   7,   ☐,   15,   19,   23,   ☐

1 mark

3 The rule for this number sequence is '**double and add 1**'

a Write in the **missing** number.

2, 5, 11, 23, ———

1 mark

Here is part of **another** sequence with the **same** rule.

b Write in the **missing** number.

———, 13, 27, 55

1 mark

4 Here is a number sequence.
Write in the **missing** numbers.

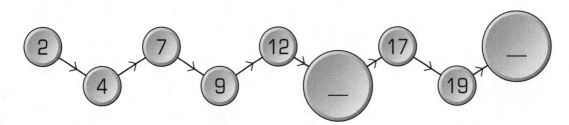

2 marks

A1 Assessment

5 a Jane thinks of a number.
She says, '**If I multiply my number by 5, the answer is 40**'.

What is her number? _____   *1 mark*

b She thinks of a different number.
She says, '**If I divide the number on this card by 6, the answer is 3**'.

What is the number on the card? _____   *1 mark*

6 Write in the **missing** number.

100 – _____ = 38   *1 mark*

7 Write in the missing number.

60 + 99 + _____ = 340   *1 mark*

Name: ....

1 Write numbers in the spaces to make these correct.
Use only these numbers:

4, 8, 12, 16, 20

You can use each number more than once.

a _____ **+** _____ **=** _____

b _____ **−** _____ **=** _____   *2 marks*

2 2.1 is marked on this number line.

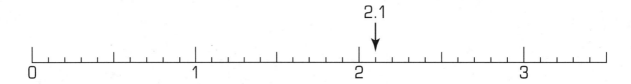

Draw an arrow to mark 1.6   *1 mark*

3 Use **all** the digits 7, **1** and **3** to:

a write a number **between 100** and **140** _____   *1 mark*

b complete this **subtraction**:

☐☐ – ☐ = 24   *1 mark*

4 Circle two more calculations that make 150.

(75 + 75)   90 + 80   85 + 65   450 – 300   210 – 70   *2 marks*

N1 Assessment

5 Circle **all** the multiples of 10.

540   500   403   180   27   295   50   531   *1 mark*

6 These thermometers show the
temperature inside and outside
a greenhouse.

Outside

Inside

a How many degrees **warmer** was it inside the greenhouse than outside?

_____ °C

1 mark

Later the temperatures were

Inside	Outside
⁻1 °C	⁻8 °C

b What is the difference between these two temperatures? _____ °C   *1 mark*

1 A recipe for bread uses 350 grams of flour.
Draw an arrow on the scale to show 350 grams.

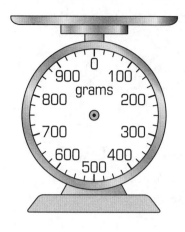

1 mark

2 Draw a **new** line 3 cm longer than this one.
Draw it underneath this line.

Use a ruler.

——————————————————————

1 mark

3 Sketch a rectangle with perimeter 18 centimetres (cm).

Label the lengths of the sides.

2 marks

S1 Assessment

4 A square window has a perimeter of 8 metres.

How long is one of its sides? _____ m

1 mark

5 Gemma says shape A has a larger area than shape B.

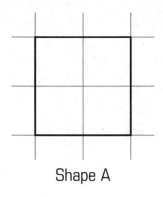
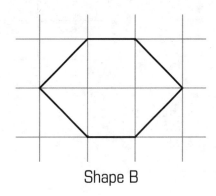

Shape A   Shape B

a Explain why she is wrong.

_____ *1 mark*

b Draw another shape with the same area as A and B.   *1 mark*

6 A rectangular field measures 60 m by 45 m.

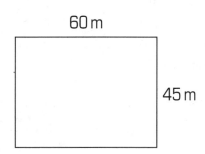

60 m

45 m

a What is the perimeter of the field? _____ m
b What is the area of the field? _____ m^2 *3 marks*

1 Colour in exactly **half** of this shape.

1 mark

2 Colour in **one third** of this shape.

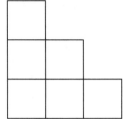

1 mark

3 What fraction of this shape is shaded?

1 mark

4 What is half of eighty-six? _____   *1 mark*

5 What is one quarter of 80? _____   *1 mark*

6 Draw a line to join each
fraction to a percentage of
the same value.
One is done for you.

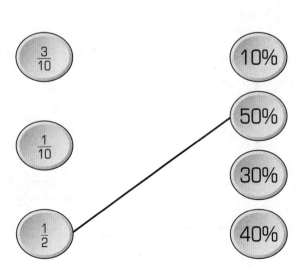

1 mark

N2 Assessment

7 Here are 12 balls.
Draw a ring around **one quarter** of them.

1 mark

8 Peter ate **half** the sweets on the plate.
These are the sweets that were **left**.

How many sweets were there on the plate
before Peter ate half of them?

_____

1 mark

9 2.1 is marked on the number line.

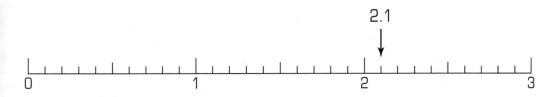

a Mark 1.3 on the number line.

1 mark

b Mark 0.65 on the number line.

1 mark

1 Write a number that it is **impossible** to throw on a dice.

_____ *1 mark*

2 Here is a bar chart of class 7E's pets.

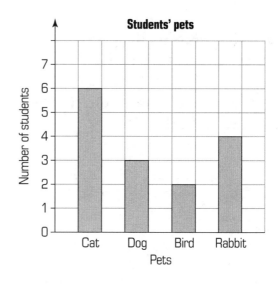

a Which is the most common pet? _____ *1 mark*

b Explain how you know.

_____ *1 mark*

3 Write these in **order of size**, starting with the **smallest** amount.

540   65   72   288   1000

_____ *1 mark*

4 Work out the number halfway between 26 and 38.
Write it in the box.

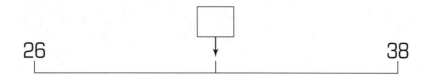

1 mark

D1 Assessment

5 Class 7P made a birthday graph.

Which month has most birthdays? _____ *1 mark*

6 Simon, Emily, Sam and Sarah work out how many apples they eat each week.

a Who ate the most apples? _____ *1 mark*

b What is the mean number of apples eaten? _____ *1 mark*

7 These black, white and striped marbles are hidden in a bag. The bag is shaken.

David **picks one marble without looking**.

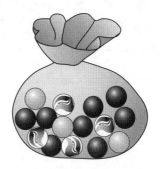

a Which kind of marble is David most likely to pick?

_____ *1 mark*

b Explain how you know.

_____ *1 mark*

1 Write in the missing numbers.

a $52 + \boxed{} = 61$

b $83 - \boxed{} = 78$

2 marks

2

Big popcorn	**£1.50**
Small popcorn	**90p**
Big drink	**£1.20**
Small drink	**75p**

a Peter has **£2**.

He buys **one** thing and has **exactly 80p** left.

What does he buy? _____

1 mark

b **Ayesha has 90p.**

She buys a small drink.

How much money does she have left? _____

1 mark

3

Boat Hire	
Motor boats	**Rowing boats**
£1.50 for 15 minutes	£2.00 for 1 hour

How much does it cost to hire a **rowing boat** for four hours? _____

1 mark

4 A box of doughnuts contains 5 doughnuts.

Gemma buys 7 boxes of doughnuts.

How many doughnuts does she buy altogether? _____

1 mark

A2 Assessment

5 Draw arrows to complete the diagram. Each arrow means 'is 7 less than'.

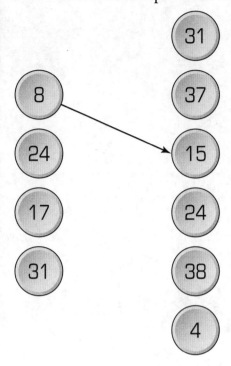

3 marks

6 Jon picks 60 apples. He sells some and has 25 apples left.

How many does he sell? _____

1 mark

1 A train should arrive at 8:25. It is running 20 minutes late.

What time will it arrive? _____   *1 mark*

2 Here is a clock:

How many minutes until it shows 1:30?

_____ minutes   *1 mark*

3 The clock shows when a film starts.

The film is $1\frac{1}{2}$ hours long.

What time does it finish? _____   *1 mark*

4 Draw lines to match the times on the analogue clocks with the same time on a digital clock. One has been done for you.

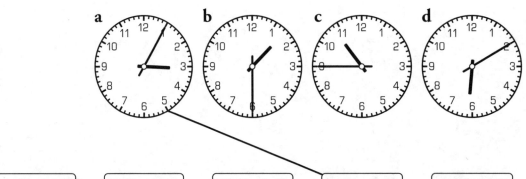

3 marks.

S2 Assessment

5 P, Q and R are three corners of a square.

Write the coordinates of the other corner.

_____

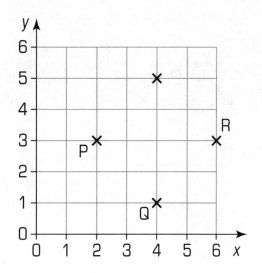

2 marks

6 (4, 5) is a point on this line:

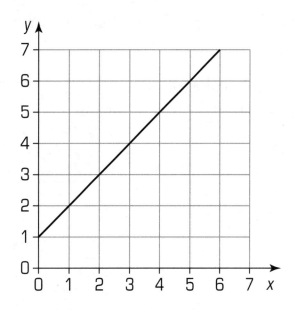

a Circle the coordinates of the points that are on the line:

(1, 2)   (4, 1)   (3, 3)   (5, 6)   (2, 5)   *1 mark*

b How do you know that (8, 9) is on the line?

_____   *1 mark*

1 A shop sold 10 ice lollies on Wednesday.

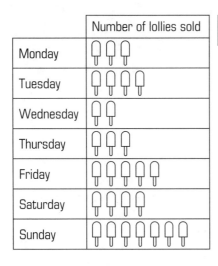

 = 5 lollies

	Number of lollies sold
Monday	
Tuesday	
Wednesday	
Thursday	
Friday	
Saturday	
Sunday	

a How many lollies were sold on Tuesday? _____   *1 mark*

b How many more lollies were sold on Thursday than on Wednesday? _____   *1 mark*

2 Write each number in its correct place on the sorting diagram.

30   12   15

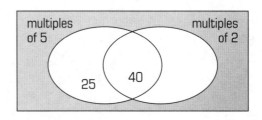

2 marks

3 a Complete this tally chart.

Fruits we like best

Fruit	Tally	Frequency
Orange		6
Apple	ⅢⅢ Ⅲ	8
Pear	Ⅲ	3
Banana	ⅢⅢ ⅢⅢ ⅢⅢ Ⅰ	
Mango	ⅢⅠ	4

1 mark

b How many people were asked altogether? _____   *1 mark*

c How many people chose banana or apple as their favourite? _____   *1 mark*

D2 Assessment

4 Chris tallied the number of people going into different shops in one hour.

Shop	Tally
Newsagent	III
Bakery	JHT JHT IIII
Post Office	JHT JHT JHT JHT I
Pizza take-away	JHT JHT III

a How many people went into the **Bakery**? _____   *1 mark*

b How many **more** people went into the **Post Office** than into the **Pizza take-away**?

_____ *1 mark*

Here is part of a bar chart of the information.

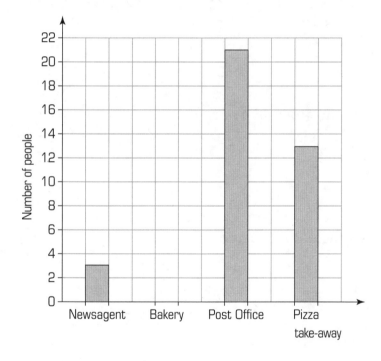

c Draw in the **missing** bar.   *1 mark*

1 Write different numbers in the circles so that all six numbers are in order.

23 ◯ 104 ◯ ◯ 203

smallest ——————————————→ biggest

1 mark

2 Draw lines to match the answers.
One has been done for you.

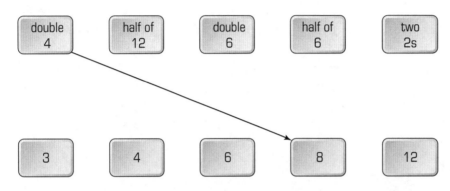

| double 4 | half of 12 | double 6 | half of 6 | two 2s |

| 3 | 4 | 6 | 8 | 12 |

1 mark

3 32 people share pizzas. Each pizza is for one group of 4.

How many groups are there? _____   *1 mark*

4 Write the lowest number you can using these three digits:

| 3 | 7 | 1 | _____   *1 mark*

5 Find the missing numbers:

a $30 \div \boxed{} = 5$

b $4 \times \boxed{} = 28$ *2 marks*

N3 Assessment

6 A shop sells doughnuts in packs of 5 and packs of 8.

   a Janet buys 6 packs of 8 doughnuts.

     How many doughnuts does she buy? _____

   b Rhona buys some packs of 5.

     She has 45 doughnuts altogether.

     How many packs did she buy? _____   *2 marks*

7 Draw lines to match these numbers to their nearest 100.

162

293

145   100

         200

421   300

         400

362

         500

204

2 marks

1 Circle the three numbers that are multiples of 5.

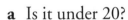 62 65 66 81 82 89 98 99 100 103 108 115 *2 marks*

2 Claire and Sîan play a number game –
What's my number?

a Is it under 20?   Yes

  Is it a multiple of 3?   Yes

  Is it a multiple of 5?   Yes

  What is the number? _____   *1 mark*

b They play the game again.

  Is it under 20?   Yes

  Is it over 10?   Yes

  Is it odd?   No

  Is it a square number?   Yes

  What is the number? _____   *1 mark*

3 Complete this two-digit number so that it is a multiple of 6.

4	

1 mark

4 Write the missing numbers in the circles using these rules.

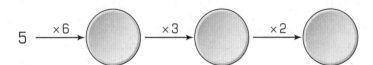

2 marks

A3 Assessment

5 Explain how you know that 16 is a square number.

_____

_____ *1 mark*

6 (7, 6) are the coordinates of the point × on this line.

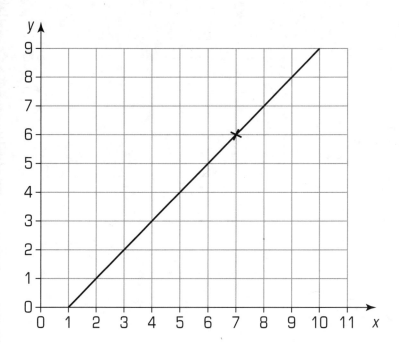

a Tick (✓) the coordinates of other points on the line.

(3, 2) ☐   (7, 10) ☐   (5, 4) ☐

(4, 5) ☐   (10, 9) ☐   (7, 8) ☐   *1 mark*

b Explain how you know that point (11, 12) would not be on this line?

_____

_____ *1 mark*

1 Hannah puts **5 pegs** in a pegboard. Draw how the board looks now.
She turns the board through
1 right angle clockwise.

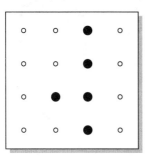

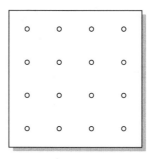

1 mark

2 Use a ruler to draw **2 more lines** to make an **isosceles** triangle.

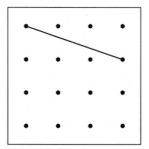

1 mark

3 a On the grid join dots to make a triangle which **has a right angle**.
Use a ruler.

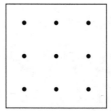

1 mark

b On the grid join dots to make a triangle which does **not** have a **right angle**.
Use a ruler.

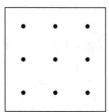

1 mark

S3 Assessment

4

a What number will this clock hand point to after a quarter turn **clockwise**?

_____ *1 mark*

b What number will the clock hand point to after a half turn? _____ *1 mark*

c What number will this clock hand point
to after a quarter turn **anticlockwise**?

_____

1 mark

5 What will this rectangle look like after a half turn?

Tick (✓) the correct answer.

      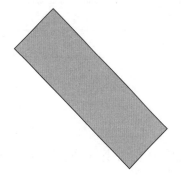

1 mark

6 Complete these sentences.

a All **isosceles triangles** have _____ *1 mark*

b All **equilateral triangles** have _____ *1 mark*

1 Shade more squares so that exactly **half of the shape** is shaded.

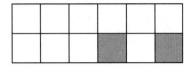

1 mark

2 Shade more squares so that exactly **a quarter of the shape** is shaded.

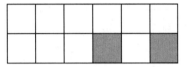

1 mark

3 Put a tick (✓) in **each row** to complete this table.
One has been done for you.

	Greater than $\frac{1}{2}$	Less than $\frac{1}{2}$
0.9	✓	
0.4		
$\frac{6}{10}$		
0.21		

3 marks

4 What is half of four hundred and sixty? _____

1 mark

N4 Assessment

5 Draw a line to join each fraction to a percentage of the same value.

One has been done for you.

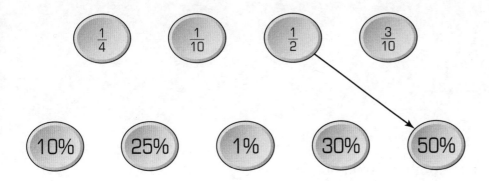

2 marks

6 John has 27 apples. He gives one third of them to Steven.

a How many apples does he give Steven? _____ *1 mark*

b How many apples does John have left? _____ *1 mark*

1 Write in the missing numbers.

   a $84 - \underline{\hspace{2cm}} = 76$

   b $3 \times 20 = \underline{\hspace{2cm}}$

   c $\underline{\hspace{2cm}} + 78 = 97$

   d $65 + 35 = 120 - \underline{\hspace{2cm}}$ *4 marks*

2 Write in what the missing numbers could be.

   a $\underline{\hspace{2cm}} - \underline{\hspace{2cm}} = 66$

   b $\underline{\hspace{2cm}} \times \underline{\hspace{2cm}} = 48$ *2 marks*

3 Each card on the left matches one on the right.

Draw lines to match the cards which are **equal** in value.

One has been done for you.

4×6	2×30
10×6	12×2
5×6	50×2
8×10	4×20
4×25	10×3

2 marks

A4 Assessment

4 Use these signs.

$$= \quad < \quad >$$

Write the correct signs in the boxes.

a 3×4 ☐ 2×6

b 8×6 ☐ 9×6

c 4×7 ☐ 4×5

d 10×6 ☐ 6×10

2 marks

1 Each of these shapes has one or more **lines of symmetry**.

Draw **all** the **lines of symmetry** on each shape.

a 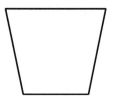 **b**  **c**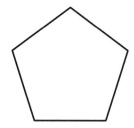

3 marks

2

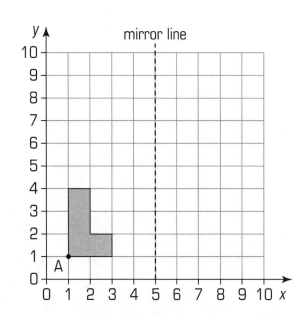

a On the grid, draw the **reflection** of the shape **in the mirror line**.

You may use a mirror and tracing paper. *1 mark*

b What are the coordinates of point A? (_____, _____) *1 mark*

c What are the coordinates of the reflection of point A? (_____, _____) *1 mark*

S4 Assessment

3 Draw the **reflection** of this triangle in the mirror line.
Use a ruler.
You may use tracing paper.

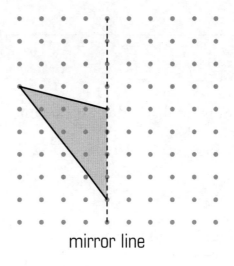

mirror line

1 mark

4 Follow this route with your pencil.

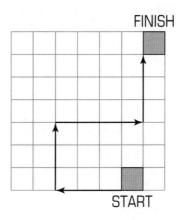

FINISH

START

a Complete this chart showing the route from START to FINISH.

START
Left 3
Up 3
....
....
FINISH

1 mark

b Give your own directions to move from START to FINISH.
Use as many directions as you need.

START
....
....
....
....
....
FINISH

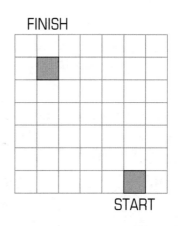

FINISH

START

2 marks

Name: ....

1 What is twice four hundred and thirty?

_____

1 mark

2 Circle the number that is **nearest in value to 650**.

470   599   710   752   950

1 mark

3 Write the missing numbers.

a $20 \times 4 = \boxed{}$

b $48 \div \boxed{} = 24$

2 marks

4 The outside of this circle has 11 squares fitted around part of it.

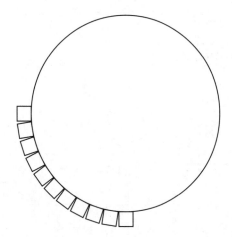

About how many squares could be fitted around the whole circle?

Circle the answer.

80   40   25   100   65

1 mark

N5 Assessment

5 Draw arrows to match each number to its nearest 10.

The first one has been done for you.

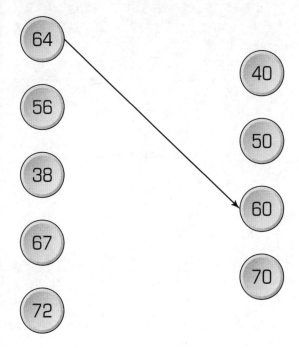

2 marks

6 Write the answer.

$24 \times 5 =$ _____

1 mark

7 Calculate 326×6
You **must** show your working.

_____ *1 mark*

8 What is $\frac{1}{3}$ of 27 balloons? _____ *1 mark*

1 Here is a table showing the number of children at 5 schools.

Number of children attending 5 schools

School	Number of children
Henry Compton	161
Sedgehill	108
Paxton	170
Woodbridge	99
Sydenham	145

Tick (✓) the school with the most children.   *1 mark*

2 Tom makes a graph of buses passing a school in 1 hour.

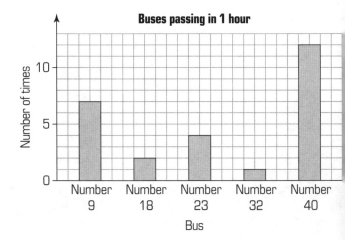

a Which number bus passes most often?   Number _____   *1 mark*

b Tom says, '***Bus number 32 passes least often in the hour.***'

Explain how the graph shows this.

_____   *1 mark*

3 Suzy recorded information about cars passing the school.

Colour of cars passing in one hour

Colour	Number of cars
Red	15
Yellow	7
Green	3
Blue	10
White	2
Silver	1

a Which colour was the second most popular? _____   *1 mark*

b Which two colours of cars were seen the least? _____   *1 mark*

D3 Assessment

4 This graph shows class 7B's birthday months.

Birthday months

a In which month does no one in class 7B have a birthday? _____ *1 mark*

b How many children are in class 7B? _____ *1 mark*

5 Class survey of favourite fruit

Flavour	Number of students
Pineapple	4
Orange	8
Blackcurrant	8
Grapefruit	6
Apple	9

a Complete the pictogram for the class.

Flavour	Number of students
Blackcurrant	🍎🍎🍎🍎
Apple	
	🍎🍎🍎
Orange	
Pineapple	

Key: 🍎 = 2 students

1 mark

b How many students altogether chose the three most popular fruits? _____ *1 mark*

c Write another question you can ask someone about the results of the class survey.

_____

_____ *1 mark*

1 Here are some counters.
Some of them are grey, some are black, some are white:

James puts these **7** counters into a bag:

He takes **one** counter from his bag without looking.

a List all the colours James **could** get when he takes **one** counter from his bag.

_____ *1 mark*

b Which colour is James **most likely** to get? _____ *1 mark*

Explain your answer. _____

_____ *1 mark*

c Geena has these counters in her bag:

She wants to put some more counters in, to make it **equally likely** that she
will pick a black, white or grey counter.

What **extra** counters should Geena put into her bag?

_____ *2 marks*

D4 Assessment

2 You can throw any number from 1 to 5 on this spinner.

Write a number that is **impossible** to throw. _____   *1 mark*

3 Peter uses an **8-sided** spinner.

Choose one of these words to complete each sentence:

| IMPOSSIBLE | | UNLIKELY |
| EVEN CHANCE | | LIKELY |
| CERTAIN |

a _____ to spin the number 12.

b _____ to spin a number less than 9.

c _____ to spin the same number twice in a row.

d _____ to spin an even number.   *4 marks*

Name:

....

1 Continue this sequence.

96   97   98   99   ____   ____

1 mark

2 Write in the **missing** numbers.

a $4 \times \boxed{} = 80$

b $\boxed{} + 69 = 81$

c $60 - \boxed{} = 36$

d $30 \div \boxed{} = 6$

4 marks

3 The rule for this number sequence is

'double and subtract 1'

Write in the **missing** number.

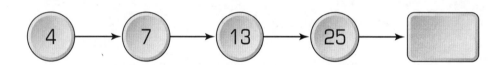

1 mark

4 A shop sells doughnuts in boxes of 12.
John buys 6 boxes of doughnuts.
How many doughnuts does he buy altogether? _____

1 mark

5 How many twenty pence pieces are there in two pounds? _____

1 mark

A5 Assessment

6 Paul is thinking of a number.

He says: 'If I double my number, the answer is 24.'

What number is Paul thinking of?   _____   *1 mark*

7

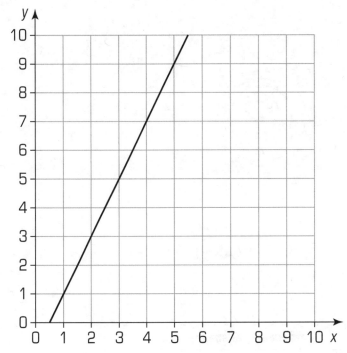

(1, 1) (2, 3) (5, 9) are all pairs of coordinates on this line.

Write another pair of coordinates on this line.   (_____, _____)   *1 mark*

1 Each of these shapes has one or more **lines of symmetry**.

Draw **all** the **lines of symmetry** on each shape.

a

b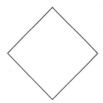

1 mark

2 Here are three badges.

A

B

C

You may use a mirror and tracing paper.

Put a tick (✓) in the box if the badge has **reflective** symmetry.

A ☐   B ☐   C ☐

1 mark

3 Complete the table.

Shape	Property of shape		
	4 sides only	one or more right angles	two pairs of parallel sides
a 	✗	✓	✗
b	☐	☐	☐
c 	☐	☐	☐

2 marks

4 Complete this sentence.

All **equilateral triangles** have _____

_____ *1 mark*

5 Circle the letters that have rotational symmetry.

A   Z   F   H

1 mark

S5 Assessment

6 Here are some shapes.

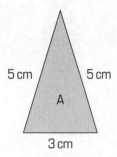

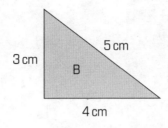

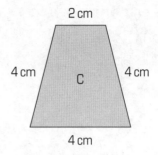

Write the letters **B** and **C** in this **sorting diagram** below to show where shapes **B** and **C** should go. Shape **A** is done for you.

Shapes	**No** sides equal	Only 2 sides equal	**More than** 2 sides equal
3 sides		A	
More than 3 sides			

2 marks

7 Draw **two more straight lines** to make a rectangle. Use a ruler.

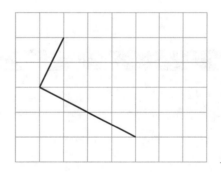

1 mark

8 Where will the hand be pointing after a quarter turn anticlockwise?

Tick (✓) the drawing **a**, **b**, **c** or **d** which shows this.

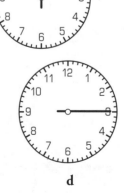

      a   **b**   **c**   **d**

1 mark

Assessment Answers

A1

1 200, 201

2 11, 27

3 a 47

 b 6

4 14, 22

5 a 8

 b 18

6 62

7 181

N1

1 a 4 + 12 = 16   or   8 + 12 = 20

 b 16 – 12 = 4   or   16 – 4 = 12   or

 20 – 12 = 8   or   20 – 8 = 12

2 Arrow at 1.6

3 a 137

 b 31 – 7 = 24

4 Circle 85 + 65   and   450 – 300

5 Circle 540, 500, 180, 50

6 a 15°C   **b** 7°C

S1

1 Arrow at 350 grams

2 Line 8 cm long

3 Rectangle with perimeter 18 cm, lengths marked.

4 2 metres

5 a They have the same area: 4 cm^2.

 b Any shape with area 4 cm^2.

6 a 210 m

 b 2700 m^2

N2

1 5 squares shaded

2 2 squares shaded

3 $\frac{3}{12}$ or $\frac{1}{4}$

4 43

5 20

6 Lines joining $\frac{3}{10}$ and 30%, $\frac{1}{10}$ and 10%

7 Ring 3 balls

8 18 sweets

9 1.3 and 0.65 marked on the number line.

D1

1 Any number 7 or above.

2 **a** Car

 b It has the highest bar.

3 65, 72, 288, 540, 1000

4 32

5 May

6 **a** Emily

 b 2 apples

7 **a** Black

 b There are more black marbles.

A2

1 **a** 9

 b 5

2 **a** Big drink

 b 15p

3 £8.00

4 35

5 Lines joining: 24 and 31, 17 and 24, 31 and 38

6 35

S2

1 8.45

2 40

3 12.50

4 **b** `13:30` **c** `10:45`

 d `18:10`

5 (4, 5)

6 **a** (1, 2) and (5, 6)

 b Because 9 is 1 more than 8.

D2

1 **a** 20

 b 5

2 30 in intersection

 12 in multiples of 2

 15 in multiples of 5

3 **a** Orange: ⦀⦀⦀ ⦀

 Banana: 16

 b 37

 c 24

4 **a** 14

 b 8

 c Bar height = 14

N3

1 Number in order.
2 Lines joining: half of 12 and 6, double 6 and 12, half of 6 and 3, two 2's and 4
3 8
4 137
5 **a** 6
  b 7
6 **a** 48
  b 9
7 Lines joining: 162 and 200, 293 and 300, 145 and 100, 421 and 400, 362 and 400, 204 and 200

A3

1 Circle 65, 100, 115
2 **a** 15
  b 16
3 2 or 6
4 30, 90, 180
5 Because $16 = 4 \times 4$.
6 **a** Tick (3, 2), (5, 4), (10, 9)
  b Because 11 is less than 12.

S3

1 Pegboard drawn after 90° clockwise turn.
2 2 lines making an isosceles triangle.
3 **a** 3 lines making a right-angled triangle.
  b 3 lines making a non right-angled triangle.
4 **a** 6
  b 9
  c 3
5 Tick second diagram.
6 **a** Two equal sides
  b Three equal sides

N4

1 4 more squares shaded.
2 1 more square shaded.
3 0.4 = less than $\frac{1}{2}$
  $\frac{6}{10}$ = greater than $\frac{1}{2}$
  0.21 = less than $\frac{1}{2}$
4 230
5 Lines joining: $\frac{1}{4}$ and 25%, $\frac{1}{10}$ and 10%, $\frac{3}{10}$ and 30%
6 **a** 9
  b 18

A4

1 a 84 − 8 = 76

b 3 × 20 = 60

c 9 + 78 = 97

d 65 + 35 = 120 − 20

2 a Any two numbers that subtract to make 66.

b Any two numbers that multiply to make 48.

3 Lines joining: 10 × 6 and 2 × 30, 5 × 6 and 10 × 3, 8 × 10 and 4 × 20, 4 × 25 and 50 × 2

4 a =

b <

c >

d =

S4

1 a 1 line of symmetry

b 2 lines of symmetry

c 5 lines of symmetry

2 a Shape at (7, 1), (9, 1), (9, 4), (8, 4), (8, 2), (7, 2)

b (1, 1)

c (9, 1)

3 Reflection of triangle

4 a Right 4, up 3

b Any route describing path.

N5

1 860

2 599

3 a 20 × 4 = 8

b 48 ÷ 2 = 24

4 40

5 Arrows joining: 56 and 60, 38 and 40, 67 and 70, 72 and 70

6 120

7 1956

8 9

D3

1 Tick Henry Compton

2 a 40

b It has the smallest bar.

3 a Blue

b White and silver

4 a November

b 26

5 a Apple = $4\frac{1}{2}$ pictures
Grapefruit = 3 pictures
Orange = 4 pictures
Pineapple = 2 pictures

b 25

c Student's question

D4

1 **a** Grey, white or black.
   b White, because he has more of them.
   c 2 extra grey and 1 extra black.
2 Any number more than 5.
3 **a** Impossible
   b Certain
   c Unlikely
   d Even chance

A5

1 100, 101
2 **a** $4 \times 20 = 80$
   b $12 + 69 = 81$
   c $60 - 24 = 36$
   d $30 \div 5 = 6$
3 49
4 72
5 10
6 12
7 (3, 5) or (4, 7)

S5

1 **a** 1 line of symmetry
   b 4 lines of symmetry
2 Tick Box B.
3 **b** ✓, ✓, ✓
   c ✗, ✓, ✗
4 Three equal sides
5 Z and H
6 B = 3 sides, no sides equal
   C = more than 3 sides, more than 2 sides equal
7 2 more straight lines making a rectangle.
8 Tick **a**.

R1 | **0–9 digit cards**

0	1	2	3	4
5	6	7	8	9

R4 Place value tables

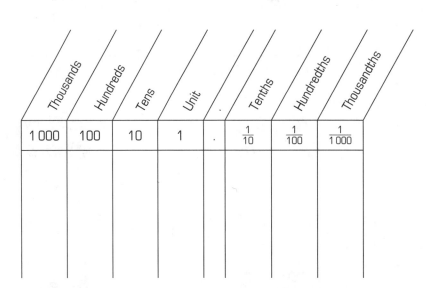

Thousands	Hundreds	Tens	Unit	.	Tenths	Hundredths	Thousandths
1 000	100	10	1	.	$\frac{1}{10}$	$\frac{1}{100}$	$\frac{1}{1\,000}$

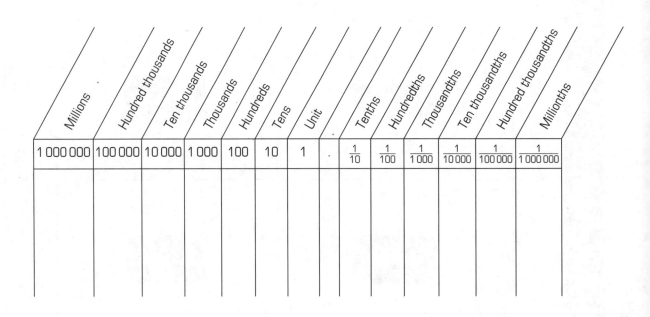

Millions	Hundred thousands	Ten thousands	Thousands	Hundreds	Tens	Unit	.	Tenths	Hundredths	Thousandths	Ten thousandths	Hundred thousandths	Millionths
1 000 000	100 000	10 000	1 000	100	10	1	.	$\frac{1}{10}$	$\frac{1}{100}$	$\frac{1}{1\,000}$	$\frac{1}{10\,000}$	$\frac{1}{100\,000}$	$\frac{1}{1\,000\,000}$

All tiers

R5 | Number ladders

FRAMEWORK MATHS

R6 Number lines

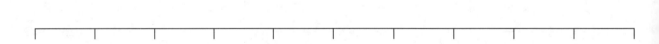

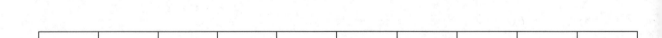

All tiers

R7   Function machines

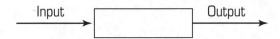

Input → [ ] → [ ] → Output

Input → [ ] → [ ] → Output

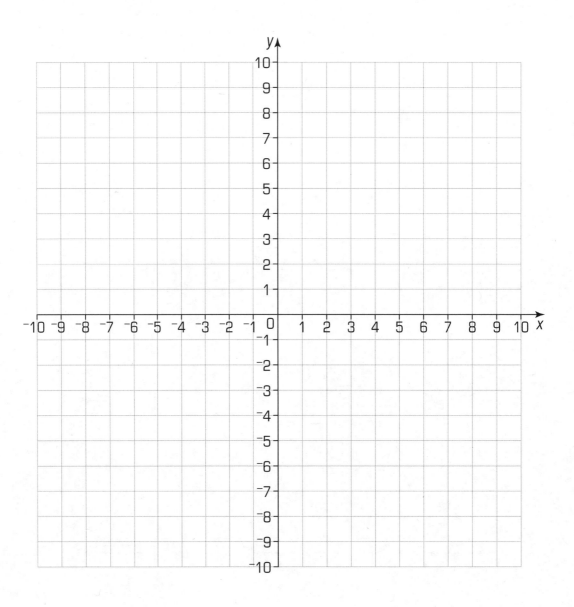

All tiers

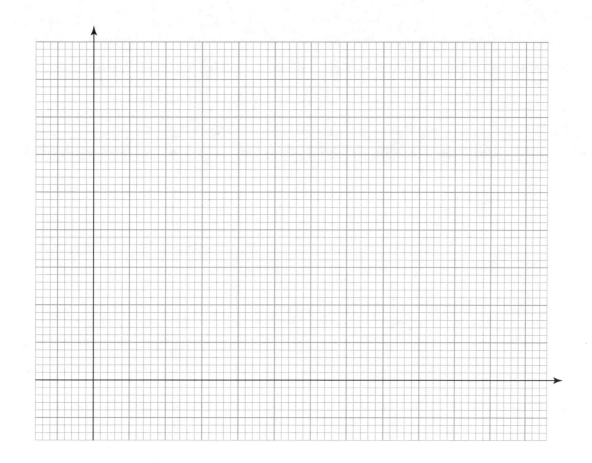

R11 Tally chart

Frequency table

Value	Tally	Frequency
	Total =	

All tiers

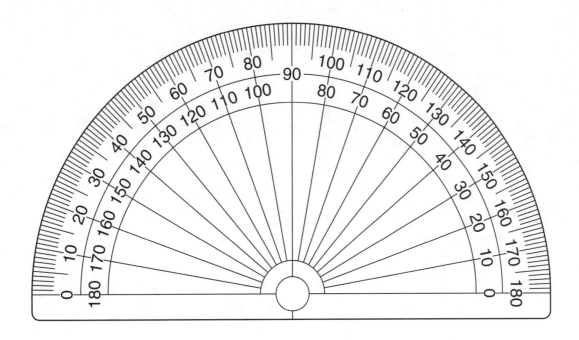

R14   Triangles

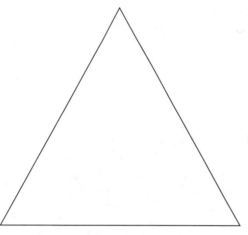

Equilateral

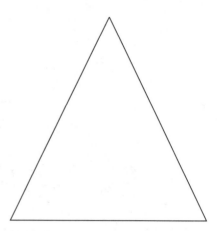

Isosceles

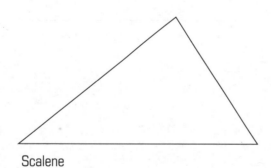

Scalene

Right-angled

All tiers

R15 Quadrilaterals

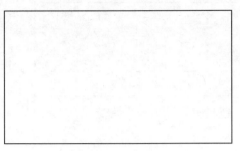

Rectangle

Square

Parallelogram

Rhombus

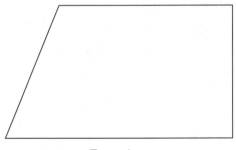

Trapezium

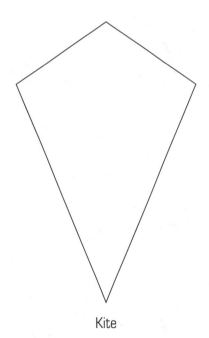

Kite

Isosceles trapezium

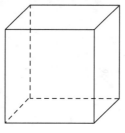
Cube

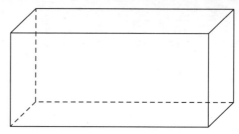
Cuboid

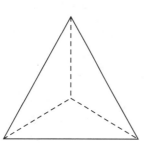
Tetrahedron

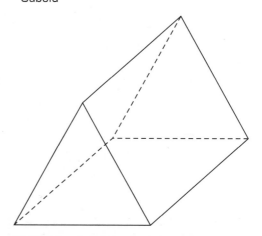
Triangular prism

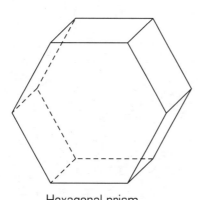
Hexagonal prism

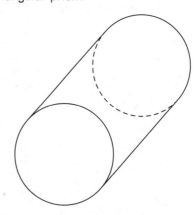
Cylinder

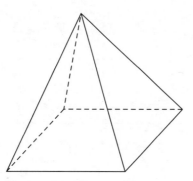
Square-based pyramid

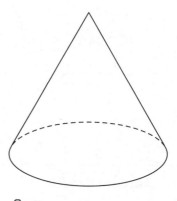
Cone

1	2	3	4	5	6	7	8	9	10
11	12	13	14	15	16	17	18	19	20
21	22	23	24	25	26	27	28	29	30
31	32	33	34	35	36	37	38	39	40
41	42	43	44	45	46	47	48	49	50
51	52	53	54	55	56	57	58	59	60
61	62	63	64	65	66	67	68	69	70
71	72	73	74	75	76	77	78	79	80
81	82	83	84	85	86	87	88	89	90
91	92	93	94	95	96	97	98	99	100

Resources

R19 Ruler

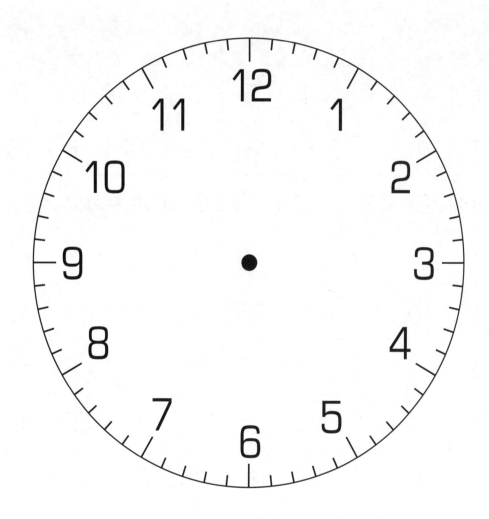

×	1	2	3	4	5	6	7	8	9	10
1	1	2	3	4	5	6	7	8	9	10
2	2	4	6	8	10	12	14	16	18	20
3	3	6	9	12	15	18	21	24	27	30
4	4	8	12	16	20	24	28	32	36	40
5	5	10	15	20	25	30	35	40	45	50
6	6	12	18	24	30	36	42	48	54	60
7	7	14	21	28	35	42	49	56	63	70
8	8	16	24	32	40	48	56	64	72	80
9	9	18	27	36	45	54	63	72	81	90
10	10	20	30	40	50	60	70	80	90	100

All tiers